"No" I said "you have done nothing. It is only that I—"

But finding no plausible excuse, I lifted my face to him offering my lips, and said: "All right—kiss me then."

But behind my back I had my hands clenched into fists; I was pressing my nails hard into the flesh in order to think rather of the pain than of our lips touching. But when they did touch and Charles took what I had wanted to deny him today—took it hungrily, more closely than usual and longer—it happened as I had feared. My fingers loosened; my arms swept forward; and in an uprush of uncontrollable passion I flung them around his neck and glued my lips to his in a hungry and eager abandon . . .

All My Sins

by

Norbert Estey

ace books

A Division of Charter Communications Inc.
A GROSSET & DUNLAP COMPANY
360 Park Avenue South
New York, New York 10010

An ACE Book

Published by arrangement with A. A. Wyn, Inc.

First ACE Printing: June 1978

Published simultaneously in Canada

Printed in U.S.A.

Prologue

NICOLAS GÉDOUIN was my lover when, according to the calendar, I was eighty years old, and I firmly resolved that this time should really be the last.

When my eightieth birthday approached I was surprised with a gift appropriate to the solemn occasion. What more suitable present could there be for a former *grande amoureuse* than a night of long foregone pleasures? An experience to turn the head of an eighty-year-old woman indeed!

Thirty years have passed by since I withdrew from my amatorial pursuits and ceased to be "the fickle Ninon," recognized past mistress of the high art of love-making. Since my fiftieth year I have become the distinguished "Mademoiselle de Lenclos," who has shared the sublimest delights of the mind with her friends; among whom I had the honor to count La Rochefoucauld, Saint-Évremond, Corneille, Racine, Scarron, and above all Molière. In my "yellow salon" in the Rue des Tournelles the quintessence of culture and art would gather around me to cultivate music and conversation, iridescent with gaiety and brilliant esprit in an atmosphere of distinction and in a tone of *bon goût*.

Though my hair was snow-white—my admirers said that it was only to enhance the youthfulness of my face—Nicolas Gédouin, a tall, narrow-shouldered and dark-eyed, handsome man of learning and elegance, loved me. How flattered I was! He was young. Graduated from the Sorbonne, he already wore the collar of an abbé. But he was no hypocrite. Unlike quite a number of my ecclesiastical visitors in the past, he made no pretense of trying to save my soul, but admitted his passion outright. He declared that for my sake he would gladly give up his career if only I would make him my lover.

I had been unapproachable to any man for many years, and Gédouin's pleading I had resisted for months. But when on the eve of my eightieth birthday his pleading became so insistent and desperate, I lost my head once again, and, struggle as I would against the very idea of giving myself up to the youthful charmer, I yielded at last. "But there is one condition," I said. "You must promise me that after this night you will withdraw and never lapse into sin again. At least not with me."

He protested, but, seeing me adamant, he gave in at last and solemnly promised.

In the morning, however, Gédouin fell on his knees and implored me for Heaven's sake not to send him away. I protested my canonical age.

"You are younger than the youngest of all," he insisted. "In you all the enchantments of love are imprisoned forever!" He went on arguing and begging and coaxing.

I felt sorry for him and suggested a compromise. "Travel," I said. "Go away from Paris; go to foreign lands. Learn, observe, and examine yourself. If you find after one year that you would still rather renounce your abbé's *collet* than give me up—and if I am convinced by your absence that I should not like to be deprived of you and your love—then perhaps——Come exactly on the day of my birthday anniversary, which—don't forget—will be my eighty-first, and I'll give you my answer."

I made this suggestion because I took it for granted that, away from me and in foreign countries and in the arms of some blonde Gretchen or fiery Spaniard, Gédouin would forget his silly passion for me, the old woman, and that next year he would have no inclination to tempt me. So I sighed with relief when he accepted my offer and—on the same day—departed. For from now on, I was firmly resolved, *amour* should belong only to my memories.

My days still belonged to my visitors, my clavecin, my lute, and above all to my books. For my mind was still as fresh as my body, and it took an eager interest in all the affairs and currents of our time, in which everything seemed to be outgrowing itself and expanding into colossal dimensions; in the struggle between the mystical and militant forces of the Roman Catholic Church against modern "enlightenment," of which the world, unaware of the deep religious streak in my soul, would still consider me an ardent champion; and last, not least, in the

French theater, in the development of which, thanks to my friendship with its greatest playwrights, I had played a modest but such a happy, exciting part!

But when the shadows fall and my visitors have gone, my time belongs to my past amours. Then I rummage in my old letters, most of them turned yellow and the ink faded, and in old keepsakes— dried flowers and miniatures. There—out of them and out of the shadows and of the flickering candle-light—my lovers emerge and with them returns the memory of all the thrilling adventures, the flighty follies and caprices that, if catalogued, would not be overshadowed by those of Boccaccio or of the Queen of Navarre. And with them also my former would-be lovers would mingle—the proud Louis XIV begging me on his knees to become his *maîtresse en titre*, France's uncrowned queen; men in armor and men in cardinal's purple; and all those of my poor "martyrs" who, like impatient pages, had been awaiting their lady's pleasure. . . .

But far more passionate, surpassing them all in undying devotion, remembered always, was my love for my Charles, that first and only and wonderful love. Ever since he had left me when I was a silly young girl I had been searching for him in the arms of all the others, until after more than thirty years, by a strange play of circumstance, he did reappear in the full bloom of his youth.

But, alas, that trace of the Devil in me that tinged everything I touched with sex has been a source not only of enchantment but also of tragedy. It has been the destruction of those whom I loved most on this earth.

But—*c'est fini*. They are all over—the pleasures, the lusts, the rebellions of the mind, the struggles of the flesh, and the laughs and the tears as well. I long for the coolness of peace. There are moments when the ticktock of the ebony *Théodore Denise* clock on my mantelpiece brings a sweetly joyous feeling of quiet to my heart, and I wish it would last for ever and ever. . . .

PART ONE

1

CHARLES BEAUMONT was my first lover, but by no means the first man to have been in bed with me.

Remembering these things, I do not count my father, into whose bed, as quite a little girl, I used to crawl in the morning to kiss him and press myself as close to him as I could. "Ninon, you sweet little wildcat!" he would say, and laugh, returning my kisses and fondling me. "*You'll* know how to drive a man crazy." Only Maman wouldn't like our doings. My protest, "It's *my* Papa, and it is *I* who should be permitted to sleep with him, and not you," was of little help. One day I had to stop my morning visits to Papa once for all.

I was a little more grown up, though not much above seven, when I had my first adventure in bed with a stranger. At the time when this was about to happen, I was not only a little wildcat but a veritable little devil. If I was not immersed, with my cheeks glowing, in one of my books—I had already started to learn Italian, Spanish, and Latin; I played the lute,

3

danced, fenced, or rode on horseback, all this passionately and with my dear father as my instructor—I was roaming busily about house, courtyard, stables, and garden, singing, whistling, chatting with everybody, laughing because I had discovered something to laugh at, or just laughing for no reason from sheer *joie de vivre*. "The Cayenne pepper in your blood you have from Papa," my mother would say, and smile—sometimes with a hint of resentment in her side glance at Father. And he would often call out: "What, drunk again—from your milk bowl?"—as people tease me nowadays, too, when they say that to become cheerful they have to wait for their wine, whereas I "get drunk from the soup."

In spite of my loud and quicksilverish sprightliness—or perhaps just because of it?—people did like me, I think. At least they made a great pet of me. My dear mother and I were outwardly alike. We had the same brown hair, the same brown eyes that could deepen to profound black, and the same oval, smooth-skinned face. But she, unlike myself, was soft-spoken and delicate and often suffered from bad migraines. She not only bore my noisiness with patience, but even delighted in it, hoping that I would settle down and take after her when I grew up. What a dear optimist she was!

Even my aunt the Baronne de Montaigu, father's sister and a childless widow, prudish and with all the traits of sour, conservative spinsterhood, seemed pleased with my liveliness when she came to Paris to pay us a visit. "What a brisk little filly!" she exclaimed, tapping my behind with her long skeletal

4

fingers in the manner of a horsebreeder, and then she proposed: "Why, shouldn't you like to come this summer to Loches and stay in my château, all three of you?—It would do a lot of good to your petite, wouldn't it?—There is so much space in my park to race about the whole day!" Her proposal was accepted. Though we owned estates in the country, too—one in Virey-sur-Bar, the other, La Douardière, in the Touraine—we never went to live in either. Preferring the pleasures of the capital to country life, father would visit them only for inspection. The mansions were otherwise neglected and hardly fit for longer sojourns.

But when summer came Papa, an army captain, could not absent himself from his regiment in Paris. Neither could Maman go, because Grandma had fallen seriously ill, and Maman wanted to remain within her reach and call. But my part of the plan was carried out, and one day in July my father took me, both of us riding on horseback, to Loches.

My aunt's castle was a massive antiquated structure, its sternness softened by luxuriantly growing ivy and by lichen and ferns on the battlements. But, situated on the bank of the Indres River and with its ancient overgrown park and pastures and woods stretching far to the blue horizon, it promised unlimited freedom. It was just the right place for me.

My first night I spent on a couch, sharing the room with Mademoiselle Amélie the *femme de ménage,* who, with her long hard head, drab dress, and spinsterish ways, seemed my aunt's perfect replica. But in the morning I stole over to my father's chamber and, as I had done as a very little girl, crawled into his bed, cuddled up to him, and coaxed him: "Please, Papa dear, don't go away. Stay with me! For a few days at least! We could gallop together all over the country in daytime, and by night I should not have to sleep with the old bore of a scarecrow, but could come and sleep with you, and without Maman knowing of it!" (I still believed that Mother was usurping my place and that by right Father belonged to me—a conviction that seemed justified, because at home he busied himself almost exclusively with me and my education. I didn't know that his time outside the house was spent not only in the service of the king, but also in that of gay, pretty ladies and particularly of one who was later on to become the cause of great trouble.)

My father laughed and said that I was a good one. "I'd like to stay with you, darling, but it cannot be done. But before I go I'll see to it that you need not sleep with that old witch. You shall sleep alone and in this good, comfortable bed." After breakfast in the hall he had a confidential talk with my aunt, and then he led me back to his chamber. "You'll get the bed," he said. "And as I have spoken in so high terms of it, your aunt has told me I can keep this 'old piece of lumber' if I like it so much, and that I can take it with me in the autumn when I come to fetch you. She is unable to appreciate it, but it is one of the noblest works of cabinet handicraft of the time of Henri IV." Bidding me look at the bed carefully, he went on: "With these carved pillars and this gabled canopy it looks like an old Greek or Roman temple. And that's what it is about to become to you, my dear girl—a temple, a sanctuary; because it will be yours not only here, but also when we are back in Paris and for your whole life. Look at those caryatids—the four wooden women carrying the pilasters. They are the four seasons, and like the seasons these four figures will symbolically enclose your whole life—witnesses and confidantes of your joys and pains, your repose and oblivion.''

There was an ever so slightly sentimental vibrancy in his voice. I noticed it well, because until then I had known him only in inexhaustible good humor; also the pause that he let follow his words had a solemn touch. But then he took me under the chin and, laughing again said: "But mostly joys, my petite—joys as many and pleasant as possible! Just joys.''

I missed him much, my dear Papa, when he had gone! At night, lost and lonesome in the deep center of the enormous bed, I wondered what he could have meant by wishing me joys in this bed when I couldn't have him there with me. But in the daytime, at least during the first weeks, I was too much absorbed by my almost unchecked wild life in the country to notice my loneliness. Left to myself—for my aunt and Mademoiselle Amélie were busy with household administration from morning to night—I roamed not only about the park, but also across meadows and woods. I raced with the dogs. I climbed the old oak trees, or preferably the cherry trees with their round black sweet fruit. I explored turrets and cellars and battlements, and when I found some boys' old swords I made a furious attack on a knight's rusty mail in the armory. On rainy days I would linger in the corridors and galleries thickly hung with dusty, neglected, and blackened but interesting paintings—family portraits, battle scenes, and outlandish Italian landscapes. Or I would rummage in the heavy oaken chests of the library, discovering wonderful leatherbound books that no one seemed ever to read. A special pleasure was making fun of the two old women. I would shake with laughter when I succeeded in exchanging the apple cider in their cups for vinegar and they made sour faces. In those days every practical joke of mine was condoned and even laughed at.

As the weeks advanced, though, I began to miss company. I missed my mother's sweet, tender ways, her care and her caresses, and above all I missed my father's lusty joviality and intelligent talk. If only I had at least someone of my age to share in my pleasures, were it a boy or a girl, but preferably a boy! But there seemed to be not the slightest chance of such company.

But one afternoon when I returned from a roving expedition to the woods I found Aunt and Mademoiselle Amélie very excited. And then I learned the news. A letter had arrived in which Father Ambrose, a distant relative and a prefect in the Jesuit College of La Flèche, requested my aunt to take the Prince de Marsillac, who was one of his pupils at Loches, over the summer. Upon his suggestion the prince's father, the Duc de La Rochefoucauld, had decided that the boy should spend his vacation together with his tutor in a rather secluded place in order to make up subjects in which he had not succeeded during the school year. Father Ambrose had thought of Aunt's castle. There were never hunting or hawking or other parties on her estate, to distract the boy from his studies. And as it was the duc's wish that the boy's life, his chamber, and his food should be extremely modest, of almost cloistral simplicity, the boy's sojourn would not cause her any great expense, and furthermore she could be sure that the duc, generous as he was, would remunerate her in a lavish way.

At last, someone coming to Loches! and moreover a boy! and certainly one not much above my own age! I gave a cry of delight, and in my first uprush of joy I jumped on Aunt's lap, embraced her and even kissed her cheeks, though they felt like old crumpled paper. "You'll invite the boy, of course," I said, flushed with happiness. "Won't you? Oh, do, please do!"

"Certainly I will," my aunt said. "To have him in my château will be a great honor to me. The Duc de La Rochefoucauld is one of the highest-born and mightiest and richest nobles of France, and the young prince is to become an heir to his fortune and title. But pray do have these facts well in mind, when he arrives. To *you* he won't be 'the boy,' but *Son Altesse le Prince*. You'll have to speak and behave well and be neatly dressed. You'll have to stop all those wild fooleries that soil and tear your dresses and can bring only disgrace to me and you in his eyes."

All this dampened my joy at having company. And so I looked rather glum when, a few days later, in my pretty pink Sunday dress I stood with the others in front of the entrance gate to welcome the high-born bore. My aunt, mistaking my unwonted stillness for a result of her exhortations, nodded acknowledgment as if to say: "Quite right, always behave this way, my child." The awful crunching of the coach on the gravel seemed to register the end of my days of sweet freedom.

When it drove up at last and the prince jumped out, I had a moment of pleasant surprise. I must confess that even as a very little girl I always let myself be prejudiced by any kind of beauty, especially if it were that of a man. And the unusually tall and slender boy who sprang from the coach with an elegant leap was decidedly handsome—not so beautiful as Papa, because no man in the world could compare with Papa in either looks or charm; but I was caught by the boy's smart figure, his beautiful great eyes, black and round like the sweet black cherries in my aunt's garden, and above all his magnificent forehead, with the high temples so in contrast to his supposed backwardness. But my pleasant feeling for him was of short duration. He bowed to Aunt and Mademoiselle Amélie *comme il faut*, but to me, though I made my prettiest curtsy and gave him a welcoming smile, he paid not the slightest attention—as if I didn't exist at all! My aunt said: "May I present to Your Altesse my little niece Ninon de Lenclos," and only then did he look down at me. For a moment he gazed at me fixedly: then, as if he had wasted too much time in honoring me with his princely attention, his head snapped suddenly back and he said in a voice alternately nasal and husky: "What a charming little niece you have, baronne!" But not a word to myself, and not another look! Stung to fury, I felt myself getting scarlet. "And what a pretty white cat my aunt has," I blurted out, aping his funny voice, "and two tamed green siskins, and a whole bunch of puppies, too"; and then I laughed right in his face, wheeled around, and made for the park at a run.

"Your father would spank you for such naughtiness," my aunt said afterwards, explaining to me that it was only natural that the prince should speak in this odd way, because his voice, like every boy's of his age, was changing.

"It is also only natural," I said, "that he is a boy and I only a girl, and he must not look down on me for it. And my father has never spanked me and never would. And I can't help saying your prince is a nuisance." But upon my aunt's entreaties I apologized to him. He did nothing, though, to placate me, but continued his irritating, haughty ways. I didn't take it too tragically, but I got the idea into my head that I must find an opportunity to show that conceited boy that a girl is just as good as any man. And after a few days an occasion arose.

I had gone to the armory in order to attack the knight's mail. Entering, I saw the prince in the half dark of the vaulted salle, practicing fencing positions. "Go out of here or you'll be hurt," he cried at me without interrupting his exercise. "An armory is no place for a girl."

Once again I was stung to fury. "Don't be so conceited!" I retorted. "*I* know how to fence, too." He let out an ironic laugh but he stopped both his laughing and his practicing when he saw me go over to the swords on the wall and, taking up my boy's sword, exhibit a few thrusts that I had learned from Papa. And while I was doing it and watching his stupid stare, I was suddenly full of fight, and an idea struck me.

There had been in Papa's house a famous Italian rapier fencer, a certain Cavaliere d'Oltrecastello—a lean, black-clad, black-eyed, black-haired man who had taught my father the secret of his *fulmine improvvisato*, a riposte delivered from a defense position with the point of the foil, taking an opponent unaware like a flash from a clear sky. At my Papa's urgent request the Italian taught him the point-thrust, and by an intensive training of certain muscles my father had acquired the necessary skill. And so had I.

"If you'll take up another boy's sword and fight with me, I'm sure that I shall beat you," I challenged the prince.

"I don't fight with a girl," he said, with that intolerable contempt in his voice again.

"Afraid?" I mocked him.

His black, thick eyebrows contracted. "Well, have it your own way," he said, taking up a boy's short sword, "and be taught your lesson, you silly girl."

I must confess that I had a hard time to ward off his attacks, which, though he had granted me generous advantages, were brilliant and powerful. But while the blades flashed and whistled between us I was in wait for my opportunity, and at last I got it. I delivered my *fulmine improvvisato*. The prince stopped short. He caught his breath. "What devil's trick was this?"

"A thrust just as fair as any of yours," I said, throwing my sword away and turning to go. "And you will still have to study and train very hard if you are going to fence with a girl." And out I went.

He kept on being haughty. But I flattered myself that his rudeness was now a cloak to the aversion, if not hate, that he felt because I, a little girl, had outdone him. Either suited me better than his previous indifference, and I was mischievous enough to taunt him by frequent visits to the armory and by watching his fruitless attempts to get to the bottom of the trick. But at last he brought himself to ask me how it was done, and I, proud of my triumph, showed him. He thanked me and said it was a pity that we couldn't become good friends.

"Why can't we? Is it because I am only a girl?"

"Yes."

"Why?"

"Because I don't like little girls."

"Then let it go," I snapped back. "I don't care for your friendship. *Je m' en fiche!*" "*Je m' en fiche,*" I repeated to myself all day long, indignant at his thanklessness and his obstinate contempt for little girls.

That night I could not fall asleep right away, because I was brooding on how to teach my odious companion another lesson. Gazing across the moonlit room—because of the August heat my bed curtains had not been drawn—I could suddenly see the handle of my door latch moving down noiselessly. In another moment the door had opened a slit, and through the slit came the head of the princely boy, his hair glossy in the moonlight and his eyes cautiously spying about. My first impulse was to put him to rout with a cry; but some stronger instinct made

13

me incapable of defensive action. All I could do was to close my eyes and feign sleep.

I heard the door creak faintly as it opened another slit and then closed. What did he want? Had he realized that he was wrong to treat me with disdain, nose in air, and had he come to make peace with me? But if so, he did not need to come by night. By a quick glance through a slightly opened eyelid I saw him move—and how stealthily!—across the floor to my bed. How funny he looked in his long white nightshirt! A bubble of laughter rose within me, but I fought it down, closed the eye again, and kept still.

He stood now at my bedside. Though he was obviously trying to hold his breath, I heard it flutter in and out. A long moment passed, and I wondered whether I should not open my eyes and ask him outright what it was that he wanted at this unusual hour. But again my instinct said no. He certainly didn't want me to know why he had come, and if I spoke or even betrayed that I knew of his presence, I should never learn why. And I was *so* curious!

After another long moment I knew that he was bending down and seizing the corner of my blanket. He was not about to draw it off—or was he? I could not possibly tolerate that. Because of the heat, I had no nightshift on, and if he removed the blanket he would see me stark naked. But, strangely enough, my curiosity increased, and it was stronger than my shame, and again I remained passive.

I had guessed right. Slowly and anxiously, inch by inch so as not to waken me, the impertinent boy removed the bedspread, first little by little, but in the end completely. It was novel and mysterious to feel a stranger's eye darting about my naked body, but it was curiously exciting. I decided, though, that I would cry out if he dared to touch me ever so slightly.

But he did not touch me. Instead, after having stared at me for another long moment, he replaced the bedspread softly and stole away just as slyly as he had come.

I was a little puzzled the next morning, more than a little ashamed, and very glad that he tried to avoid me. But when we met in the corridor he was again *de haut en bas*—just as arrogant as he had been to me from the start—and I was angry at myself that I had not cried out by night and put him to flight. If he was curious about how a girl looked under her dress, he should observe his sisters at home and not bother strange girls.

But when he came to my bed again in the same way as the night before, I could not help acquiescing. And this time he not only removed my blanket and stared at me, but sat down on my bed; and then—what impudence!—he lay down by my side, leaving, however, enough space between himself and me not to awaken me.

It was a pleasant enough feeling to have someone with me in this lonely giant bed; and as he did nothing more than lie there and watch me, I felt strangely secure and was slowly lulled into sleep. In the morning he was gone.

I cannot absolve my early girlhood from some premature sinfulness in the endearments with my beloved father, but as to this boy there was—but for

15

a faint vestige, perhaps—none to be found in me. At least, so it was in the first days and weeks, even when his nightly visits had become regular, and we lay close together night after night, body to body, my head on his breast, and I at first feigning sleep, but then falling really to sleep and sleeping soundly through the whole night, until the wild cock would crow in the woods and the boy would leave me.

But even then nothing changed in the boy's harsh and contemptuous ways towards me when we met during the daytime. Our scuffling and trying to outdo each other, whether in racing with the hounds or in fencing or in bickering—he aggressive and I in my repartees as biting as I could be at this age—all this continued and became an inexhaustible source of amusement, not only to the ladies, but to the servants as well.

But one day I was called to the dining room in the *rez-de-chaussée*, and the moment I entered and saw Aunt and Mademoiselle Amélie and the pinch-faced, spare-haired Monsieur Bou-Bou (which is what the prince would call his tutor, Monsieur Bouffler) sitting at the round table, stiff and looking at me as sternly as Aunt's ancestral portraits were staring down at me from the walls, I felt that something unpleasant was brewing.

"I am sorry," Aunt started the proceedings, "but Monsieur Bouffler has submitted a complaint to my hearing which I must bring to your attention, my dear little niece." The "dear little niece" sounded somewhat sharp, and I was afraid that something had come out about the prince's nightly calls to my bed; but, *Dieu merci*, this was not the trouble. The tutor's charges were aimed only at my daytime doings with the prince. The prince, so he said, had unusual qualities; his mind was full of esprit; but the trouble was that it was difficult to get him to learn if he weren't enough interested in a subject. He had hoped that here in the solitude of this château where nothing else would divert his mind, the prince would find Latin syntax and mathematics attractive enough. But now all the fencing and racing about and arguing with me was so engrossing his pupil that he, the mere humble tutor of a high-born prince, had not the power to keep him at his books. If this went on, he was afraid that he must give up, break off the sojourn in Loches, and return with the prince to La Flèche.

"It is not my fault," I said. "I never did ask your prince to play or race or scuffle with me. It's he who always crosses my way, though he knows that I can't stomach him."

"That is not the way to speak about a prince and a future de La Rochefoucauld," my aunt said. "And I think you like him well enough," Mademoiselle Amélie chimed in with a venomous look in her bird's eyes. And neither did Monsieur Bouffler accept my defense. It was I, they asserted, who was provoking the prince by my precocious ways and constant opposition to all that he said.

This wounded my pride. "What?" I blurted out, shaking my locks and stamping my foot. "You want me to pocket all his impertinence and let him treat me like a little dog, without a word? If so, you had better write to Papa, and he'll take me home." Mademoiselle Amélie, by a side glance at Aunt, indicated that this wouldn't be such a bad idea, but

Aunt shook her head No. Anxious to keep the prince in her home, she too would have liked to pack me off, but at the same time she feared offending my father.

"I really am at a loss what to do with this obstinate child," she said plaintively.

At last Monsieur Bouffler succeeded with me. He knew that I respected him as a scholar, and he was clever enough to appeal to my "intelligence" and to my "understanding of his precarious position." He almost begged for my co-operation. I gave in to his pleadings and promised: "Count on it, I am going to avoid him like the plague."

Thereafter I met the prince very rarely. But just at that point I came to like him much better. The windows of my chamber overlooked the park in which he used to walk back and forth with his tutor, and I often watched him from behind the curtains. My first impression that he was a beautiful boy returned. I admired the nobility of his head, the strongly marked features, of which only the mouth was soft, and his teeth so whitely gleaming in the now brown-tanned face. I also revised my first idea of him as a backward boy and learned to understand what his tutor had meant in extolling his esprit. Once when the prince was discussing a historical subject with Monsieur Bouffler the tutor supported his own view with a rather lengthy quotation from Cicero.

"You didn't listen, my prince," he said resentfully when he had ended and was waiting for an answer.

"No," said the prince, "I didn't, and I didn't on

purpose. I prefer to form my own ideas and not copy the opinions of other people—even authorities.'' His words struck me because they showed such determination to be mentally independent, and I think I owe it to them that all my life I have considered persons with weak memories fortunate because they couldn't quote. And there were many other remarks, too, in which I recognize now the germs of some of the *Maximes* that were one day to make him so famous.

The nightly visits went on without a break, and I had got so used to them that I couldn't fall asleep until he had settled himself in my bed. But once, on a hot night, sleep would not come—perhaps because the sultry air stifled me, perhaps because the song of the crickets outside was so unusually strident. And all of a sudden I heard the prince give a deep sigh and then speak in a soft whisper. At first I thought he was memorizing a lesson; but then I perceived that his words were addressed to me. And I was amazed at how tender they were. I strained my ears to hear what he had never told me in the daylight and would never say now if he thought me awake.

The longer he whispered, the more excited and the less understandable his words became. But then, trying with obvious difficulty to keep his voice down, he murmured under his breath: ''What the devil is the matter with me, little Ninon? What have you done to me? It—that—has never happened to me before. When I came, and you smiled at me in your pretty pink dress—— What is this that you have done to me? How have you done it? You have no breasts; your little body is without a curve; and yet—I cannot help it. This is driving me crazy. Mad! Completely mad.''

His words frightened me. What did he mean by all this? Crazy? Mad? Was he really mad, and was that the reason why they wouldn't have him at home, why they wouldn't have him in the college, why they had put him away at Loches? Many odds and ends of his strange behavior to me seemed to support my suspicion. I lay still; but this time it was more because I was overcome by fear. And at the same time I felt so sorry that this intelligent, brilliant boy by my side should be insane!

''If I could only kiss you, press you close to me, closer than that, quite close, quite close——''

I felt relieved. Was this all that troubled him? I cannot say that I had particularly cared for the boy's caresses, but as he longed so much to give them, I decided that I wouldn't cry out if he tried to. Poor boy! I knew how lost one could feel by night, alone in one's bed.

''Oh, how I would love you,'' he went on murmuring, ''if you were only a little bit more grown up—a little more like a woman. How I would love you!''

My pity, my determination to endure his fondling, vanished. ''Conceited boy!'' I thought, once more fuming. ''Always showing off because you are a few years older, even when you think me asleep! Why shouldn't you love me because I am still a little girl? Papa is much more grown up than you, much more beautiful, and yet he loves me!''

But then he kissed my hair, and after that my

ALL MY SINS

shoulder—all this very softly, still afraid he would
waken me. And then I knew that he did love me,
even though I was only a little girl; and I was happy,
and I thought he should keep on fondling me gently
while I kept on feigning sleep. But then I heard him
moaning: "Oh, my God, what am I doing? No—I
must not—I mustn't." And then, with a leap, he was
out of my bed and running out of my chamber like a
boy scared off while stealing forbidden fruit. I lay
listlessly for a long while, expecting that he would
return. When he didn't, I said "Coward!" and,
turning over, decided that I would go to sleep. But
for a long time sleep would not come, because I
had got used to his nearness, and he wasn't with
me.

The next day thunderstorms and heavy rainfalls
kept me indoors. The forenoon I spent in the library
alone, my mind less on the books than on the puzzling details of the night. When I met the prince at
the dinner table he avoided my eyes. In the afternoon
I went to the picture gallery in the upper floor. I
thought the prince was in his room with his tutor, but
no sooner had I entered than he came after me. I
warned him that Bou-Bou would resent his absence,
but he brushed my words aside and joined me in
surveying the paintings; they depicted mostly hunting and battle scenes, and he made very interesting
comments on them. Then we came upon a "Suzanne
and the Elders," and I saw him first study Suzanne
and then squint down as if comparing me with the
fat, big-bosomed woman. "Do you like that woman?" I asked. "No," he said, blushing. "The
figure is too unskillfully drawn," and stepped at

21

once to the next two pictures, which represented the Vesuvius, one in daylight, the other by night. He regarded the pictures alternately, shaking his head and murmuring. A pleasant thought seemed to take shape in his eyes, and for the very first time since I had known him he smiled at me. The smile so captivated me that it transferred itself to my own face; and there it lingered, and we found ourselves smiling at each other for quite a while, without a word.

"Should you like to go and see Vesuvius together with me?" he whispered all of a sudden, softly, as if in continuation of his whispering by night, and without the slightest hesitation I said that, yes, I should like to. And then both of us fell silent again. I have never forgotten that moment of our standing before the paintings in the olive and hazel dusk; outside the thin rain and the wind in the leaves making a soft sweet music, and we two alone and absorbed in each other. It was this moment, too, that both of us remembered when, many years later, we stood close together in another gallery, moved by the sight of another Vesuvius picture.

But then the prince said: "All right, little girl, when you are grown up I will take you to Italy." Again the little girl!

"I don't need you, and I do not have to wait all that time if I want to be taken to Italy," I blurted out. "My Papa doesn't mind that I am little, and he would take me there any time."

His laugh—how amused must he have been by my naïveté!—irritated me even more, and we should have started quarreling again. But there came Monsieur Bou-Bou, complaining that this was lesson hour and no time for play; whereupon the prince turned truculent and aggressive and, instead of apologizing, said brusquely: "Leave me alone, with your damned lessons. They make me uncomfortable and tell me nothing. The only real thing I've learned here in Loches was a brilliant foil riposte, and the one I learned it from was this little girl. She has more brains in her little finger than you in your whole head." The sickly, crotchety man paled and shrank back. Without a word, though not without a reproachful side glance at me, he went out.

"Now you have offended the poor man," I said, but with a "What do I care for the old ass?" the prince brushed it aside. I was a little uncomfortable, because I felt somehow guilty. Besides, I was afraid lest Bou-Bou go and complain to my aunt. But my prince was so charming again, and his extolling my brains to Bou-Bou had so restored my accord with him, that I stayed with him in the gallery until almost evening.

At the dinner table I saw that Bouffler was glooming and also that my aunt and Mademoiselle Amélie looked rather sour. He must have made his complaint, but I didn't care. My mind was too much on fire with the question whether the prince would come by night again, or whether—since he had fled me so hastily last night—he would stop his visits. I wished and feared both eventualities because I was strangely beguiled by the thought of his coming to me; and yet I felt equally that it was not proper and was disturbed by guilt.

He did come. And, though my heart was thumping within me, I feigned sleep as usual. For a long time I waited for something to happen. But when it came, it came swiftly, and it was utterly different from what I had expected. There was a sudden short scream, and when I started and looked up I could see the bed curtains drawn open, and standing there, drab hair loose on her shoulders and candle in hand, was Mademoiselle Amélie, with my aunt behind her. Bou-Bou had emerged, too, and some of the servants, and the whole chamber was full of buzz and excitement. The prince sprang out of the bed and jerked the curtains together, and through them I heard him pleading that I was innocent—that I had been sleeping and knew nothing about his intrusion. Bou-Bou apologized to my aunt for his prince and announced that they would pack this very night and go off in the morning. But Aunt protested. If anyone were to blame, she said, it was I, who had played the innocent from the start. It was obvious that I must have been born corrupt in my very core and was no companion for a noble young prince who had only been led astray by my doings. Monsieur Bouffler must pray forgive her for having such a despicable creature in her house. She would send at once for my father, and he would take me with him, and Monsieur Bouffler must for heaven's sake stay on with the prince and forget the whole incident.

Nobody said a word to me that night. In the morning I was confined to my chamber. Though, of course, I didn't feel guiltless, I was too proud to defend myself. There must have been in me, even then, a vestige of the future *précieuse galante* who would claim her bedchamber as her own and not other people's affair; and defiantly I refused to answer.

They kept me shut up to the very hour of Papa's

arrival. I heard our horses trotting on the gravel in front of the castle. When they halted and began neighing I was sure that they scented my nearness and were greeting me joyfully. Then I made out that the two witches had led Papa to the dining room in the *rez-de-chaussée* to get in their accusations before he had a chance to see me and hear my defense. I must confess that I was sorely embarassed, because, though Papa loved me, he could hardly overlook my conduct or the shame it must cause him. Just the same, I could not master my impatience to see him, and at great risk I climbed out the window and, holding fast to the ivy branches and to projecting stones, I slipped down to the ground and a moment later stood outside the dining room windows.

With my throat thickening I could hear Aunt's sawing voice, her words laden with moral indignation. She was saying that my installation in her house had been a mistake—that I had been disorderly, mischievous, and *"impossible"* from the start —that now I had caused her a scandal so abom- minable that it could only disgrace her and her house. And when father demanded that she speak to the point, she told him about me and the prince in my bed.

There followed a silence, in which I could feel the two old witches waiting tensely for the pronounce- ment of a shocked, outraged father. But my dear Papa burst into loud-throated laughter. "Wonder- ful!" he cried, and his voice was resonant. "Seven years old, and sleeps with boys already! *My* blood! *My* flesh! Where is she, the golden darling, that I may kiss her?"

He had not to wait for an answer, for with one leap I was on the window sill, and with another to the floor I was in the room and on his lap; and then, with my arms around him, I was kissing him wildly, my tears of suspense mingled with those of relief and rejoicing.

We had already mounted our horses when I heard the prince call: "Adieu, Ninon, and au revoir." Looking up, I caught sight of him leaning forward out of his window in the upper story, waving a white kerchief.

My father looked up, too. "Handsome boy," he said. "I congratulate you on your good taste." I waved back and smiled up at my prince. For a long time, as we rode down the valley, I could see the château hovering over the woods like a dream, as if it were inhabited only by elves, and the white kerchief a tiny spot, moving and moving back and forth.

2

HOW HAPPY I was when we arrived in Paris and the red brick façade of our pretty house, graciously broken by white columns and pilasters, emerged from the greenery of our tree-lined Rue des Trois Pavillons. And with what emotion did I fly into the wide-open arms of Maman, from whom I had been separated for the first time in my life! And there was also my good bonne Madeleine, whom I kissed on the wart of her blue-veined red eau-de-vie nose, and there was Perrot the valet, who had come to the entrance, and there were the cook and the grooms and all the kitchen and stable boys to hail me and welcome me home.

My new bed arrived on the third day, and it caused quite an upset in our house. It proved too large and too ponderous to be put in my chamber or any other on the upper floor. My parents, then, moved their marital bed upstairs, and mine took its place in the spacious salon in the *rez-de-chaussée*. There it dominated the room, but the effect of its noble proportions and its new gold-yellow silk and lace draperies was graceful, and it made the salon appear even more comfortable then before.

My life at home went on as ever—gay, effervescent, and full of laughter; and if any change occurred in the next few years, it was only that of the new contentments that every hour, every minute had in store for me. Though I loved my good mother dearly, it was chiefly Father who was the source of all this happiness. I could never have him enough to myself. How impressive was the very presence of this uncommonly tall, vigorous, broad-shouldered Papa, with that reckless thrust to his chin! How engaging his jovial and affectionate ways, his swift, brilliant smile, the light always dancing in his large dark eyes! He was always spruce, redolent of cleanness and the scent of freshly waxed leather. And how elegant he was in his movements, particularly in fencing or dancing or on our daredevil rides through the environs of Paris!

But how soft and how subtle he could be, too, when we read the poets together and played and sang to the lute. (I was ten now.) Who could be more perfect than he—the man of all men? But what truly carried me away about him was his magnificent rage to live. Live your life to the full! this was the Alpha and the Omega of his philosophy, and he made it mine. To live life to the full, he taught me, one must be both stoic and Epicurean. One's answer to adversities, whether needle pricks or shattering blows, must be a calm mind and a sense of humor. (Poor Papa! the time was not far off when he would have to prove this valor of mind.) But one must also enjoy the bread and the wine of life to the last crumb and drop. It was partly his zeal for freedom of the mind, but even more this unconditional belief in life, that made him reject the Church; her antiquated superstitions and dogmas, he told me, put fetters on the spirit, and her hollow promises of a better life in the hereafter distracted man from the pleasures that a generous Nature had stored up for him on earth.

With my pleasure-loving disposition, it was only natural that I should embrace this easygoing wordly philosophy; and if I ever went to pay a visit to the Good Lord at all, it was only on Sundays and only out of love for my mother. She, devout Catholic that she was, seemed not very happy that Father was bringing me up to see the world with his eyes and thus preparing me for a *grande vie mondaine*.

Once, when I was twelve, on a horseback ride through Paris we met a stately gilded *carrosse*. It stopped as we came abreast; the puffy-faced, blond head of a lady leaned out the coach window, and a gloved hand waved at Papa; whereupon he stopped, too, and leaned down from his horse to kiss the lady's hand gallantly. After he had exchanged a few words with her he bade me dismount and enter the coach. Inside, I found myself in the presence of a voluble woman who, by the sheer expanse of her broad-bosomed, broad-hipped person, seemed to fill the whole coach. She was all dark red silk and cream-colored laces, and she was aglitter with jewels. Thick layers of powder tried to cover the many wrinkles on her broad triple-chinned and perhaps once beautiful face. But her eyes—blue eyes—were young with vitality and humor.

"What a darling she is, *mon cher* Henri," she gushed at sight of me. "May I kiss her?" and without waiting for answer she hugged me to her and gave me two smacking, booming kisses on each cheek. Then she said she would do everything, of course, that dear Henri wanted of her. "Your petite will be a sensation," she said, "and every man in Paris will grovel at her feet."

"How did you like the lady?" Father asked me as we rode on. "*Superbe!* with her four bellies."

"What *do* you mean?"

"One embonpoint under her robe and three others hanging down from her chin." My father laughed and told me that she was of high rank, this Madame de Senneterre; she was wife to old Maréchal de la Ferté, and she was very influential in court and in society. And she had promised to introduce me in the Louvre and in the great salons when the time came—a very important service, because Maman had no desire for a great social life. But I was not to tell Maman that the lady had called him "my dear Henri," because she didn't like it if other people called him that.

Sometimes Papa and I took our rides in the company of his subaltern officers. I came to like Lieutenant Évremond, much Papa's junior—not because he was a daredevil on horseback like Papa or me, and not because he was the wittiest of raconteurs, but rather because he had a kind of shyness that seemed perpetually to constrict his youthful and ardent impulses. With a young girl's instinct I sensed and soon detected the reason. He had a noble head, high temples, and very handsome features, but there was a wen in the middle of his forehead that marred his beauty and gave the whole face an irregular look, and it must be the awareness of this defect, I told myself, that made his lips look so bitter. But to me this very touch of asperity seemed particularly winsome; and once when he and I, far ahead of the others, stopped and hid in a thicket for the fun of ambushing them, and he smiled his bitter-sweet smile at me, I could not help kissing him right on the wen. He seemed a good deal touched, and I think that it was at this moment that his deep attachment to me—it was to last a lifetime—really began.

Évremond was the only one of Papa's fellow officers whom I had kissed, and not one of them would ever have allowed himself this kind of familiarity with me. I knew that they would have liked to, though, because once I overheard them talking about me and confessing what they would have liked best to do with me, even if I was still such a young girl. It all sounded like what my prince had whispered to me in bed, and I still couldn't figure out what it meant; but I did understand that it was not a game of Badminton that they had on their minds.

As for the prince, I would think of him often in these years—mostly at night when I felt lonely in my huge bed. What a pity, I would think, that he was a prince and not one of us—just some neighbor's boy who could come over to see me every night and sleep with me. But I was resolved to wait patiently, because, always mindful of his words before the Vesuvius picture, of his "au revoir" when we had parted, and of the white kerchief dancing in the distance, I had the persistent idea in my head that I

31

had only to grow up and develop a bosom and curves like Suzanne's in the picture, and he would come and love me dearly.

But once when Maman was doing some needlework on my future trousseau—I was thirteen now, almost fourteen—Papa told her she ought not to fret herself over such business, because what kind of father would he be if he ever allowed me such a bad bargain as any marriage is for a woman? ("Hush, before the child!" my mother said.) He would grudge me, Papa went on, to any man, even if he were a great prince. "Even Rochefoucauld?" I said. "Even Rochefoucauld," my father said, laughing. "But you must not think of him, because he has been married for some time."

I caught my breath and remained painfully still. It was my first great disappointment in love. It had been almost seven years since I had seen Rochefoucauld, the young prince, but I had thought of him often. At night I remembered Madame de Senneterre's offer. I had never cared for any kind of splendor, but now I wanted to be in the Louvre—in one of its most splendid salles, candles burning, and I all in silk and jewels, surrounded by my admirers, and suddenly the door would open and my prince would come in with his ugly wife on his arm. He would catch sight of me and stop, his mouth open. He would leave his wife just standing there alone and walk over to me. But I wouldn't return his smile; no, I wouldn't. And if he were to ask "Don't you recognize me?" I would say: "No, I don't, and I don't want to know who you are, because I don't need you. No, I don't need you. *Je m'en fiche!*"

I said "*Je m'en fiche*" determinedly and bitterly, several times, just as I had said it in Loches, but tears pricked behind my lids, and then they came flowing and wetted my cheeks and my pillows. I wouldn't have wept so much that night had I known that my faithless prince's *mariage de convenance* meant nothing to him and that a charming adventure and many happy times with him were still in store for me.

But all that was still far off.

3

IT WAS A very short time after I had learned that my young prince had married that a great tragedy struck. Papa was forced to flee Paris; and, as you can well imagine, our whole life changed.

It had not come about without warning. I did not know at the time, however, what was the meaning of all those summonses, briefs, and court orders, that had occupied Papa so much in the past months. It was only many years later that I learned the reason for them: Papa's passion for the beautiful Lucrèce Riberolles in the Rue de la Tisseranderie, whose husband prosecuted Papa with charges of adultery and, failing to prove them, tried to make away with Papa. Being himself a weakling and a coward, he had suborned one Chaban and his strong-armed men. But nothing of that seemed to impair Papa's inveterate cheerfulness, and for that very reason it was the greater shock when one day he came rushing home, his dear face all flushed, and in hot haste ordered his things packed and his horse saddled. He told Maman and me that he had killed Chaban on the

Place des Galles. They had ambushed him from behind shrubbery and fallen upon him, and he had fought them off singlehanded. But having killed Chaban, a man very influential at court, and having, when they raised the cry of "Murder!" no witnesses that he had acted in self-defense, he had no way to escape arrest, prosecution, and the scaffold but by fleeing Paris before the bailiffs came to take him away. He would try every possible expedient from abroad to settle the matter, but there was only a faint hope, he said, that he could ever return; he feared that it was adieu forever.

But even in this dreadful moment he made a great pretense of cheer. "Tears, Ninon?" he said, taking me under the chin. "Are you not ashamed? Have you forgotten what I taught you about being a stoic and a disciple of Epicurus? This is just the moment to show greatness of soul." He kissed and embraced Maman and me, and we were with him in the vestibule. Looking deliberately through his traveling bag, he exclaimed: "Where is the most important of all—my lute?" I hurried to bring it to him; and while my mother stood deathly white and trembling with fear lest the bailiffs come, and I stared at him in both pain and worship, he said that there must always be time for a song. And he tuned the strings and sang a poem of Froissart:

> "Days fade and others spring anew;
> Each month a new moon hangs in air;
> Take, then, the moment still in view,
> For Fortune is a fickle fair . . ."

And then he admonished me that, whatever should happen to me in life, I must follow his example and never lose my poise and my sense of humor. There was still a smile on his lips when he rode off, waving back. And I too, though only by a great effort, smiled and waved to him, while against my will the tears came running down my cheeks.

Father had left some money with my mother, but not for long would it cover the costs of our great household. Of the troop of servants only two had remained: my Madeleine and old Perrot, Father's valet. There would have been many others willing to stay on without pay, but we could not afford to feed so many. Indeed, if my aunt in Loches had not sent us food once in a while, we should have starved to death. Perrot, withered, flat-chested, bent, and hobbling ever since my father's spirited horse had kicked him in the hip, didn't count much, and the whole burden of our household was now on the square shoulders of Madeleine. She owed her inexhaustible health, so she maintained, to hard work and her eau de vie, an unfailing medicine against tooth- and headache, gout and dyspepsia and all kinds of woes. She worked hard and incessantly in a stubborn resolve that our household should keep its appearance of nobility and comfort. It was a dogged battle that she waged against any and all symptoms of its disintegration.

Maman and I bore our misfortune, in the beginning at least, in quite different ways. She found her haven in her faith. She had always been deeply religious, and even in Papa's time, grieved by his many amorous escapades, she had looked for solace to "higher spheres": she had joined the mystical movement which, originated by Madame Arcarie called Rose Mystique, was sweeping the country with the idea that not only selected souls, but everyone, could attain the experience of the presence of God. She went to Mass six times a day and missed no gathering of the Friends of the Bonnes Filles de Madame Arcarie, and when alone she gave herself up for long hours to her "prayers of the heart" and to concentrated mystical exercises.

But I, though broken-hearted to have lost my father, tried to stick to his worldly philosophy and his example, nourishing my courage on my sense of humor and on the hope that some day he would return as unexpectedly as he had disappeared. But when weeks, months, and years passed and the hope of his return proved to be a foolish dream, and in the face of our isolation and poverty and my mother's gnawing sorrow for me and my future, I had to make a great effort to keep up my pretense of good spirits. The Parlement Criminel de Paris had seized Papa's whole property upon his enemies' demand, and if we still had a roof over our heads and could keep our furniture, it was only because they had been bought with my mother's money. Certainly there was no money left for a dowry for me. By the generally accepted *tableau des mariages* every man was entitled to a dowry corresponding to his rank and profession, and there was therefore no prospect that I could ever marry. The only way left to ensure me a decent future was the way of all poor maidens of rank: the convent.

At first my poor mother didn't even dare hint at a solution so utterly opposed to my inclinations and views. But, watching her, I could recognize that she was not just the "sweet little bigot" that my father had called her. There was greatness, sincerity, and depth in her faith, and as I have always been impressed by grandeur, my mother's religious sweep could not fail to affect me. I would sit for hours and ponder about God and the world, and ask myself whether my father had been right in teaching me never to believe without evidence and never to be led astray by those teachings of the Church that were in contravention of reason. How, I asked myself, can our earth-bound intelligence have any inkling of the laws of the Universe, to say nothing of being the measure of them? And what a reservoir of spiritual power there must be in the Beyond, since Mother, and with her so many others, could draw such strength and solace from it!

My mother was so sweet, so considerate, so discreet! She didn't try to convince me by argument. And not until her fine instinct had told her of my susceptibility to the suggestion did she even mention the eventuality of a religious life. "Besides my faith in the Lord," she told me once when we were both sitting in the salon, bent over our needlework, "I have no other passion on this earth but to get for you the very best that life can afford. If it were a good, charming husband, I should welcome him with open arms and with my heartiest blessings. But it cannot be, I grieve to say, and I see only one way to save you from the meanness and vulgarity of this world.'' And then she spoke to me of the convent as the only place where an unmarried girl of culture and standing could find a refuge. There was in particular, she said, the Ursulines' Convent in the Rue du Faubourg Saint Jacques, where the finest bloom of Parisian maidenhood were gathered in the holy community, practicing the fine arts, gardening, going on errands of mercy, teaching in the Convent's girls' school, and pursuing all manner of such occupations as gave to an otherwise meaningless life a mission, a direction.

My mother had tried to paint the life of a religious in the brightest of colors, and I was sorry that I could not at once agree with her. Though I was nearer to God than ever before, Father's skepticism was still too much in my very bones. At religious services I still felt that I was rather paying a formal call on God than dedicating myself to him, and I knew that I had still not even crossed the threshold to Him and His Church. Mother replied that she understood my doubts, and she suggested that we should move to the Ursulines' Convent as pensionnaires. There, in holy surroundings, I might get into a state of mind in which God's Grace would seem nearer and more real. As yet I made Mother no promises. Deep within me were still the vestiges of all my old spirited defiance, humor, and zest for life, together with a spark of the vain hope that some day something unexpected might happen to save me from becoming a nun. But the sight of my mother perpetually drooping under her burden of grief and worry got to be more than I could bear any longer, and I gave in and let her write to the Mother Superior of the Ursulines.

Such was my situation and such my state of mind on the morning of the twentieth of May 1637, when I was still a virtuous maiden without an inkling that on this very day I was to meet the young man whom destiny had singled out to be the first of my lovers and the greatest passion of my life. Neither did my dear mother have any inkling, of course; if she had, she would hardly have surprised me with the promise that in the afternoon she would take me for a walk in the Luxembourg Gardens.

The promenade was meant as a treat for me, and so was the permission to wear for the first time my light blue dress. It was not exactly a new dress, but only one of my mother's of better times, slightly faded, but refitted to my slim figure. We could not afford to buy new things. Ever since my father had had to flee from Paris to foreign lands, more than four years before, we had been very poor, and our life radically altered.

I was not anticipating overmuch pleasure from our stroll, for I knew that Mother would choose the Promenoir des Malades, those lonely pathways among dark boxwood bushes where the ill or the elderly used to walk for the sake of their appetites or their digestions, and not the splendid and fashionable Promenade sous les Marronniers, where the youth of Paris sauntered on beautiful May days like this one. But it presently occurred to me that in order to get to the Promenoir des Malades one had first to cross the chestnut alley; and the thought that, for a few moments at least, I could get a glimpse of the *mondaine* life that I had once expected would be mine—this thought thrilled my imagination. For no particular reason I took a blue ribbon from our chest and, standing before my mirror, bound it around my curls. "Very fetching," I said, and smiled at my reflection.

The Promenade sous les Marronniers was a lovely sight that sunny May afternoon. The vivid green foliage overhead was enlivened with a profusion of pink-white chestnut blossoms, and beneath them there was a constant ebb and flow of flaneurs, the gentlemen in richly embroidered *justaucorps*, bowing, smiling, paying compliments, and doffing lacquered hats with a flourish of gaudy plumes to greet the pretty demoiselles. These, their beribboned and beflowered dresses fluttering, answered their gallant admirers, this one with a curl of her patrician lips, that one with an enamored *coup d'oeil* from under frivolous laces and forelocks *á l'espagnol*. The air seemed haunted with the whisper of secret amours and kisses-to-be. Its vibrating warmth caressed my skin, and I felt sorry that in a few minutes we must exchange the glittering promenade for the drab side path.

"Spring is lovers' paradise . . ."

I stopped. My ears had caught the song and a strum of lute chords. And then I espied, beneath a tree, an old street singer. Neither voice nor accompaniment was mellifluent, but they fascinated me, and I stood rooted. "Listen, Maman!" I said. "The rondel that Papa used to sing to the lute!"

"Hush!" said my mother, looking around apprehensively. "If someone were to hear you!"

I understood very well. Singing to the lute was for beggars and wandering minstrels; society would more readily forgive Papa the bloody affair on the Place de Galles than his demeaning himself by playing the lute—he, a nobleman and an officer! But I did not care. Papa was vividly in my mind. His voice penetrated to me out of a happier past: "Are you mad, Ninon? Where are you going? You don't belong to the sick and the old. You are young. Here, here is life. Don't leave the promenade. Enjoy your youth!"

Two young men came sauntering, one sleekly arrayed *à la mode* in silks and ribbons, the other more modestly dressed. Both were in high feather and obviously out for gallant adventures. *"Tonnerre de Dieu!"* exclaimed the dark one. "Look you there, Scarron!"—whereupon both stopped in their tracks and began to exchange remarks about my person in terms of the high-flown, flowery gallantry of the day, and loudly enough for me to hear them.

"Lovers', lovers' paradise . . ."

Listening half to the song and half to my casual admirers, I observed that the one, Scarron, had laughing blue eyes in a handsome, strikingly intelligent face; but I found the other, darker one the more interesting. He reminded me strangely of someone—but of whom? I was momentarily baffled. Papa? The prince? No, neither. There must be something out of the common in this dark stranger—something at once vigorous and gentle; for after that first booming *"Tonnerre de Dieu!"* and a few bold compliments he had fallen into an inexplicable silence and merely stared at me dreamily, almost shyly.

"Paradise : . . Paradise . . ."

The beggar had ended his song, and now he held out his shabby felt hat. My mother threw him two sous—no small sacrifice for her. But I was glad that she had done it: it was honoring the memory of my father's singing and playing. But save for Maman no one paid any attention to the street singer. Past him flowed the eddying current of flaneurs, the rustle of lavish gowns, the glitter of gold lace and silver buckles, the tittering and the flirtatious exchanges; but no more coppers fell into the hat. Neither of the young men standing so near made a move. I was suddenly angry, and—I do not know what devil was riding me at that moment—I snatched the hat from the beggar's hand and said bitingly: "As you are squandering so much counterfeit coin in gallantry, Messieurs, you may still have a few real coppers left in your purses"; and before my mother could stop me I had the hat under their very noses.

Scarron laughed and, never interrupting his *badineries*, threw in a handful of coppers. But the dark one stood silent, and only when I said, "And you, Monsieur?" did he reach into his pocket and place a silver coin in the hat. Still he said no word, but kept his eyes on me, in a puzzled and helpless way, so that I was hard put to it to suppress a bubble of laughter. With a "Many thanks!" and sweeping a mock-ceremonious curtsy I handed the hat to its owner.

"Let us go now," said Maman.

But the old man, overwhelmed by the splendid outcome of my intervention, implored me to stay and try once again with other passers-by. "Ruined by the war——" he pleaded. "I am sick—wife sick—four children—— All of us sleeping in the streets——"

Again my little imp of the perverse had its way with me. Were it for pity of the old man or for mere sudden thirst of adventure, I seized the lute from his hands, and——"I am going to play and sing in your stead," I told him.

I could see my mother's hands rise in deprecation. But there was a thrill in my blood; I was absorbed, too, in strumming trial cords and tuning the instrument; and I paid no attention. Many strollers stopped, and still more gathered around me when I struck the first firm chords. And then I began:

> *"Now are melted ice and snow;*
> *Grass and trees their verdure show. . . .*
> *Philomena sings in heights,*
> *Spring is lovers' paradise."*

A clatter of applause broke out, and now a rain of coins pattered into the beggar's hat. My dark, silent admirer actually threw in a gold coin. "Encore, encore!" cried the crowd.

But an abrupt silence stopped the clamor dead.

The press of folk in front of me melted away to give place to a man in richly embroidered livery. This lackey made me a profound bow. "His Excellency," he said pompously, "invites the demoiselle to be so kind as to give her encore before him."

Everyone turned around. A golden state coach had driven up and stood in the alley, flanked by two mounted guards in flashing helmets and cuirasses, their muskets *en bandoulière*, their mantles a flaming crimson background to large white crosses. And flaming crimson was the robe of the man who sat inside.

"Cardinal Richelieu," someone murmured.

I was all of a tingle. For years—ever since Papa's departure—I had lived in isolation; and now, within mere minutes, in one stride, I had moved out into the great world, into what a fullness of extraordinary events, into what adventures! And while the crowd stood stock-still before the all-powerful minister, I tripped gaily, eagerly after the lackey; and my mood grew even more buoyant when I saw my dark admirer threading the crowd with deft, quick movements. Who *was* it that he reminded me of? Presently he found a spot behind the carriage from which he could watch me at close quarters—as he was obviously intent on doing—but unobserved by the Cardinal.

The guards lowered their lances. His Excellency deigned to acknowledge my presence by a benign uplifting of the hand. I dropped him a demure curtsy; I was trying desperately not to giggle over all this ado. Richelieu seemed to notice my flippancy, but by no means to mind it. Quite the opposite! His

gray-yellow, liverish face brightened with a smile.
"Brava—bravissima!" he said. "Your way of be-
stowing charity is engaging indeed. And you know
how to play music, *mon enfant:* there was no flaw in
your performance. Delightful precision! every note
in its right place, the mood, the expression, the
balance, everything perfect. Tell me, where did you
learn to play so beautifully?"

"From Papa," I said.

Something in the expression of Richelieu's face
gave me the conviction that he guessed who my
father was. And in his eyes I detected a subtle light
that seemed to contradict all I had heard about this
inexorably hard man, this "mailed fist of France";
and I had an inkling that, despite my inexperience
and youth, he was taking a warm interest in me—as
in fact he was; an interest that was to outlast this
moment, and to be not strictly confined, either, to
my musical talents or to my virtue of charity.

"Pray be so kind," the Cardinal said, pointing to
the lute, "as to let me hear your encore. Such a
charming treasure of medieval song! It was composed in Limoges, and its original text was in
Latin."

Delighted to find the great statesman so
thoroughly informed about the trifling song, I took
up my lute, struck the introductory chords, and sang
the whole chant in its original Latin:

> *"Jam nix glaciesque liquescit;*
> *Folium et herba virescit.*
> *Philomena jam cantat in alto*
> *Ardet amor cordis in alto . . ."*

I had begun by watching the Cardinal's wondering and obviously delighted face; but in the middle of the stanza, on a sudden impulse, I turned a sidewise look on my young stranger. The deep tan of his handsome, sensitive features made a pleasant enough contrast, I found, with the gray old face in the carriage. For a moment he did not move under my gaze. Then—the audacity of it, behind the back of the Cardinal!—he lifted his hand and threw me a kiss. And that was the instant that brought me sudden enlightenment. His slim, dark figure leaned forward; his arm darted forward in the swift, covert gesture; and the resemblance that had so baffled me flashed into focus. He of whom the young man had reminded me was Signore d'Oltrecastello, the Italian fencer of my childhood; and in the next instant I felt a fine, sharp point touch my heart and pierce it. And I knew that it had been no imagined rapier's thrust, but a flash from his eyes. A quick, light, and sudden shock went through me like very lightning as I received this *fulmine improvvisato*. More than a little dazed, I could not help missing some syllables, my lapse covered only by my fingers' instinctive groping for improvised chords. When I looked up, all the chestnut bloom overhead was a mass of little rosy clouds driving over a deep-green, dizzily swaying ocean. In a moment I contrived to steady myself enough to go on; but I knew that my voice was tremulous now, and that a peculiarly warm and sensuous vibrancy had come into it. But I managed to sing the rondel to its end without stumbling again.

No one stirred when I had finished. Not until the great man himself had sketched a soundless clapping

47

gesture of his finger-tips was there a burst of applause. When it came, it brought me quite back to my senses.

"You have put much of yourself into your music, *mon enfant*," the Cardinal said, "and I must confess that the rondel never sounded so charming to me as it did just now. And your Latin! Your pronunciation! Exquisite! You have given me a real pleasure, and I could wish to reward you. What is it you would like best, *mon chère enfant?*"

Everyone held his breath, wondering what I was going to ask from the all-powerful minister. My mother bent forward, eyes wide, as if to dictate to me some very momentous request. But both common sense and instinct told me to say: "It was honor and reward enough that I was permitted to play and to sing before your Excellency *in behalf of the poor man.*"

"Of course, of course!" exclaimed Richelieu, obviously amused by the reminder. He turned to the secretary at his side: "My purse, please." He opened it and was about to take out some coins. But then he had another thought. He handed the whole purse to me.

"Take out for the poor man whatever you think right," he said, "and keep the rest for yourself." He was watching me intently; so were all the others. But I gave them no time for guessing. I paused only to say: "A thousand thanks!" Then I darted over to the beggar and poured into his hat the whole contents of the purse. He stared first at the clinking gold coins, then incredulously up at me. "Take it," I said. "It is all yours." His inarticulate thanks culminated in a wild scream of joy; then he burst into loud, unrestrained sobbing.

A solemn hush followed. When I turned about I saw the Cardinal beckoning me near to him. He gave one long, deep look into my eyes; then he bent suddenly forward, and his lips touched my forehead. "God bless you, my child," he said. And in another moment the carriage was driving off, pursued by cheers and a chorus of "Vive Richelieu!"

"It was like a consecration," my mother said when we had disengaged ourselves from the cheering crowd and were traversing the lonely paths of the Promenoir des Malades between the high, dark boxwood hedges. For my part, I did not feel so exalted about that ducal kiss as my mother did. The fact was, I had been tickled by the old man's goatee as by flies, and I was slightly annoyed that I could not scratch my nose in so eminent a presence. But my mother was transported. She called me a darling of God—one from whom He would assuredly not withhold His vocation. So many were seeking admittance to the convents nowadays, she said, that it was extremely difficult to get a novitiate, but she had no doubt that the Cardinal, after witnessing my charitable deed, would help me. From my own mind, however, nothing was more remote just now than the convent. A boundless sense of well-being, exhilaration, and lightness had flooded over me, and I had in my heart the secret but powerful conviction that the miracle for which I had hoped had actually happened. It had happened in that very moment when, as I sang, the young stranger's dark eyes had reached my heart. This had been and was to remain, I was persuaded, the great moment of my life.

I had lost sight of him when we diverged from the chestnut alley; but a crackling in the bushes, and then footfalls behind us, told me that he was following. When we got back to the entrance gate he was standing there; apparently he had taken a short cut. He was watching me in brief stolen glances of unmistakable eloquence and ardor. I knew that he would follow us all the way to the house to make sure who I was, and in fact, when Maman and I left the Luxembourg, I felt him behind me, very near.

But suddenly a woman's voice was calling Maman and me from a carriage. It was Madame de Senneterre, offering to carry us home and evidently in a hurry. What a long face, what unhappy eyes, were those of my dear young stranger when he saw me being whisked off out of his sight by carriage! I was certain, though, that he would find a way to locate me. I fancied him turning up in our street the next morning, sauntering back and forth under the trees, casting covert glances up at our house; and I would stand behind the curtain and watch him. And then, for just a moment, I would show myself and smile down at him. How wonderful was life now, coming into its own again! How enticing, with its promise of thousands of unknown delights!

4

BUT THE NEXT morning and through the whole forenoon our street lay silent and unstirring, dreaming in
the shade of the sun-bright trees. No young man put
in an appearance. Towards noon Maman announced
that this afternoon she would take me to a meeting of
the Friends of the Bonnes Filles de Madame Arcarie.
Monsieur Vincent, a holy man, would be present,
and the fire and grandeur of his inspiration would not
fail to take me one more step onward toward the
divine goal that we both desired so dearly. I looked
away from her and down at the street, but it still lay
silent and deserted in the midday heat, and my spirits
sank leadenly.

But at the last moment, just as we were ready to
start, a carriage dashed up, and Madame de Senneterre burst in, an explosion of colors, vociferating
extravagant congratulations. "Why didn't you tell
me yesterday, both of you?" she exclaimed, burying
me in her massive arms. "The whole town is talking
about nothing but you and the Cardinal. He even
kissed you, the lecherous old bird!"

51

My mother said: "I beg your pardon, Madame——" and Madame de Senneterre, aware of having made a faux pas and disturbed that my pious mother should have taken offense, hastened to assure her that there was nothing wrong with Richelieu's being an *homme à femmes*, because she knew from reliable sources that his priesthood was invalid. The bishop had had a cold on the day of Richelieu's consecration and had not pronounced the essential formula loud enough to make the ordination valid. But to be a cardinal one had not necessarily to be a priest, and on that basis Richelieu had even got a secret pontifical license to marry. But, observing that my mother's countenance was still strained, she changed the subject to say that I had warbled myself into all hearts, and that we were to go with her to the Promenade sous les Marronniers to be introduced to her friends. "Let the petite come with me," said Madame de Senneterre. Maman looked at me as if I were at the crossroads of virtue and sin; but my heart leaped. Incapable of renouncing the chance of meeting my admirer again, I said that, yes, I should like to go with Madame. To my surprise, my mother showed no sign of disappointment, and, wishing me a great deal of pleasure, she thanked Madame for the honor and entrusted me to her care.

In the carriage Madame de Senneterre, exultant that she had carried me off, kissed me over and over and said that it was time she lived up to the promise given to "my dear Henri—pardon me, your Papa." She had heard that Maman wanted to send me to a convent, and that made her flesh creep. "How can she?" she said. "Doesn't such a pious lady as your

mother know her Gospel? Does she want to make
you the unprofitable servant and bury the treasures of
your charms?'' And shrieking with laughter over her
interpretation of Holy Writ, she squinted at me with
one eye shut and added: ''I know you wouldn't
commit so inexcusable a crime. Do you imagine for
a minute, you sweet little rogue, that I didn't see you
yesterday casting a furtive eye at the young man at
the entrance gate?'' She laughed, pinched me
roguishly, and said that it must not be just that one
alone, because there were many charming fellows
with illustrious names, and that every one of them
would be overjoyed if I deigned to favor him with my
attention.

When the carriage reached the chestnut alley we
were quickly besieged by a press of gentlemen, and
Madame de Senneterre was kept busy introducing
them. Finally, at her suggestion, I left the carriage
with Alice, her lady's maid, to be escorted by her
and a score of young men along the promenade to the
perron, the outside staircase of the Palais Luxembourg. The steps were alive with splashes of color,
bubbles of laughter, and the busy prattle of the young
people who sat there enjoying the sunny May day
and the broad and splendid prospect of lawns and
flower beds. I chatted with my cavaliers and smiled
as politeness demanded, but my eyes were searching
for my stranger. Foolishly, I had taken it for granted
that I must find him here on the same spot and at the
same time, and when for a long time I failed to do so,
my heart misgave me. But then it missed a beat.
From my lofty seat on the steps I had descried him
emerging from the alley.

I saw his slim dark figure, the sun in his face, moving in my direction with the sure step of a sleepwalker making straight for an invisible goal. At the foot of the staircase he stopped and stood still; only his hand went up to his heart, and his eyes looked up at me with an overwhelmed and appealing expression. Not until I had encouraged him with a smile did he trust himself to the stairs. He looked around as if searching for someone who could introduce him to me, only to be measured by the glassy, hostile eyes that greet an intruder. But he slipped adroitly through the crowd, stopped short on the step just below me, lifted his hat, and called up to me in the tone of a long-established acquaintanceship: *"Bon jour*, dear demoiselle. Here you are at last. I was looking all over the park for you and Madame your mother. How is she? And how are you?"

Nobody marked that his address was nothing but a bold expedient for breaking through barriers of convention, and I, with my inveterate pleasure in little pranks, was delighted. Choking down my laughter, I accepted the game. It would have been deplorable, I said, if he had not appeared, because Maman, who could not come as she had promised, had especially charged me to give him her greetings. I extended my hand, and he bowed over it and carried it to his lips. They were glowing, those lips; they seemed to burn through my glove. But I had the self-control to appear casual and to ask my cavaliers to make place for monsieur; and they complied, though not without long, sour faces.

Though my young man was, in appearance and demeanor, modest by comparison with their ornate costumes and their clamor, I felt only his presence; and I was seized by the wish to be alone with him. Reading the same wish in his eyes, I made myself very gay and audacious and whispered to him: "I've had enough of sitting in the sun, and I had rather walk in the park."

He jumped up at once, and I with him, and before the others could realize what we were up to we had slipped through the crowd, down the stairs, and off into the park. Looking back, we saw the young swains and Alice making their way after us. Presently my young man sprang into a clump of young birches and rosebushes, and I, without the slightest hesitation, followed; and in a moment we were laughing together to see the pursuers hurrying by and gazing vainly about with silly faces.

But after that outburst of high spirits we both fell silent, and so we remained for a long, long moment, just standing there, face to face and our looks locked. Then he said: *"Bénit soit l'heureuse étoile qui m'a jeté sur votre route"*—words that my memory had cherished ever since. From anyone else, that praise of the happy star that had thrown him in my path would have appeared as a flowery commonplace of love talk, but in his voice there was something so momentous, so beautifully honest and humble, that it could only be felt as the expression of a heartfelt belief in a higher force drawing him irresistibly and inevitably toward me. Feeling the same way myself, I answered him with a surrendering smile, no less solemn than his. He murmured: "I cannot explain how it came about so quickly, so all of a sudden, but I love you. I have never known what love is; never before. You are my first and will always remain my only love.'' Then he said that since the moment when, yesterday, I had disappeared from his sight, he had wandered all over Paris in search of me. Sometimes he had thought that the whole episode in the alley had been but an elusive dream, and I myself a saint and a legend, never to be met in reality; but then his heart had told him that when he went to the Luxembourg he must find me, and since we had now the chance to talk together for a little, I must have mercy on him and for the love of God tell him when we could meet again.

I wanted nothing more than to meet him again. But now, so near to the fulfillment of hope, a shadow fell across my happiness. How exquisitely everything had begun! But how was it going to end when he found out that I was a poor and dowerless girl? He must have detected the trace of depression in my face, for the next he was frowning reflectively. After an intense scrutiny of my features he said: ''I must humbly apologize for my temerity, that I, still a stranger to you, dared ask you for a rendezvous. But believe me, dear demoiselle, I honor you highly, and my feelings are completely sincere.'' He went on to tell me that he was Charles de Beaumont, Vicomte de Chamausy and Sieur de Saint-Étienne of Toulon; that he had come to Paris to obtain a position in the King's household or Richelieu's—a position that he would hold until he could take over his father's estates; that he could present letters of introduction from high personages; and that, if I consented, he would call and ask my mother for permission to see me in our house and to pay his homage.

I should have preferred to tell him: "Pray do just that." But the ugly image of my poverty and the thought of the *tableau des mariages* had me in a panic. "It would be of no use," I said, and tears sprang to my eyes.

"Why not?" he insisted, an infinitely tender concern in his voice. "What is the trouble?"

For an instant I wavered: then I saw that it would be dishonest and shabby to deceive him, and diffidently, though haltingly, I told him straight out about our poverty and the uselessness of expecting any dowry with me.

But he took my hand, pressed it warmly, and protested that I offended him by the assumption that he attached any importance to a dowry; he needed none, and if *that* were the only obstacle, I should forget it and never mention it again.

Overwhelmed, I said shyly, awkwardly: "Well—if it is as you say, then I—I should be glad if you came."

"Thank you, thank you!" he exclaimed. He bowed low and kissed my hand; and though it was, as before, through the glove, I felt the ardor of his lips send the same sweet lightning through me that his look had sent yesterday, except that this time it was not so much sharp and swift as lasting—the steady illumination of a flooding brightness that I had never known before.

This greatest moment that I had ever lived through seemed to expand the world into a universe and time into eternity. Yet I remained aware throughout of the smallest, subtlest of its attendant details, and to this day they abide in my memory—the slim white shafts of the birches, the hazy green of their new leafage; a half-opened rosebud catching the sunlight and looking like a small suspended heart; a white butterfly zigzagging past as if it had been some tiny billet-doux snatched up by a capricious wind; the chirrup of siskins, the plashing of a fountain close by us. And at the center of it all was *he*, with my hand in his and pressed to his lips, his head humbly bowed, yet somehow eloquent of pride and power. For it came over me in a rush of certainty that there was a greatness in him, little as I could then have told what manner of greatness it might be. But save for that one flash of questioning surmise there was no room in my great moment, or in my heart, for anything more than the pure, simple, and radiant awareness of a heaven in me, of myself in heaven.

Next morning, in extraordinarily solemn *tenue*, with his three-plumed tricorne pressed tight to his heart, Charles appeared in the Rue des Trois Pavillons. He had presented his credentials, signed by the bishop and the president of the Parlement de Toulon. Admitted to our house, he became our daily visitor, beloved not only by me but also by my mother, who declared him to be "the most exquisite young man" and "the soul of decency and honor." Madeleine adored him, too. She displayed all the tricks and miracles of her cuisine on Sundays when he came to dinner; and nobody knew then that all the good roasts and the delicacies came, not from Aunt Montaigu's sparse generosity, but out of Madeleine's own savings, which she doted on sacrificing for the "good gentleman" who was going to "snatch me away from the *bon Dieu*."

To me the hours of his presence were purest delight. His presence in itself would have been enough. But I had the ineffable joy of discovering that he had the same interests as I. He loved music and poetry, and when he read me Villon's love poems it was only through his voice and intonation that I came fully to understand their quivering passion. But more exciting to me than the greatest love poem of Villon or Petrarca were his own words of love, whispered when Maman's attention was diverted from us to her mystical meditations—words even more beautiful when muffled by overmastering passion or dissolved into inarticulate exclamations, languishing sighs, or long silences. In short, his courtship had the dream-like exaltation that, I was sure, could come only from the spirit.

There came a day when my mother told me: "The love that your Charles offers you is so romantic, so utterly different from an everyday love, that you should take good care to keep it that way. In a few weeks or months you will be his wife. I warn you, child, until then be patient and avoid anything that could disillusion him in his belief that you are what you are—a fine and perfectly virtuous maiden."

I blushed and said that I was aware of nothing that might look unseemly. But when I gave it an afterthought I discovered that Maman had been right: I had done little things better avoided. I didn't know as yet that they were the first successes of a refined scheme of my suitor himself—that he was exercising all his ingenuity to arouse and to tantalize me, and then accepting my responses with the most innocent mien in the world. Like my mother, I took it for granted that it was I who was to blame; and I resolved to be irreproachably self-controlled and decorous in the future.

At first I managed fairly well. But the little fleshly irritations accumulated, and with them my discomfort lest my unrest become perceptible in my demeanor. And as the weeks drew on, this unrest grew and grew and seemed to be propelling me toward a crisis.

One day, with Charles and Maman in the salon as usual, I went to fetch a book from a little table by the side of my bed. In the instant before I bent to pick it up, a strange sensation ran down my spine, and, turning quickly, I saw my lover's eyes on me. And suddenly it was as if, under his stare, my dress were falling from me and leaving me stark naked in his presence. I started back and, for a moment, stood there trembling. "What is it?" he asked, turning an astonished look on me—a look so beguilingly innocent that once more I believed the obscene imagining to have been created by my own mind, and that he would have been shocked if he had realized what I had been thinking. I sighed involuntarily, said that there was nothing, and returned with my book, trying to appear casual and, when it didn't quite work, covering my discomfort with hectic, overdone merriment.

That night, alone and about to go to bed, I did not undress carefully, as on other nights, folding my frock in orderly fashion, laying it over the back of my chair, and placing stays, lingerie, and stockings on the seat: I undressed in nervous haste and dropped everything in a heap on the floor.

When my body emerged out of a cloud of light blue and white I looked down at it with mounting wonder, aware that it had become something new to me—something quite different from what it had been before.

A few steps took me into the white quadrangular spot that the moon cast on the floor before my mirror. Surrounded by the frame, my naked figure stood in the glass like a life-sized painting.

Was I beautiful? Or was I not?

In modern and Cinquecento paintings the women had chubby faces, full figures, voluptuous and proudly arched bosoms, lavish embonpoints, and massive flanks and thighs, like Suzanne in the painting in Loches. And I was not at all like that. Rather, my oval face, slender limbs, narrow waist, my frail, sloping shoulders, small hands and feet, and daintily pointed little breasts were like those of some of the Roman white Carrara marble statues in the gardens of Paris. Yet, though I was not like the curvaceous Suzanne, I thought I liked my body better. For a long while I stood lost in tender contemplation, absorbed, smiling forlornly.

At last I turned with light, soundless steps; my bare feet glided over the carpet. I walked erect, like a somnambulist or as if performing some ancient and solemn ceremony. Before the drawn bed curtains I stood still, touched by mystical excitement.

I thrust the curtains aside. On other nights I would put on my nightgown, slip under the covers, snuggle down among the pillows, tuck myself in, roll up, and fall soundly asleep at once. But not tonight. Tonight I found myself posing my nude limbs on the dark blue counterpane, head relaxed, hands clasped together behind my neck, one leg bent at the knee, the other hanging lazily down.

"What would he think if he saw me thus?" I wondered, and smiled, because I knew he would like my body. But then I stopped smiling and closed my eyes; because another question had taken possession of me: "And—what would he *do?*"

I tried to imagine. I summoned memory to my aid. Had I not been with other men in bed?—with Papa, with my princely boy in Loches? For the first time in long years the desire to have another body with me in my bed returned; and it was Charles's body that I longed to have by my side. I realized that it would not be, as it had been with Papa or with the prince, a matter of nothing more than endearments or of lying quietly side by side the whole night long. Curiosity and restlessness set my cheeks to burning and my breasts to rising and falling. I think I had not a wink of sleep that night.

The next day I was plagued by feelings of guilt and by the tacit fear that they might be written on my face. But I could not help it if every droop of my lover's eyelids, every inflection of his voice, and the slightest of his gestures were in my blood, or if I connected them with my nocturnal imaginings.

Though we were not formally engaged as yet—we had to wait for Beaumont père's official acceptance of the *sommation respectueuse*—on parting Charles got his good-night kiss, and Maman, I knew, didn't mind, for she would let me see him to the entrance door in the vestibule. When I returned she would smile, obviously in tender recollection and not begrudging me the same joys of youth that had been hers when Papa was courting her. But that day I didn't want to be kissed, because, all wrought up with excitement, I feared that the contact of his lips would confuse me and make me commit some unpardonable silliness. But when he saw me shrink he seemed perturbed, and he asked in a pleading voice whether he had done anything to displease me.

"No," I said, "you have done nothing. It is only that I——" But I was stammering and finding no plausible excuse, and, seeing the hurt in his eyes, I lifted my face to him, offering my lips, and said: "All right—kiss me, then." But behind my back I had my hands clenched into fists; I was pressing my nails hard into the flesh in order to think rather of the pain than of our lips' touching. But when they did touch, and Charles took what I had wanted to deny to him today—took it hungrily, more closely than usual and longer—it happened as I had feared. My fingers loosened; my arms swept forward; and in an uprush of uncontrollable passion I flung them around his neck and glued my lips to his in a hungry and eager abandon.

Had it but stopped at that! But not only did my lips and my arms cling tight to him, but also my bosom, my thighs, my knees, my belly. An inner voice warned me to withdraw, but I could not. A little flame ran like a wildfire through all my blood, and I was powerless to quench it.

For a long moment I was wholly breathless and swimming with bliss; but when at last we disengaged ourselves, I was terrified at what I had done. Now he must despise me, I thought.

"Go," I said, turning my face away. "Please go."

"Yes, my love," he said gently. "Now I *can* go, and let me thank you. Because, had you not given me my good-night kiss, I should have been tormented by the fear that you don't love me any more, and I should not have found a single minute of rest. But now I can go in peace. Only one last look at you!—So!—And now I feel the way an angel must feel in the sight of God. Good night, my love."

I looked at him in amazement. Was it conceivable that he had noticed nothing of my wicked behavior? His eyes were utterly limpid, with nothing in them but purity, tender reassurance and honesty; not a trace of reproach, of suspicion. And before he went he bowed and kissed my hand with devotion, as if it were the hand of a saint's statue. Was all this naïveté and candor, or was he generously overlooking my lasciviousness to spare me the sting of shame?

But just then, with senses still in a turmoil, I had no time for reflections of that order. No sooner had Maman withdrawn for the night—I could hardly wait for the moment!—than I undressed with feverish haste and threw myself naked on my bed. Closing my eyes, I allowed my thoughts—now enriched by a new experience—to extend their fancies of the night before, and to imagine that my Charles, naked as I, was approaching my bed. I was all aquiver with restlessness and an almost intolerably sweet craving. I brought my hand up to my cheek. The cheek seemed afire. I felt my breasts, cupped my hands more closely against them, clasped them; and they, as if responding, began to tingle and to grow. The tingling passed up into my arms; my fingers strayed down delicately and slowly. Once more I heard the warning voice inside me, and I made an effort, a real effort, to keep my hands in check; but they would not obey. I caressed and squeezed my soft skin savagely; I heard myself uttering little moanings and then a half smothered cry.

It was a sound such as I had never heard before, either from myself or from any other human being. It was hoarse and yet squealing, and its beastliness at once terrified and sobered me. The fire in my veins went out. All that remained was a dull ache of unsatisfied emptiness. I withdrew my hands; I flung the covers over my body, ashamed of its nudeness, loathing myself.

I wept for hours. And I resolved never again so to debase myself. But the power of my excited flesh was stronger than my will. In the daytime my head was aching and my heart pounding from my experiences of the night. I managed to keep my lewd impatience out of my eyes and deportment, but I rejoiced in the strictness of the usage that never left a girl with a man without chaperon, for I was afraid I might let myself go once again. Charles must not know that I was, as my aunt had once put it, "born corrupt to the core."

But one day my mother explained to us that she had promised to join the Friends of the Bonnes Filles de Madame Arcarie in a pilgrimage to Longjumeau, and that on the 15th of June they would set out in the morning and not return until nightfall. Because my position was still skeptical in matters of the Faith, she did not plan to take me with her; but neither might Charles come to see me in her absence. He said that she was not to worry: he would use the day to go to Vincennes and see a distant relative, *châtelain* of the royal castle, whom he would ask for support in his overtures toward employment in the royal household. It had been agreed that Charles should not write to his father about his plan to marry until he could prove that he was able to support a household in Paris by his own efforts. For that reason I ought to have welcomed my suitor's going to Vincennes, which must help speed the day of our engagement and that of our wedding. But the prospect of separation from him for a whole day crowded every other thought out of my mind, and the nearer the day, the more desolate I became. Presently a fantastic notion came into my head from nowhere: the thought that it might be not such a bad idea if I were to go with him to Vincennes. And the idea kept on taking definite shape and plaguing me.

I didn't mention my silly idea to anyone; not until, on the evening when Charles was taking leave of me in the vestibule, I heard myself broaching it to him as if in jest. To my astonishment he said: "Why, yes, why not?" It could easily be done, he went on. After my mother's departure he would come with a carriage and wait on the Place Barbette, around the corner from our house. We could travel together to Vincennes, have dinner with his people in the castle, and be back by early afternoon, long before Mother. My heart leaped, and we laughed with each other as on the day when we had made our escape from the staircase in the Luxembourg Gardens.

"At last," he said, "we shall be quite alone by

ourselves! I have waited long for such an occasion, for I want to give you something that I can give you only in secret, and which no one but you, my dearest, shall have forever and ever.''

In a fever of curiosity I asked him to tell me what it was, but he just shook his head; and when I pouted and insisted he said I might know that he was talking about the key that would open the door to our happiness.

For some reason I blushed. But when I saw his clear, guileless eyes I felt ashamed for having had a vicious thought about whatever it was that he wanted to give me. I asked no more questions, but gave myself up to innocent anticipations of the expedition that was to take me through the spacious countryside with my beloved.

That night I found myself taking my bridal chemise from the trousseau chest. It was made of the finest linen and Malines laces, and when I put it on and in the mirror, saw how my developing curves thrust themselves against the clinging material, I felt my face getting feverish. I well knew that if anything wrong happened on the morrow, it would be all my fault. But from where was I to get the will and the strength to resist the promptings of my perverse flesh and to refrain from tempting him? If I did tempt him and we were guilty of any wrongdoing, how disgusted he would be with me afterwards! He would be grievously disappointed in me; his pure heart would be broken; and he would certainly abandon me.

My eyes, darting tormentedly about the room, caught sight of my little white marble statue of the Holy Virgin. In the blue radiance that filled the room the statue shone with unearthly brightness. Oh, if I could but believe in her! If I could have a little of my mother's faith! So insistent became this longing that I slid out of my bed and, when I had put on my simple nightshirt, walked over to the statue and, kneeling down, faith or no faith, began to pray: "Have pity on me, O Immaculate One. Let there be nothing to make me lose him, for I love him so much! I will never be ungrateful to you, and if you will help me and let nothing happen tomorrow, I will take it as a sign: I will believe in Thee and in Thy Son and in my immortal soul for all time to come."

As soon as I had finished this compact with the Virgin I felt at once deliciously aware of the freshness and whiteness of the nightshift clinging, cool and protective, to my body and of an inner joy in virtue for virtue's sake, which, I found, was much lovelier than the obscure thrills of overwrought flesh. I said a fervent *"Je Vous salue, Marie"* and, feeling heavenly clean and secure, covered myself to the chin, closed my eyes, and, lying straight and on my back, fell happily asleep.

But of what I dreamed in my sleep I felt a little ashamed in the morning.

5

THE EARLY MORNING light was still dim when I stole around the corner and climbed into the carriage in which Charles had been waiting for me on the Place Barbette. It was one of those poorly constructed old coachman-driven vehicles called "fiacres" because one hired them beside the convent of St. Fiacre. They smelled of the stable and had straw peeping through worn-out upholstery. But to me this one was a heavenly chariot that was to carry me with my beloved into a day of sun, freedom, and happiness.

"Remember our compact," I reminded Saint Mary as we passed by her church, its great gate wide open, and the flicker of its candles and the admonitory reverberation of its choir reaching out to me.

On the market place in front of the *halle au blé*, the city's granary, our fiacre was stopped. A thick throng had gathered around a buxom fishwoman, and she, hands on hips, was chiding an elderly lady customer: "What are you talking about? My fish stinks? You stink and I stink, but never my fish. What? Dead it is, you say? Oh my! yes. But it was still alive a minute ago. It must have laughed itself to death when it saw you coming, you old hag!'' The harangue was rounded off with a selection of those scabrous epithets that, despite the *ordonnances* of the city authorities, were still current coin in the market place. Father had left behind him a little leaflet called *"Nouveaux Compliments des Dames de la Ville."* It was fun to read this resourceful vocabulary of the market women's insults (it was said to be resorted to by even the old Queen Mother herself), and it was even more fun to hear them at their source.

When the fishwife saw me laughing she broke off her flatteries and shot me a resentful glance. But then she fell to grinning. "A nice couple!" she said. "On your honeymoon trip, eh?" She picked up a baked fish from her stand and thrust it at me. "Here, take this as a wedding present. For you, Madame, is the tail, and for the young Monsieur the nice middle piece." Everyone around us burst out laughing, and in the midst of it her neighbor, a baker woman, passed me a longish loaf of the famous bread of Grenelles: "Here, Madame, there's another wedding present—and, as you can see, quite the right thing for the bride: long, big, and crisp." I felt myself blushing, and my face became even hotter when I noticed Charles watching me sidelong. But I managed to thank the two women and to take the presents, and our fiacre moved on, followed by a chorus of *"Bon voyage!"* and "A happy wedding night!"

On the Place du Dauphin we were stopped again by a crowd. Bugles sounded. From the Rue des

Sorties Saint Honoré du Louvre a platoon of red-and-blue musketeers came marching along, followed by green falconers on horseback and a tremendous pack of hounds. "Today is the King's hunting day," Charles said. "He is off to St. Germain." Surrounded by noblemen *en grande tenue* the King, himself dressed in simple black, came riding by. The few scattered cries of "Vive la roi!" he answered haughtily and morosely. But when he had passed by, the crowd broke into loud cheers: "Vive la reine!" and there were also cries of "Peace!" "Peace!" "Peace with Spain!" Bowing from her heavy six-horse carriage, the emerald-eyed, copper-blonde, extremely pale Infanta Queen rewarded the crowd with a sad but pretty smile. "Poor Queen!" I said. "It must be terrible for her that we are at war with her native country."

"And that's not the last of her troubles," said Charles. He launched into anecdotes about the queen's childless marriage—the papal nuncio's urgent but futile remonstrances with the king for being so persistently lethargic about his marital duties, the keyhole watch kept every night at the Queen Mother's order by her ladies in waiting, who continued unable to report any promising developments on the royal bedstead.

Meanwhile our carriage had reached the Place de la Bastille. We passed through the Porte Saint Antoine and left the city. Like a symbol of my future life at Charles's side the pleasant landscape of the Île de France unfolded its prospect to my delighted eyes. Beneath an unusually deep blue sky, wide meadows and fields, interrupted by clumps of bushes and little groves, undulated to the far horizon—a horizon that was a dazzle of sun-shot white mists and a promise, as it seemed, of an even more dazzling if still mysterious fulfillment.

We were sitting each in his corner, with a kind of neutral zone between us; and this Charles seemed to respect—to my thinking, a little too strictly. Yet I know that I should have been grateful to him for his caution, for I could trust neither myself nor even Saint Mary.

After some two hours the carriage stopped. The coachman alighted to announce that we were in Picpus and that his horses needed a rest. Charles frowned, but he made no protest. "Shall we get out and have our refreshments in the open?" he suggested; and on my welcoming the idea he picked up the woolen laprobe and the food basket that Madeleine, conspirator in our plot, had prepared for me. We crossed a roadside pasture toward a little grove that promised protection against the sun, which was beating down much too fiercely for so early an hour.

Charles stopped to point out a soft wooden elevation in the distance. "Look," he said. "What can that be over there?" I caught sight of something that shimmered indistinctly at the top of the hillock, something white and rosy in the far distance; but I could not make out what it was, either. A herd of sheep was grazing near by, and we went to question the shepherd, a man with a withered skin and a toothless mouth but clever blue eyes. "Some tumbledown structure," the old man said. "An old-time heathen temple or a castle ruin. All I know for sure is that it belongs to the Comte de Coligny." The romance and mystery of the distant ruin drew me. "Let us go over there and see," I suggested, agog for exploration. Charles demurred, because of Vincennes; then he changed his mind and said that, if I wished, he could go to Vincennes some other day instead. We finally decided on that and took the way that the shepherd pointed out. It led us along a little brook and past blue ponds surrounded by buttercups and marsh marigolds.

We came upon a hemlet alive with gay countryfolk all decked with flowers and ribbons, celebrating a wedding. It would have been an offense to reject their invitation, and we stayed for a while. We congratulated the bride—a stout, stubby, slit-eyed lass, full of bounce, whose inflated belly bore witness that she was a less dilatory worker than her good country priest. We shared with them no end of their heavy but delicious *andouilles* and *boudins* and sour wine, and in exchange we presented them with our food basket. And then, having danced with groom and bride, we set out again and made for the ruin.

The trail that we were following soon became unrecognizable in a tangle of undergrowth, moss, and grass. Charles led the way with confidence, as if perfectly familiar with it. Adroitly he picked out little detours, removing stones and bent branches from my way. As earlier in the carriage, his gallantry was impeccable, and when, close enough to have touched me by a very slight movement, he did not make that movement, I decided that even a nun would be annoyed at such excess of chivalry, and that I had to make an ever so slight concession to my good resolutions and tempt him a little. I could always withdraw if he became too forward and took too many liberties, could I not? I swayed toward him as if inadvertently, and when nothing happened I had him tighten my shoelaces. When we came to a ditch—which I could have taken easily in one jump—I made helpless eyes, so that he had to carry me over in his arms. And it was all in vain. He took me up and put me down as if I were the Holy Virgin in fragile faïence. Only once did his arm make an encircling gesture as if about to press me to him—but it was only to snatch an insect that had settled on my shoulder. My head was a swirl of love and exasperation mingled, and I didn't know which I should have preferred—to kiss him or to scratch or bite him.

But then I became aware of a shadow falling. Whether because a suspicion had stolen into my mind that behind Charles's exasperating reserve there lurked a purpose that had nothing to do with chivalry and honor, or because the deepening dusk of the wood had communicated itself to me, or both, I knew that a strange misgiving was fast growing upon me.

"Who is this man, really?" I asked myself anxiously, "—this man whom I love above everything in the world and whom I still do not know?" From the moment when I had met him in the Luxembourg Gardens I had sensed grandeur and a tremendous power beneath his fascinating amiability, and I had tried many times to find out of what kind they were. They had remained unfathomable; and when my awakening sex had become dominant in my mind I had given up puzzling about his character altogether.

But now, in my alarm, I began to puzzle again, and I wanted to know.

"You look weary," Charles said. He had stopped walking and so had I. Facing him, I looked squarely into his eyes.

"Yes, there is something," I said. "And I will tell you straight out. I love you with all my heart, and I want you. But I want you whole, and not only a part of you. There is something about you that I can only guess at—something that I cannot grasp. I can only feel that it is *there*. And you are not really mine until I know you completely—all of you."

A flash of surprise showed in his eyes, and a narrow line between the brows told me that my words were not welcome. When he bent forward and studied me he reminded me once more of d'Oltrecastello, the Italian fencer. There went through me a shiver of apprehension lest a word spring suddenly from his lips—a word, sharp as a foil's point, that, like the *fulmine improvvisato*, would pierce my heart.

"I *know*," I said, breaking the strained silence, "that you are not merely the charming marquis, the sieur with delicate manners, that you try to exhibit to me and to the world. That is only your shell. Deep inside you there is something else entirely—an artist, a philosopher, a man carrying the burden of some great idea or some momentous design; something unusual—unusual and, it may be, terrible."

"Terrible?" he said. His dark eyes were upon mine for another long and reflective moment. Then he said with a slow, a strangely insinuating smile: "And you are afraid of it, darling?"

"Yes," I said, "I am afraid. But I think that that is only because you are concealing your innermost self from me. My instinct tells me that I shouldn't be afraid and shouldn't mind and should even love it—if only I were permitted to *know*."

At that his face lit up. "What a fine and sure instinct you have, my dearest! I am glad that you told me outright how you feel. Yes, there is something in me, something powerful—more powerful than I—that I have never so far been able to get to the bottom of. That is why I cannot tell you what it is. But when I know—the very first moment I know—I will tell you. I promise it. Can you be patient enough in the meantime, ask no questions, and wait until I am ready to tell you myself?"

Though his words were evasive, his promise, the charm of his smile, and the honesty of his look disarmed me once more. He is shy, I thought, like everyone who has greatness in his soul. "I will wait, dear," I said.

"And you trust me? Unconditionally and fully?"

"Unconditionally and fully. I am yours."

"Yesterday I promised you something," Charles said suddenly, "—something that will bind us together for the rest of our lives." I must have looked very foolish at this moment, because there was a mocking glint in his eye when I saw him reaching inside his coat and producing a little round rosewood box encrusted with coral and enamel. While I stared in fascination he took a ring from this box and showed it to me. I had received many gifts from Charles before—books, flowers, confections, trinkets, even a precious Chinese silk-and-ivory fan; but the marvelous great turquoise of this ring eclipsed all of them together in beauty and in value as well as in meaning. "It is—like moonlight!" I stammered.

"Quite right. That is what this stone got its name from—'Moonlight on a Lover's Face.' An ancestor of mine brought it from Persia, and it has been in our family ever since. Take it as a token of our knowledge—yours and mine—that I am bound to you for all eternity." Solemnly he put the ring on my finger. Then—at last!—he reached out to put his arm around me, and his lips came to meet mine.

Thunder growled in the distance, and a great rain threatened. "Come," said Charles. "We shall have to hurry to escape the storm and to be back before your Maman."

The reminder of Mother brought me to my senses. I arranged my disheveled hair and adjusted my dress. Tenderly, in order to protect me against the wind, Charles wrapped me in our woolen rug, and I followed him meekly.

When we reached the fiacre we found it all ready. In my confusion I did not even notice that it stood turned in the direction of Paris. The sky was swept clear by now, and the sun shone again. There were peace and brightness over all the world, but not for me. In the coach we sat apart as before, each in his corner; only Charles, anything but sprightly as he had been that morning, sat dispirited, brooding, silent. When I saw him suffering, all suspicion vanished. For a long time maidenly decorum held me back; but the moment came when I knew that I must be held back no longer, and that something had to be done about us two. Taking his hand warmly, I said:

"I cannot bear to see you so sad. I love you, and you gave me your ring, and I will be yours."

I saw him drinking in my words, his face lighting up with a great joy. We gazed at each other, he with triumphant possessiveness, I in smiling submission. Then he drew me passionately on to his lap. Our mouths met and clung, teeth and tongues glued together in our madness, and our bodies' pulses singing "Soon, soon, soon—tonight, tonight!" And soon not only our pulses, but also our voices, were saying it; and before we reached Paris everything was agreed upon between us.

Arrived at home, I found it easy to persuade Madeleine to leave the door in the garden wall open tonight. The good soul had always slipped candies or pickled fish or other tidbits to me behind Maman's back, and her face was beaming because now she could help me to the greatest of all the sweets her petite could ever have. And, to round out my luck, a horseman came with the message that the pilgrim ladies had been surprised by a thunderstorm and would spend the night in a wayside convent and not reach Paris until the next afternoon.

And then came the night, my first of love—the night of nights that was always to remain in my memory. A tranquil moonlight drifted into my room. I undressed and stepped to the mirror. "Yes, he will like you," I whispered. The lines of my body seemed to fluctuate. In its whiteness there were nuances of cream and rose; it was smooth, satiny, inviting to the touch. The white marble statue had come to life. I had become a woman grown, with sex visible on every part of me, and with sex glittering at me out of the wild, soft strangeness of my eyes.

In my bed I lay in the posture in which I had so often imagined that I would be awaiting my bridegroom—arms back, hands under my head, one of my legs drawn up and bent at the knee, the other dangling relaxed over the edge. With my eyes closed I listened to Charles's stealthy steps in the hallway. I heard the handle of the door latch going down, the door opening, and then Charles tiptoeing toward my bed. There he came, first to stand in breathless silence, then to whisper to me: "How beautiful you are, my beloved one!" I opened my eyes a slit, just the way I had done as a little girl in Loches, and I saw him undress and stand before me like a statue of dark bronze against the white moonlight, every line of his slim body admirable.

But he did not throw himself upon me as I expected. Instead, he let himself down on his knee; he took my foot into his hand with a tender solicitude as if it were a precious white blossom; and, humbly adoring what he had conquered, he laid upon it a long, desirous kiss. And then his lips came working up along my thighs, my loins, higher and higher, to my belly, my breast. And then it was not only his lips, but also his tongue, that made a little flame spring up on every spot it touched; and then there were a thousand little fires, and at last a single and all-consuming incandescence.

We made love only once, but that once went on for hours—not because Charles found any impediment in the physical armor and symbol of my chastity, but because, in our fury of abandon, we passed without a moment's interlude from one crisis to the next until exhaustion overtook us. His head fell on my breast, and I, after having contemplated long the moonlight on my lover's face, closed my eyes, to open them only when the sun stood high and he was gone.

6

IT WAS THE same bed at which I looked on wakening, the same armchair, the same recess with the hanging lute, the same window, the same outlook into a bower of trees—but what a difference! Everything made over new, invested with a freshness, a brightness, and I myself every whit a new being, my brain swept clear and free, my blood cleansed, profound contentment in all my limbs, full of lightness and strength and thrill about the great mystery lifted.

With a great zest I fell upon the honey-and-barley soup that Madeleine brought me for breakfast. Her little eyes and her whole broad peasant face were radiant, as if for a sweeping victory won.

"You never know about a man," she said, "even the finest, but you are on the safe side now. My sister Louise had a fiancé when she was a girl, but when it came to leading her to the altar the good boy was a little slow. But—my sister Louise was a clever one. She got him to make love with her and became pregnant, and so he was caught and had to marry her.

As for me, I was coy and offish with my lad, and see what it made of me—an old maid!''

She was of great importance to us, my good Madeleine. By night she saw to it that my lover could enter and leave our house unobserved, and in the daytime she was on the lookout when Mother had gone to the Friends of the Bonnes Filles de Madame Arcarie or to the church, trusting us to Madeleine as decorum demanded. For no sooner had Mother left the house than we would throw ourselves at each other with so violent an impulsion that we did not wait to reach the bed, but made love forthwith wherever we happened to be. There was no place, no situation, that we should have found too uncomfortable, no spot or part of our body with which we could not have found a way to make love. And I not only had all the voluptuous delights of what the Romans called *dulcis insanitas*, sweet lunacy: I *loved* Charles, too, with my whole heart and soul. There were moments, quite outside our wild moods, when only our souls seemed to touch—moments of reading the poets together, or making music, or just gazing wordless into each other's eyes. So great was my happiness, so blinding its radiance, that I did not perceive any danger signals.

One day a young woman appeared in our street and hid herself in the bushes on the empty plot opposite our house. She had a white, freckled cat face with round green cat eyes and a mass of glossy red hair. But those bushes across the way were a rendezvous for many couples, mostly of neighborhood servants, and I paid no attention to this girl. It never occurred to me to connect her appearance in any way with Charles, nor did I become suspicious when she appeared again and again.

One day I got an anonymous letter warning me that Charles had a mistress, Yvonne, a red-haired girl of obscure descent and lowly station; also that he frequented the Pomme de Pin, a tavern that had taken an ill name from the inordinate excesses of its guests. I did not hesitate to show the letter to Charles.

"Only that black rascal Count Miossens could have written this," said Charles. He frankly admitted that before he had met me in the Luxembourg Gardens he had been a frequent guest in the Pomme de Pin and that up to that moment red-haired Yvonne had been his mistress. He told me a touching story. The girl's stepfather, his shoemaker, had counted on selling her first night to the highest bidder, and Miossens, shown the naked charms of this *primeur* by a peep through the keyhole, had paid him five hundred écus in advance. But Yvonne loathed Miossens, a fat, bleary-eyed revolting satyr, and fled from home. Charles, feeling sorry for the girl's predicament, took her to himself and made her his mistress. Nevertheless Miossens went on pursuing the girl, and when she continued deaf to his overtures he warned her that he would denounce her to the authorities as a prostitute. "You will get a hundred lashes on the Place des Halles, your hair will be shorn, and you will be banned from the city under penalty of death," he threatened her. Though Charles said that he had dismissed her as his mistress, she still looked to him for protection and tried to keep near him, and Miossens, wrongly assuming that Charles was still the reason for her dogged resistance, must have written this shabby anonymous letter to me in the hope of my becoming jealous and keeping Charles away from the girl. Of course I believed every word of the story, and I would not even allow Charles to frighten Yvonne away from the neighborhood, as he declared that he would.

Then Charles began to ask me strange questions about the turquoise ring. As we were not yet officially engaged, he had requested me not to wear it and not to show it to anybody. His request had hurt a little, but I obeyed. I kept the ring in its rosewood box in my lingerie chest. Once, upon his special demand, I showed him the hiding place. A few days later he wanted again to know the whereabouts of the ring. I was a little puzzled. Had he been looking for it without telling me? I had, in fact, changed the hiding place: instead of keeping the ring in my chest I had put it away behind my books, which nobody was supposed ever to touch. A few days later still, he told me that the time of our official engagement was approaching, and that I should give him the ring so that he could take it to a goldsmith for precise adjustment to the size of my finger. ''That's not necessary,'' I told him. ''The ring fits as if it had been made for no one but me.'' He seemed disappointed. I experienced a vague malaise, but I would not admit to myself the suspicion that he wanted to have the ring back. I loved my ''Moonlight on a Lover's Face,'' and for nothing in the world would I have parted with it.

One afternoon Charles failed to appear. He didn't come to me even by night. This and following nonappearances—they grew in number and length—he would explain to me by journeys that he had to make to obtain a position. I, wishing to trust him fully, was foolish enough to believe him. And when, in contrast to previous occasions, he began to show preoccupation and neglect of my person, I took these for signs of a hidden worry because his efforts to find a suitable post were getting nowhere. I pondered the question whom to approach to help me find him one. I thought of my father's fellow officers, especially Évremond, but they were all in the field. Then Madame de Senneterre came to mind, and finally, when Charles had stayed away for two full days and nights, I determined to go and see her. But just then, quite unexpectedly, there was brought to me a piece of great news, which, if I could only put it to the right use, seemed to warrant the most sanguine hopes.

The bearer of the news that seemed to me so fortunate was Père Luc, the pastor of our parish church and my old instructor in the catechism, on whom I had always inflicted so many sorrows with the sincerity of my disbelief and so much embarrassment with my confessions. How often had I shocked the good old man by telling him in the confessional of dreams about a naked boy in my bed and of my unrepentant wish that my dreams should come true? But whenever I confessed such or other mischiefs and sins, most of them invented, he would always kindly tell me: "Say a hundred *Je Vous salue's* to the Holy Virgin, and that will help you, my poor child," and he had never ceased loving me.

Today there were red spots of excitement on Père

Luc's lean, withered face when, in his best cassock, he came hurrying to our house. "A great honor is to be bestowed on our little Ninon," he said breathlessly, producing and unfolding a letter signed by Boisrobert, secretary to Cardinal Richelieu. "His Excellency," the letter said, "would be pleased to receive Mademoiselle Ninon de Lenclos in a private audience," and Père Luc, her *parocchus ordinarius*, was requested to escort his parishioner to the Palais Cardinal at two o'clock of this afternoon.

"How extraordinary!" Père Luc said, looking at me lovingly and almost with awe. "Cardinal Richelieu, a Prince of the Church, the highest ranking statesman in France, overburdened with responsibility and work, finds the time to see you, a young girl, in a private audience!" Maman agreed that this was extraordinary, and she seemed swept into ecstasy. Not for a moment did it occur to her humble soul that it ought to have been she, my mother, who was chosen to take me to Richelieu, and both she and Père Luc agreed that the only purpose of the audience must be that His Excellency wanted to reward me for my exemplary deed of charity in the Luxembourg Gardens. But I, remembering that Madame de Senneterre had called Richelieu an old lecher, assumed that this reward would be only an official pretext to get me into his presence, and that Père Luc had been chosen as chaperon because he could be sent away, whereas it would be less easy to be rid of my mother.

There came to my mind the many piquant *historiettes* that Madame de Senneterre and Papa, and also Charles, had told me about the great Richelieu,

"aimant la femme et craignant le scandale"—
Richelieu and Marion Delorme, Richelieu and the
Duchesse de Chevreux, Richelieu and Queen Anne,
and so on and on. Did the great man think that now
there would be another *historiette,* Richelieu and
Ninon de Lenclos? I felt a little mischievous smile
curl my lips. Of course, I did not think of betraying
my Charles in the slightest way. But playing a little
with His Eminence—why not? Playing as a cat with
a mouse—but just playing and nothing more. And in
the meantime I could coax out of the old lecher a
position for Charles! What a wonderful prospect! No
more torment of long separation from my lover, all
his unconfessed worries about a proper billet done
away with, and—above all—our wedding day
brought tangibly near!

I dressed in the linden-green high-buttoned Sunday frock of my mother's that had been altered for
me for my official engagement, and upon her insistence I hung her gold chain with her big golden cross
around my neck. Secretly, to have it with me for
luck, I also took my ''Moonlight on a Lover's
Face,'' hiding it in a little bag under my dress.
Shortly after one, and followed by Madeleine, I left
the house with Père Luc, walking so fast beside him
that, though long-legged and still very hale, the old
priest could hardly keep pace with me. I should
hardly have adopted so elastic and swinging a gait,
or felt so full of enterprise, had I known for what I
was heading.

WHEN WE REACHED the end of the Rue Saint Honoré and got sight of the gold-lettered inscription "PALAIS CARDINAL" a crowd was gathered in front of the entrance gate, watching and commenting on the personages who arrived, some on horseback, some in splendid stage coaches. "The Maréchal de Brézé," we heard, and "The Maréchal Chatillon," "The Sieur de Soyecourt." Someone said: "There is a war council on, I wager."

Two officers came riding by in a rather disheveled state, covered with dust. They dismounted in haste and disappeared through the entrance gate. "Must have just got here with news from the front," someone murmured. "Bad news," another said, and the rest agreed. They told what they had been hearing from refugees who were driving their cattle and carts toward Paris. The Spaniards had massed formidable forces on the frontier, ready for an invasion of Picardie. The French fortresses to the north of Paris were much too weak to resist the powerful Spanish siege artillery being brought in from the Spanish Netherlands. The French troops, low in morale because long unpaid and half-starved, were too weak to block the advance of the well-trained, well-equipped Spanish army. The populace was in wild flight at the mere rumor that vanguards of the "infantry," the Cardinal Infanta's élite foot-soldiery, had crossed the border. Would the Spanish break through and actually reach Paris? Others were trying to calm the crowd. "Curs! Milksops! Even if the Spaniards should get the places in the north, we still have the Somme and the Oise. The defensive works at La Corbie are impregnable, and as long as they can't get La Corbie they can't advance towards Paris." "And we have forts at Paris, too." "And as long as we have Richelieu we have nothing to fear." Some of the crowd agreed, but the anxious murmur would not die down.

A six-horse chariot drew up. Shouts of command sounded, drums beat, bugles blew, and the carriage rolled through the gate between files of the crimson guards, their breastplates and helmets a blinding glitter in the June sunshine. "The British Ambassador," the crowd murmured. Then an outcry: "Richelieu is going to make an alliance with the British!" "That means that the Spanish are done!" "Didn't I tell you that Richelieu will do the trick?" "Thank God we have him!" A great wave of relief went through the crowd, and they broke into cheers of "Vive Richelieu! Vive Richelieu!"

"I am afraid the Cardinal won't be able to see me today," I told Père Luc. I hoped we should be sent away and invited for another time, for even if Richelieu could receive me today, it seemed likely that it would be for only a few minutes, and I could hardly find my opportunity to coax an appointment for Charles out of him. But when Père Luc presented his letter at the gate the captain of the guards bade us enter at once. He escorted us across the outer court-yard to a salon in the *rez-de-chaussée*. Shortly an undersized dark, modestly dressed man entered and came toward us without the sound of a footfall. His face was a grotesque composition of foxlike and bulldog traits, and with his head drawn in between his shoulders he looked almost like a hunchback. I recognized in him the man whom I had seen in the Cardinal's carriage in the Luxembourg Gardens. With an elegant bow he introduced himself as Bois-robert, secretary to His Excellency. He told me with bland deference that he had instructions to escort me upstairs to the apartments of his master. "The visit of the British Ambassador," he explained apologet-ically, "came quite unexpectedly; that is why you'll have to be so gracious as to wait a little while." Then he turned to Père Luc, and suddenly he was the meek hunchback no more, but a man who could tower and trample. He said with authority: "But you are much occupied, Reverend Father, and His Excel-lency does not wish that you should be kept from your priestly duties. Thank you for having brought your parishoner here, and—you may go now." *C'est ça!* just as I had thought.

Père Luc looked crestfallen. Obviously he was disappointed that he was not to share the honor of the audience. But there was nothing to be done, and with a "God bless you, my child" he took his leave and went. Madeleine, though, was permitted to wait for me downstairs.

"You cannot imagine," said Boisrobert as we ascended a red-carpeted staircase of white marble, "how His Excellency appreciates your charitable generosity, your lute-playing, your lovely voice, and above all your faultless Latin. In fact, on the very day when I heard you in the Luxembourg I suggested to His Excellency that he should engage you as his private reader of Latin books."

He peered at me sidelong. The pattern of his plot now seemed clear enough; and it was quite like him to have hatched such a scheme. Charles had told me about Boisrobert, whom he had known at the Pomme de Pin. He was a former provincial lawyer who had escaped the consequences of an amorous intrigue with his landlady's maidservant by taking holy orders. He had been suspended from his canonicate at Notre Dame for refusing to give up his habitual resort to the disorderly Pomme de Pin. There was a reason for his refusal: his share in the drinking bouts of the aristocratic town gallants was a matchless opportunity to collect important information for his master. Uncannily and diabolically shrewd, he was extremely useful to Richelieu, for whose *affaires de femme* (so Charles had told me) he spun the webs.

"It is not easy to find a really good reader of the Latin classics," said Boisrobert. "The worthy Père who serves him now was reading from Ovidius yesterday as if it were the recipe for a soup. And in Ovidius, as you know, every tree, every flower, has its story—and always a love story."

I said not a word. But, mindful of my mission, I pursed my lips in an enigmatical expression that might mean Yes, No, or Perhaps, or mere absentmindedness, or anything, or nothing.

We had entered a very large oblong room with a high ceiling. Between its darkish brown, carved, and gold-leafed crossbeams flowers and amoretti were painted on a light blue background. The sunlight, dimmed by beige silk hangings at high windows, suffused the whole room with a golden hue. In this light the tapestry on the walls—an all-over floral pattern with innumerable figures of women and men, dogs, deer, hares, grotesque masks, and intricate ornaments—glowed in every imaginable shade of green, yellow, and red. There were also paintings in rich stuccoed frames and any number of statues and statuettes on consoles and tables.

"All these are His Excellency's very favorite *objets d'art*," Boisrobert said. "He chooses and arranges and dusts every one of them himself. Few are ever permitted to enter this room, but His Excellency hoped that a little sight-seeing might help shorten the time of waiting for you." He offered me a lady's gilded chair, made his elegant bow, and withdrew.

I stepped diffidently over the mirrorlike parquet and confronted the huge statue of a lion tearing a steer to pieces. Beyond it was the bust of a Roman emperor, then a black marble Hercules. Impressive, yes, I thought, but—too much bulge of muscle; altogether too heavy a man. A cast-iron gladiator gave me the same feeling. A bronze Mercury pleased me better. And even finer was a nude discobolus with a nobly proportioned body, slim legs, and graceful loins. Like Charles! Furtively I looked around. I approached the discus thrower and leaned my cheek against his cool thigh. When I passed my hand over his hip a delicious thrill went through me.—Oh, Charles! Two days and two nights you've been away from me. But today, tonight, you must come. Tonight I shall have news for you—and such glad news! You will never again have to wear yourself out running after appointments, and can stay with me by day and by night!

But I must not give myself up to dreaming. To get what I coveted I must have all my wits about me. I drew myself away from the beautiful discobolus and turned to the other statues.

It occurred to me that, so far, I had noticed only the representations of men, though the women's figures there actually outnumbered them. Here was a *dormeuse*, a young girl relaxing her slim, virginal limbs; there, a rosy marble Venus with fulfillment in her whole body. Another Venus, and another—and all these figures so placed as to make the most of their specifically female charms. No doubt Madame de Senneterre was right: Richelieu was an *homme à femmes*. My prospects were of the most promising.

Then my eye lifted to an immense portrait of Richelieu above a fireplace hedged with swords, muskets, pistols, and other weapons and trophies of war. This Richelieu had the Cardinal's small erect head, his thinker's high forehead, his fine moustache; but what severe, what terrifyingly arrogant eyes had this man dressed, not in the robe of a Cardinal, but in a silver armor with a black coat floating martially from his shoulders, and guns and

burning towns in the background! He was over-
whelming. This was no man to fall an easy prey to a
woman. How could I have fancied that I could play
with him as cat with mouse?—I, a nobody, a poor,
unfashionably dressed young girl.

I looked quickly around, and my eye rested on the
small portrait of a copper-blonde woman in green
brocade that revealed her neck and her gracefully
shaped arms, and partly revealed her white bosom. It
was Queen Anne.

I looked around for a mirror. There was none. But
in one corner hung a highly polished suit of armor. I
stepped to it and, studying my reflection in the blank
polished breast plate, I undid the button that fastened
my dress at the neck and turned the silk inside. The
golden cross hung from my bare throat, glittering
between my breasts. Not just the right place for the
cross, I thought—between those breasts that already
knew so many of the delights of the flesh. But I had
better not be thinking about them, I told myself: the
point was simply that I looked a little more frivolous
this way. There were still the sleeves! I was just
about to roll them up and leave my forearms bare like
those of the Queen in the picture, when a red shimmer appeared in the breastplate. I turned around. In
the doorway stood Cardinal Richelieu. The sight of
him gave me a little shock. Had he observed my
tactics? Had he, by any chance, been watching them
from beginning to end?

"I am happy to see you," he said with a friendly
smile. I hurried to him and was about to kneel and
kiss his ring as Père Luc had advised me; but
Richelieu grasped my hand, and the pressure of his

kept me standing. With an inviting gesture he bade me pass through the doorway into his study.

It was much darker than the room in which I had been waiting. The window curtains were of a deep brown and heavy, and only one of them had been pulled aside to let a slim shaft of daylight fall on the writing desk behind which the Cardinal seated himself, after seating me in an armchair near him. The confusion of papers on the desk and of the stools grouped around it showed that pressing business had been going on. The face above the crimson robe looked even more yellowed and ashen than in the Luxembourg Gardens, his eyes even more deeply sunken in their sockets. But a gentle smile had taken possession of his face, and I knew that I was the cause of it. My embarrassment began to ebb, and when he offered me chocolate-with-ambergris from a gold wire basket and told me that he had known at once in the Luxembourg Gardens who I was, because Papa had been the only nobleman in Paris who would play the lute, I felt at ease and quite at home with the great man.

"I met your Papa at the siege of La Rochelle more than ten years ago," he said, "—a long and boring siege, indeed. All the endless waiting in the positions and the foggy, damp weather made us all feel rather sour. But where your father was there was fun, there was life. A *bon causeur* and *bon viveur*, he was full of wit and esprit. He would play and sing to the lute, and that not only to his fellow officers, but also to his men, and on the day of the general attack he and his company stormed the batteries with his chansons on their lips and fought like lions. A wonderful man! A pity I could do no more for him than drop a hint to let him pass when he was reported fleeing from Paris and about to cross the frontier. Unhappily it does not fall within my powers to have the King dismiss the charges. Chaban, whom your father killed, was Master General of the Venetian Artillery and a close friend of the Venetian Ambassador, and reasons of state make it impossible for me to antagonize Chaban's friends, who are very influential at court. I feel sorry, of course, not only for your father, but also for you, my child, whom I never think of but with pleasure." He launched into reminiscences of the scene in the Luxembourg Gardens and extolled my charity, my singing, and my Latin. He ended by handing me a parchment on which a poem was written in medieval Gothic letters, the initials red, blue, and gold-edged and adorned with daintily painted spring flowers. "*Jam nix glaciesque liquescit . . .*" Papa's spring song!

"That is the original," Richelieu said. "I sent for it to the Diacre of Saint Martial in Limoges. It has been on my desk for two weeks; urgent business kept me from inviting you earlier. But here you are now, and this parchment is yours."

I was not sparing of my thanks. Richelieu received them with a gracious nod; but then a faint frown appeared on his brow. It alarmed me somewhat: I imagined that pressing affairs of state had crowded back into his mind, and that with the passing of the parchment the audience must come to an end. The moment was critical. If I were to wheedle a position for Charles out of this busy man, something must be done instantly. I made my lips soften into their best smile; I leaned back in my armchair in a way that accentuated my breasts and made the hem of my dress creep up. Was I not fascinating him with my little game? I thought I must be: he peered, he smiled. My heart began to thump. I was succeeding! The play had begun. The cat with the mouse!

Richelieu said with a slightly ironic intonation: "What is it that you have on your mind, *mon enfant?* Is there some particular thing that you want me to do for you?"

I felt the red flush mounting from my bosom, and I was glad when a sudden interruption gave me a chance to collect my wits. Without warning an invisible door in the paneled wall opened noiselessly, and Boisrobert entered in haste, his face deathly pale. He presented a letter, at which Richelieu glanced; then the two conversed in a low, excited whisper. But I could make out that La Capelle was reported to have fallen to the Spaniards. Richelieu ordered Boisrobert to instruct the commander of the Arsenal at once that all available guns and munitions must be shipped from Le Havre to Paris. "No actual danger," Richelieu said, "but——" The great man's face seemed almost green now, and the eye sockets black within it. But no sooner had the secretary gone than the smile returned to Richelieu's face, and he said as if nothing had interrupted: *"Eh bien,* proceed."

I took heart and asked if he could employ a young nobleman of Toulon in his household. I should be so grateful——To my keen disappointment, the shadow instantly returned to his face. Sensing difficulties, I made an effort to picture my protégé's virtues, his exquisite character, his chivalrous manners, all in the brightest colors. But I was only deepening the frown. "Who is this paragon?" he asked; and now there was only ice in his voice. He must be jealous, I thought. But I did not let myself be irritated. I told him Charles's name and all his titles—de Beumont, Sieur de Saint-Étienne, and the rest.

"H'm, yes—Charles Beaumont," Richelieu said gravely. "As a matter of fact, I wanted a word with you about him." My eyes must have widened, for Richelieu fell silent. He sat there measuring and probing me. "I must warn you against him," he said at last. "He is a dangerous fellow."

"Oh, no!" I started up. "There must be some mistake. This cannot possibly apply to Charles de Beaumont. He can give Your Excellency a complete account of himself. He has introductory letters signed by the Bishop and by the president of the Parlement of Toulon."

"It is precisely from Monsieur le Président that we have our information," said Richelieu. He produced a letter from a bundle of papers. "There is no nobleman of that name in Toulon—no *de* Beaumont. The Beaumont in question, son of an obscure inn-keeper of ill repute, acquired these titles by the purchase of a field with which they have been connected by a special centuries-old privilege. The prés-ident writes that Beaumont must have acquired them for improper purposes, the most obvious of them being to dazzle guillible women. Because he is a cynical, cunning, and dangerous adventurer whose special obsession it is to concentrate all his efforts, all his power of fascination—and this, in some dark way, he seems really to possess—on one woman at a time, only to drop her as soon as he has seduced her and turn to a new victim of his depraved lust of adventure.''

I felt a constriction at my throat, but I believed no word of it. These are all lies, I thought—all inventions to drive a wedge between me and my beloved. I said nothing; I could not speak. But I shook my head violently.

''And not only had this been his reputation in Toulon,'' Richelieu went on, ''but he is also doing the same in Paris, and, as I well know, he has tried it with even you, my poor child. You had better forswear your trust in him, and forswear it at once, because——''

''I not only put my trust in him,'' I could not help interrupting sharply, ''but I also love him. There is no man in the world more gentle, more honest, more lovable than he. You have only to know him, only to look once into his clear, guileless eyes, to convince yourself that he is utterly incapable of anything wrong. But if you insist on letting yourself be prejudiced by slanders and lies, than I had better trespass on your time no longer!'' I had stood up, hot and flushed with indignation.

''One moment.'' Richelieu motioned me back to my seat. ''Let me tell you more; and try to have a little confidence in my judgment, which is based on records of fact not to be gainsaid. I am sorry to see your heart so deeply engaged and to hurt your feelings, but your position has become so alarmingly critical that I have to reveal the full truth to you. Your Beaumont is not only a deceiver of women, but he is also a filthy swindler in money matters. Not to put too fine a point upon it, he is a thief.''

I had heard enough. I had seated myself again, but now I was resolved to bear no more, but to spring up and leave the scandalmonger on the instant. Yet, somehow I could not make myself move. Richelieu's eyes were upon me; a deep pity could be read in them, but at the same time they were implacable like those of the Richelieu of the portrait in the other room—commanding eyes that cast a spell and paralyzed my will.

''It was but yesterday,'' he went on, ''that a lady sat in that very chair and implored me to discontinue a criminal investigation that seems to have taken a serious turn against Charles Beaumont and will obviously send him to the gallows. Two or three weeks ago that lady noticed that a ring of immense value had disappeared from her bedchamber. Her husband, just returned from the field and greatly excited over the theft, informed the authorities. They questioned the servants. Suspicion was finally narrowed down to a maid who had waited on Madame the evening before the theft. Threatened with the torture, she revealed that Charles Beaumont was Madame's lover, that he had spent the critical night with her, and that it could only be he who had stolen the ring. Madame, discreetly questioned, could not but admit Beaumont's visit, though she protested his chivalrous character, just as you did. But the judges of the Chatelet have different information about your Beaumont, and they decided to send bailiffs for him. He must have had forewarning, for he disappeared and is now in hiding. But I know where the bailiffs will find him, and it is my duty to inform the Châtelet. There remains just one possibility of averting his arrest. If the ring is returned, and Madame can pretend that she had mislaid it and has found it again—— Would you, by any chance, know something of the ring? The stone is an unusually beautiful and very large turquoise.''

His voice was soft, but it cut me like whiplash. I received the stroke like one tied to a stake, and much of my anguish was simple shame that my beloved should have done such abominable things. But when I heard the Cardinal speak of criminal procedure, of the gallows, of Charles hiding from bailiffs, anxiety for him prevailed. And then the thought irradiated me: Perhaps he stole the ring, but if he did, he stole it for me! For love of me! And a wave of pity rose in me. When Richelieu pronounced the words ''turquoise ring'' I knew on the instant that there was only one thing in the world that I cared about, and that was saving Charles—saving him at any cost.

''I suppose this is it,'' I said, producing the ring from under my dress. ''Charles gave it to me. He besought me not to wear it on my finger yet, because it was to be our engagement ring.''

Richelieu took the ring, scrutinized it carefully. ''Yes, this is the ring. I once saw it on the lady's hand. Should you like me to return it to her?''

''Yes,'' I said, ''please do so. And with that the whole affair will be settled for Charles, once and for all—won't it?''

Richelieu nodded, and upon my demand that he tell me where I could send Charles the message that he now had nothing to fear, he gave me a paper with an address in the Rue des Trois Pas, behind the Hôtel de Cluny, with a sketch of the place of hiding. He told me, though, that I had better not be too sanguine about Charles's future, for there were still other charges against him, and it would be to both my interest and that of the state if so unreliable a subject as Beaumont were put out of the way of doing further harm. For one thing, the city was full of Spanish spies, and such men as Charles were fully capable of betraying their country if they saw enough money in it.

"No, please no!" I cried. I was determined to fight for my lover with every weapon I had, of body or of soul. "You must not do him any harm. Don't think that I do not feel appalled at what he has done. He will not do it again. I will put all my love, my whole life, into making a better man of him. I promise it."

"I fear that you waste your generosity and your trust on one wholly unworthy of them. You love him, but he does not love you, because such a man has no heart. He cannot love anybody. He will take from you all that you can give him, and then he will leave you."

"You don't know him!" I cried passionately, "—neither you, Excellency, nor any other person. There is some deep center in him, some great secret, that escapes all of you; and neither do I exactly know what it can be. But I feel that he has great qualities, which, if they are employed in the right way, will make him achieve something noble and great in this world, and that the day will come when all of us—you too— will be proud of him. But you must help me, and you must leave him to me."

Richelieu looked at me long, studying my face; and I am sure that he saw a glow on it. "After what I have told you about him," he said at length, "I admire your faith and your courage, and it seems to me that it would make but little sense if I tried to talk you out of your love. Well—have it your way. Though my opinion of the man and my warnings stand unchanged, I say this to you: Make the trial! It *has* happened that some very ill blackguards have been turned into honest men by the love and the faith of women. For your sake, and for that alone, I will make the experiment of leaving him to you. I will shut my eyes to his past for a time, and if he does well, his past shall be dropped and forgotten. But if he should dare play the same foul game with you that he has played with other women, then woe to him! You may tell him that." Then he stood up and released me with a raising of his Cardinal's cap. I lingered for a moment, standing before him; then—was it because I felt him expecting it, or because I myself had the impulse?—I brought my face nearer to his to be kissed.

He kissed me on the forehead. But it was—or so I imagined—more tenderly than it had been in the Luxembourg Gardens, and though he said once more "God bless you, my child," I knew from his voice that he thought me no longer a child or an eventual plaything, but a woman whom he respected and would have liked to love; and this changed attitude suited me well for the sake of Charles.

I left the Cardinal with a sense of keen triumph. My Charles was safe, and it was I who had saved him. He could leave his obscure haunt now and return to the world—return to me and begin a new life, a life without terrors that he must hide from me. Did he imagine, poor silly fellow, that I cared for titles, estates, and money? I forgave him his pretensions to them, forgave him his past and even his recent affair with the woman from whom he had taken the ring for me. If I wanted the world to forgive him, it must be I, the woman who loved him, who had first to forgive him everything—yes, everything.

When night fell and Mother had gone to bed, I wrapped myself in my father's old mantle and left the house with Madeleine.

The night was hot, dusty, and but dimly lighted by the young moon. When we crossed the quarter behind the Hôtel de Cluny with its maze of archways, turrets, and connected old houses the world seemed strangely restless and teeming with dark and dangerous secrets. But I walked through the eerie shadows unafraid, my heart beating with impatience to tell my lover that I was bringing him deliverance, generous forbearance, and the whole of my soul. And it was my soul that—as I had discovered in the hour of crisis—was the greater, the more beautiful, the supreme part of my love.

Arrived at my destination, a somber old two-story building in the Rue des Trois Pas, I gained admittance with the help of the password written on my sketch and of an écu slipped into the hand of the old woman who opened the gate. I left Madeleine on the landing of the upper floor and climbed the ladder to the garret. I climbed very stealthily lest a noise awaken the sleeping house. Nevertheless, when I got to the top the hush was broken by a sharp outcry. I saw a shapeless shadow moving out of the dark, and the next instant it was upon me like a huge, gross cat with yellow-flecked phosphorescent eyes, sinking sharp claws into my arm and hissing at me with concentrated fury and hate: "Get out of here! Get away out of here!" I had recognized Yvonne by her glossy red hair and had got hold of her hands. She bit and spat and flung foul-mouthed insults at me. "Get out!" she kept shrieking at such a pitch that I thought the whole house would be aroused.

But no one else stirred, and even as I struggled with the girl I was thinking what a good augury it was that she had to sleep outside my lover's room. It was true, then, that she was his mistress no longer. "Where is he?" I demanded when I had got the better of Yvonne and was holding her pinioned. "I have to speak to him."

"I don't know," she wailed.

But at that moment a door opened, and, though I saw nothing distinctly, I knew that my beloved one was on the threshold. I pushed Yvonne aside and all but rushed toward him. But at the last second something strange and chill held me rooted, and I could only whisper: "It is Ninon."

I had expected, I think, a happy outcry of surprise, and impulsive movement toward me, or at the least a tender word. All I met was a stiff, taut silence. When at last he said "You—here?" there was dismay in his voice—dismay and extreme annoyance. "What do you want here?'' he asked, his tone rough with anger. He continued sharply, without a flicker of kindness, to say nothing of love: ''What do you want of me?''

Was this Charles? Was this my lover? Was this voice that met me with so harsh a hostility really his? I could not understand. But I thought perhaps he understood as little, and I gathered myself together and said: ''You do not have to fear anything. I am here to help you. I am bringing you good news— freedom!''

There was an ugly, offensive sneer in the voice that said: ''You—and bringing me freedom! If that was really what you wanted, you had no need to hunt me out in the middle of the night.''

''Get out of here!'' Yvonne howled again. I was utterly perplexed, and the only explanation that I could think of was that some sinister intrigue must have been spun to cause this terrible misunderstanding. But I said resolutely: ''It is imperative that I speak to you right away and quite alone. It is about the ring.''

''About the ring?'' He seemed utterly amazed, but there was a sudden unmistakable pleasure in his voice. ''Let the lady's arm go,'' he ordered Yvonne, and then he stepped aside to let me enter his high-gabled garret.

For a moment I thought I had won. Face to face with me alone, and with all misunderstandings cleared away, he must realize what I had done for him; with a thousand regrets and apologies, he would surely fold me in his arms and cover me with kisses. But while I was crossing the garret my cour-

106

age ebbed away. In the pale light that filtered in through two hatches in the roof and a front window, I saw a low unmade bed, a half-broken armchair, a small warped table, and an agglomeration of old dusty lumber that crackled with the nibblings of rats or mice. The whole room seemed haunted by some malign spirit, and though rooftree and rafters still held the heat of the day, I shivered as I let myself sink into the chair.

"Well—where is the ring?" Charles demanded, his hand out to receive it.

I looked up at him amazed. In his face, pale in the moonlight, I thought I saw the ghost of an exultant smile, but no sooner had I said "The ring? No, I didn't bring it" than his face clouded again. "But it is in safe hands," I quickly assured him. "You must not worry." And in hurried words I gave him an account of what I knew and had done about the ring.

When I had ended he burst out with annoyance: "It is a pity about the precious ring. What a fool you were to fall into their trap! That old Red Fox, Richelieu, needs that woman, the Comtesse de Paur, because the Spanish spies think she is on their side, but she tells them nothing but what he, the Red Spider, wants them to know, and she is too much afraid of her husband not to do anything to avoid a scandal. It would not suit her at all if I were to be arrested and say a word to the judges. She and the Red Fox would have hit on some other way out of it. They would never have molested *me*."

"If you were not afraid, then why did you have to hide in this terrible garret?"

He measured me with a look of suspicion. "Do

you really suppose it was on account of this silly ring affair?''

''Surely. Why else?''

''Let us have this straight,'' he said bluntly. ''I didn't hide here because of the ring. I hid because I was afraid you would chase after me, the way all the other women do when I am through with them.''

I had been prepared for anything but this shock. ''Through?'' I stammered, ''—through? You are through with me? Why? What have I done?''

Something like a sympathetic warmth seemed to flicker in his eyes, but it was quickly gone, and he said grimly: ''I part with all my other doxies as soon as I have got what I want. I tried to do the same with you, and yet I carried on with you for all of three weeks. That is what you have done!''

''And I thought,'' I murmured in a complete daze, ''that with us it was to be forever—for all eternity!''

He made an ugly sneering grimace. ''Three weeks come to the same thing, or too near to it.''

My head sank. I was staring at the floor. ''Then Richelieu was right,'' I mumbled. ''He told me you would leave me, too.''

''What a clever prophet! Yes, every word he told you about me is doubtless true.''

Something seemed to burst in my head. I still could not raise my eyes from the floor.

''Accept the inevitable, my girl,'' he said at last. ''It is all over between you and me. Put a cheerful face on it and don't try to stage a scene. I hate scenes.''

I sat as if turned into mute stone. Only once or twice did I start, when sudden nocturnal sounds split the silence. I felt him watching me sidelong, then getting up to pace the garret; the floor boards creaked under his boots. I knew that he was discomfited and not so indifferent to my suffering as he had tried to make himself think.

"Listen, Ninon!" he said. I had to turn to look at him. He stood at the window, his dark figure a shadow. "I have something to tell you," he went on, and his voice seemed to come to me out of some cold alien world. "I can see that it was sheer cowardice to hide instead of telling you to your face where you and I stand. In two days and nights in this filthy garret I have given some little thought to us two, and it only confirmed my certainty that it is in the interest of both that we part. Either we part, or we perish."

A spasm crossed his face, as if the words were costing him a great effort. He was very pale, but there was concentrated determination in his brows as he went on: "Damn me, I cannot love just one woman—love her all the time. It is simply not given to me. I know people call me a blackguard, a treacherous brute, a heartless seducer. You asked me once what it is that I keep back from you—the great secret, the unknown center that you said must be something unusual and perhaps terrible. I have pondered your question these two days and nights, and now I can give you your answer: *I am an artist*.

"I am a very great artist, even if I am not one in the common meaning. For the material of my artistic expression is not dead stone or canvas or brass or catgut strings or mere words—not any substitute for Life, but Life itself, manifested in Woman. You, if no other, will understand me. Have I not everything that an artist has? Did I not go to work as an artist when I began by playing on your romantic need for 'pure love,' 'love enduring,' marriage, and after that when, discovering the little beast of prey in you, I provoked it, withdrew, provoked it again, and so on until you were helpless to do anything but throw yourself into my arms?

"Now, Ninon, the performance is over. But there is nothing that you have to reproach me for. These weeks with me have been good for you. Haven't I saved you from the horror of a life in the convent? Now that the little beast in you has licked blood, could you ever dream of becoming a nun? Haven't I taught you well and developed your talents?

"And if you still have any doubt of what kind those talents are, let me tell you this—and hear my words, not with the stupid prejudice of the hypocritical world, but as the greatest compliment that I know how to pay a woman: From head to foot you are made for nothing but love. You have a gift for *amour* that I have never met before or in any other woman. In the time of our liaison you invented any number of caresses and kinds of love-making that I didn't know myself, that not the most refined courtesan would know; and you invented them on the spur of the moment. You are a born past mistress of love. I am still a match for you, but you will outdo me before the world is much older. And just there is the point: we are evenly matched, and therefore it would be dangerous to both if we stayed together any longer. We had great pleasure in each other; but the favor was mutual, and therefore our accounts are honorably balanced once for all."

I had jumped up so violently that the mantle dropped from my shoulders. "How dare you!" I cried, my voice hurt and outraged. "I gave you everything—my body and my soul; and if I was unrestrained in my passion, there was nothing low or obscene in it, because I loved you deeply and completely. I was a woman in love, but no whore."

He backed away as I approached him, but I could not contain my agony or my outrage, and I followed him. "Yes, I loved you," I said, "and, though you may not like hearing it, I love you still and will never stop loving you." I had cried out thus much without restraint, and there would have been more of my outburst, but I was suddenly aware of a strange expression in his eyes—one that was drawing him to me, but at the same time apparently haunting him with a nameless fear, so that I could not help seeing him with pity. "I am sorry," I said in a softer voice, "that I had to speak to you so, but I did have to. But—you needn't be afraid. I shan't struggle. It would be like struggling against fate. You want your unscrupulous freedom, and that want is stronger than you. If you feel that you must go, then go wherever you wish. But I want one last favor from you; I *must* have it. Wipe out your ugly words from my memory. Leave me at least the reminder of that other Charles whom I love—the dream, the remembered beauty. Let us part in kindness, and—kiss me one last time, for good-bye."

"Very well," he murmured. At first he did not move; it was as if he were afraid. Then two little dark flames sprang into his eyes, and I became instantly aware that he had misunderstood me. The word "kiss" had come to mean, for us two, something quite different from what I meant now. I drew back. But the two little flames followed me—burned into my brain and set me trembling. "No, not that!" I said. "All I asked was—was——" But his hands were already on my hips and his breath hot on my face.

"Your last kiss," he said in a thick voice, "—you shall have it, my girl!"

I broke away, and I hoped that I looked outraged and defiant. But my reluctance maddened him. I thought I was about to scream; but now his mouth was on mine, my body in his frantic embrace. I still resisted, but he kept on pressing me toward the bed; and then he whispered into my ear with that old, now bewildering tenderness of his: "Come, just this once, and then never again."

The whispered words overpowered me, and after that there was room in my brain for nothing but their echo: "Only once and never again." No need to put my helplessness, my surrender, into words: the sudden quiver of my lips told my faithless lover that he had triumphed. With a savage inarticulate cry he flung me on to his bed and himself upon me.

It was a tempestuous fury, the holocaust of our love. It was infinitely stormier than our first night together, for the physical smart that had whipped to a rapturous frenzy the delights of those hours had been no more than a pinprick compared with the burning agony of knowing that this time was the last. All the wild yearnings I had ever known, all devotion, all tenderness for what my lover had ever been to me, my whole being, my whole life, we fused into one in this final tormenting embrace.

When at last Charles released me and stood up, I was clutched by an almost physical pain. How could I ever endure these torments, I asked myself in desperate anguish, how could I keep on living, without him and his passion? Hands pressed to my temples, I heard him pacing up and down. Was he merely impatient to see me rise now and go?

But no: he sat down on the edge of the bed and began to talk. "That was quite a wonderful kiss, wasn't it, my dear? I think it would be a pity if there were no more of them. I see you are in a reasonable frame of mind, and I wonder if we could not come to a sensible agreement to keep on with each other and at the same time both keep our freedom." His proposal was fantastic; it was utterly disgusting; it was nasty. And yet I nodded weakly to it, for nothing in the world counted for me at that moment if only I could keep him on any terms.

"No more mention of marriage," he went on. "No questions like 'Do you love me?' 'Shall you always love me?' 'Where have you been?' 'Will you come again?' Nothing, nothing at all on either side, but absolute freedom."

When I accepted this shameful pact that night it was not only because I was panic-stricken by the prospective final loss of my lover: there was also a trace of the idea that the power of my sex had made him change his resolve to bring about an absolute break, and with it there was a irrational hope that if I only used this power aright and strictly avoided everything that could antagonize his passionate urge for freedom, I might yet hold him to me.

The hours that we had together after that nocturnal bargain were charged with delight and with horror. The delight was in our wild abandon; the horror in my constant terror of loss and in the humiliations to which I must submit. These touched bottom at the times when Charles would tell me, with shameless candor and in gross detail, of new amorous conquests of his, while I, heedful of the danger in the least false move, made myself listen and admire his exploits. He seemed to take an actual delight in tormenting me with such *fabliaux*, all in coarse and cynical terms. And when he left me he invariably took pains to remind me that he had no idea when he would come again or whether he would come at all.

There were better days, too—days when I knew with a sure instinct that my hope had been not unfounded; and sometimes he would even give way to a tenderness that not all the artfulness in the world could feign. These moments betrayed the devotion and, yes, the love that at all other times he tried to conceal. And one night, as he lay asleep in my arms and I studied his face, I saw a frown and a smile struggle on his beloved features, and he moaned in his sleep and said: "Try as I may, I can*not* escape you!—I love you, Ninon; oh, how much I love you!"

At that instant my spirit soared. All was momentarily bright again as in the first days of our love. And sometimes, after staying away for one day or two, on returning he would atone by seeming to love me twice as much.

But after one such two days' absence there came, not himself, but a letter from him. I tore it open, thinking to find new evidences of his love. Instead, its words reached my heart with the thrust of the *fulmine improvvisato*, and there flashed upon my mind the picture of Charles as I had first seen him in the Luxembourg Gardens—dark, slender, bent forward in the pose of the Italian fencer, darting out the steel of his foil at the very second when it was least expected. "I have come to realize," the letter said, "that if I stayed with you any longer, I should never be able to extricate myself from your charms. And so I have joined the *armée brigantine* of Monsieur de Courtveville to battle the Barbaresques, Spaniards, and Napolitains, and to sail with him after that to the Far East or to America. I shall never return to Europe or to any place from which I might be tempted to reach you."

The rest did not matter. The one sentence was enough to topple me into a bottomless black pit of anguish. I was lost. I had ceased to exist. Nothing remained of me but an unendurable vast emptiness—an unappeasable hunger of the flesh and of the heart.

PART TWO

1

ON A GREEN LANE outside the Porte Saint Antoine stood an old-fashioned hostelry, the Truffe Noire—Black Truffle. Aforetime, under an ancient royal privilege, it had served a last sumptuous worldly repast to prospective novices on their way to one of the neighboring convents. This function had long since lapsed; but the inn was still renowned for a fine rich cuisine and a noteworthy wine cellar, though the present beneficiaries came without the pious aspirations of their predecessors. Adjoining the inn there was a charming little grove of maple, gray birch, and larches, with dense shrubbery, in which they could promenade by couples; and those who wanted even more privacy could safely avail themselves of transient lodging in the inn, for it lay outside the jurisdiction of the Provost of Paris, and no one bothered to scan the entries in its register. By way of tribute to this hospitable complaisance the modern habitués of the inn had made a standard pleasantry of calling it the Truffe Rouge—Red Truffle.

When, on a pleasant summer afternoon a few weeks after the letter from Charles, I set out for the Truffe in the company of Madame de Senneterre, I had as yet no inkling what manner of establishment it was. Nor did I care; for, though the good creature was trying in a thousand ways to cheer me and set my mind atingle, I was still numb, paralyzed, and in a state of emotional shipwreck.

I had not confided to Madame de Senneterre how far my affair with Charles had gone, and I didn't know why she should take my *pas fatal* so readily for granted; but since I made no demur, she hastened to reassure me as to a worry that had not even crossed my mind. "My dear," she said laying her chubby bejeweled hand comfortingly on my arm, "if you have not been cautious enough with your lover and are afraid of consequences, you just come to me. I know someone that will help you. And when it comes to future adventures, I will show you how to be really discreet. Caution, they say, is the mother of wisdom, but I say that true caution never becomes a mother at all!"

We were just passing an elevation from whose summit two octagonal turrets emerged and pointed serenely to the blue skies from the greenery of aged oaks. They belonged to the Convent of the Ursulines, which I had often visited with my mother. Had I followed in her footsteps and kept myself aloof from the world, I should not now be feeling so utterly woebegone. This peaceful house would have become my haven and home, and the young novices with the happy faces my sisters. And I was seized by a sudden longing to go and bury my scalding pain, too grievous to bear before the world's face, in the shadow of those tranquil walls.

"Poor little thing!" said Madame de Senneterre with warm maternal patronage. "Never mind my *plaisanteries*. I know just how you feel. I know it hurts. I've gone through such a *malheur* myself. But it was much worse with me, because it caught me when I was on the *mauvaise côté de la trentaine*. It is like the measles: serious at a later time of life, but not at yours. You are so incorrigibly healthy! You will get over it easily, and in a few weeks the charming rascal will be quite forgotten."

For some time I merely looked at her in silence, with distraught eyes. But she was trying so hard to bring me to life with her vivacious talk and her anecdotes that I could not very well refuse to respond. I promised her that I would try to get a little amusement out of the hours ahead.

The carriage turned off the road into an ascending green lane. At the head of it was a square white house with white pigeons trailing over its red thatched roof and a soft blue plume of smoke curling skyward. "Truffe Noire," I read mechanically from the cast-iron signpost when we had stopped in front of the house." Truffe Rouge," Madame de Senneterre corrected, her merry eyes blinking shrewdly.

Our carriage rolled into the courtyard through a broad gateway. From a half open kitchen came a cheerful clatter of pots, a smell of roasting meat, the shine of mighty copper caldrons, and glimpses of snow-white aprons and linen caps on red-faced cooks, all hard at work. The courtyard was filled with elegant people at long tables decorated with flowers and sumptuously laden with appetizing dishes.

We were greeted by a cluster of ladies and their cavaliers, and for a while Madame de Senneterre held majestic court, regal in her pompous wine-colored velvet robe. Vaguely I heard name after familiar name: Pequigny, Chevalier de Raré, Yvetot, Corbeille, La Brosse, Fleurac, and many another. Amidst all the animation and chatter I remained rigid and aloof. Gradually I became aware that all the ladies wore light, bright-colored chiffon frocks with liberal lace-edged décolletages, and that their single topic was fashion. An officer remarked that the ladies ought to think it unpatriotic to cling to the Spanish hairdress now that the Spaniards had invaded their country, but he was unanimously condemned. "Where should we go for fine taste but to Madrid?" a spirited brunette cut him short, and against this assault and the challenge of her almond-shaped eyes the poor fellow was helpless; he had to admit with admiration that the coiffure à l'Infanta, with side hair trimmed and hanging over the ear in short ringlets and the fringe across the forehead, was wondrously becoming to the indignant charmer.

Gentlemen's clothes, too, came in for attention. Some of the officers were producing a sensation with a novelty in the form of a folded piece of white mull finished with lace and hanging loose down the chest. This they had copied from the neck shawls worn by Croat officers serving in the French army, and hence the new adornments were called "croats" or "cravats." Madame de Senneterre found them very becoming; she predicted that every man who aspired to be thought well dressed would shortly have to wear them.

Many of the young men assured me that they had known me from the Luxembourg Gardens, but the only one I recognized was the lusty, florid-faced, blue-eyed Scarron. Upon his request Madame de Senneterre introduced him to me, and after that he devoted himself exclusively to me. When we went to table he escorted me to my place and seated himself at my left.

At first I was very reserved, for I feared that Scarron would ask questions about Charles, and that if he did I might not restrain my tears. But he was tactful enough not to make any reference to Charles. Instead he produced a coruscating display of witty sallies about funny nonentities, while I regained confidence and began to listen with interest. Something infectious in his hilarity made me, willy-nilly, smile back at him.

Charles had told me a good deal about this buffoon with the kind heart and the high spirits. His austere father, holder of a high parliamentary office, had dedicated him to an ecclesiastical career, but that fitted his worldly, easygoing disposition no better than the *petit collet* of a future abbé that he wore on his gold-laced *pourpoint*. Scarron had been a welcome habitué of the *alcôves* of charming Parisian ladies, but at present he was having to live in provincial Le Mans, where, poor man, he could tipple and gormandize only in secret, and for feminine society had to make shift with his landlady and her five daughters, because in Le Mans he was secretary to the bishop and bound to conduct himself with ecclesiastical decorum. To Paris he could come only for short furloughs; he was enjoying one of them now, but unfortunately this was the last day of his freedom. "Oh, Paris!" he exclaimed; and his sigh was intended to be droll, but I thought its nostalgia rather prevailed over its buffoonery. I quoted some lines about Paris from one of Scarron's poems that Charles and I had bought from a colporteur on the Pont Neuf. Paul Scarron, later famous as the author of the *Roman Comique*, was then an unknown writer, and, like others who could find no publisher, he had handwritten copies of his poems on single leaves distributed for a sou apiece by itinerant bookmen. He gleamed at me and said I repeated the verses with the same gusto that he had put into writing them.

My neighbor to the right was the Chevalier de Raré, a rather handsome officer, dark red of face. Like most of the young cavaliers at the table, he had come down from the northern front on furlough, and, like the others, he was trying to make the most out of his leave. He assured me that since he had discovered me Paris had become even more attractive to him, and that from now on he should come to it oftener. But I was paying slight heed to his and others' bold or languishing looks. I had put the entire burden of entertaining me on Scarron's knack of amusing; and it actually did somewhat allay my pervasive suffering.

"Eat what is set before you," Scarron pronounced, quoting Gospel with such exemplary sanctimoniousness that nobody could have suspected him of poking fun at his own dignity as prospective abbé. He had seen that I was scarcely touching the dishes, and he tried to coax me into eating. Here was, indeed, such a *repas magnifique* as Papa would have liked; it followed and almost outdid the most exalted traditions of a grande cuisine. There was a rich and bright array of dishes big and small, piled up with pâtés filled with chicken and hashed partridges; there were fried oysters, broiled quails, fricassées red, brown, and white, *galantines* with mushrooms, crayfish, asparagus tips, cold eels condimented with roses and cinnamon, and, as the centerpiece of this first course, a *capon rôti à la vermeille d'orange*—a capon roasted with sugared orange peels. With all this went a choice of the finest wines—Burgundy for the gentlemen, and for the ladies a light claret mixed with honey and perfumed with jasmine. I drank a few drops, and they put me into a little fever, as Madame de Senneterre had said they would. I felt the life-blood rising to my cheeks, and by and by I even began to find some titillation in the general frivolity.

The company, all of them obviously given to the pleasures of the table, not only displayed a hearty appetite, but also commented on dishes and wines with the whole-souled zeal and exactitude of true gourmets. But this interest was decidedly not the only aspect of their tirelessness, or even the prevailing one. Torrid flirtations were going on the while, fed by smoldering looks, sensual chuckles, or amorous whisperings from behind napkins and fans. The girls were chaperoned, but their mothers and aunts seemed not to be quite the right sort of guardian angels of maidenly virtue. They were much too preoccupied with their own cavaliers.

A funny globular monster approached our table—the innkeeper, piloted by an oversized paunch. On his body sat a round neckless head, and in the midst of his moon face shone a thick nose in all the shades of purple and crimson. "Now I understand," I said, "why Madame de Senneterre calls this inn Truffe Rouge. That nose, of course!" A gust of shrill and cackling laughter spread and grew into a full-throated guffaw. "How delightfully naïve!" "How thoroughly original!" "The truffle after which this inn is called," a big-breasted matron told me through tears of laughter, "grows in the grove over there; or one can have it *en deux* in the rooms upstairs. Oh, how refreshing! This little one has actually managed to achieve a blush."

Scarron addressed the innkeeper. "You are a genius. It appears that you employ just as much esprit in inventing your *recherchés* dishes as the philosophers systems of world improvement. I certainly shall not fail to recommend you to His Excellency Cardinal Richelieu for a seat in the Académie Française."

I could hardly keep back a titter over the mock-dignified way Scarron had pronounced his eulogy, but the innkeeper took it very seriously and flushed with pride. "The red pepper stew that you happen to have on your plate is indeed one of my latest creations," he said. "I call it 'à la Cardinal Infanta.' It is what the Spaniards' army will look like when we have cut it to pieces."

Reminded of the Spaniards, the light-hearted company fell silent for a moment and listened to a far-off dull rumbling. "They are trying to force the Somme River," said one of the officers. "Are they as near as that?" asked a small-faced, freckled young lady with big green eyes popping anxiously behind her small paper fan. There followed a rather excited argument about the war situation. Most of the ladies censured the Cardinal because he had got France involved in a war against an invincible enemy, but the officers disagreed. One, a red, horse-faced, very martial-looking captain, maintained that the Cardinal had done wisely to declare war on Spain. "The Habsburgs," he pronounced, "have hemmed in France on every side, and they would have choked and swallowed us as they did the rest of Europe if at the last possible minute Richelieu had not risen to resist them. The declaration of war was a great risk, but it was a necessary one. Anyway, ladies you must not worry. That the Spaniards were able to advance as far as the Somme is only due to a shrewd maneuver of the high command to draw the enemy into a trap. Rely upon it, they will never reach Paris."

The company were glad enough to be persuaded. The feasting and the flirting and the gay chatter resumed. Meanwhile a troupe of glittering jugglers had appeared, and soon the guests' attention was on a red carpeted platform on which these artists performed tricks with gold and silver balls and with dancing bears, trained apes, and dogs. Then some wandering minstrels entered the courtyard, playing lutes and singing. Their music stole like a beam of

healing into my heart and at the same time made me
long to cry, for what they were singing was the very
poem of Froissart that Papa had sung before riding to
exile:

> *"Days fade and others spring anew;*
> *Each month a new moon hangs in air.*
> *Take, then, the moment still in view,*
> *For Fortune is a fickle fair . . ."*

It reached me like a warning from Papa. And,
happening to look at Madame de Senneterre, I saw
her eyes veiled with tears; and then I knew for sure
that it was Papa who had caused her her "measles."
The whole courtyard applauded; but upon Scarron's
remark that the song would sound much more beautiful if sung by me, everyone there, obviously informed of my having sung before the Cardinal, insisted on my taking the lute that Scarron had got from
one of the minstrels. At first I protested, but with the
lute in my hands I could resist no longer and I
complied. What I tried to exhibit was lighthearted
gaiety; but I knew that my show of exuberance had
an undertone of deep pain.

When I ended there was applause from the other
tables as well as from my own. I saw the figure of a
dark, slim young man disengaging itself from a
neighboring party and coming toward me with
Madame de Senneterre. She introduced him to me,
and his name, Coligny, struck me at once and poignantly. His was the ruined castle that Charles and
I never got to. His face was extremely long and
thin, with a thin, fine nose and great black eyes that

seemed withdrawn within themselves. He was treating the others superciliously, almost arrogantly, but to me he was suave and even showed a kind of shyness. In my admirable playing and singing, he said, he sensed more than appeared on the surface, and he asked permission to sit down by me. De Raré, on my right, had given up his attempts to capture my attention by idiotically gallant speeches and clumsy approaches of knee and foot under the table and was concentrating his attack on his other neighbor, a magnificent blonde in white. He got up and made room for Coligny.

I was glad, for Coligny was a far more interesting table campanion. Save for Scarron and the fat glutton Count Miossens opposite me—was he the same who, according to Charles, had pursued Yvonne with threats of a public whipping on the Place des Halles?—all the men at our table were officers full of braggadocio about their exploits at the front. But Coligny, himself a lieutenant, was not swaggering at all. There was a singular charm about him when, with a faraway expression in his eyes, he spoke with delicacy about my singing, and then about Froissart and other poets, and after that about a theme apparently near and dear to him: Paris and its glory as revealed in the city's monuments and archeological beauties. And all the while I felt that he was groping his way to my own mind. I had, too, the impression that, in him as in me, some intolerable ache must be smoldering. That intuition, some of his facial expressions, and certain of his gestures that reminded me of Charles brought me a little closer to him. But I did not dream of accepting his suggestion that he take me on a sightseeing tour through Paris; for I had no intention of closer acquaintance, to say nothing of a fresh adventure. I enjoyed his talk as I did Scarron's, but that was all. It merely helped me over a few hours of misery, and for that reason I did not mind their advances; indeed, I got a trifle of mischievous pleasure out of their mutual jealousy and their efforts to outdo each other in diverting talk and little attentions.

The second course was brought and served, and then a third, and as twilight settled they brought the dessert. This consisted of innumerable small china dishes filled with sugared cherries and *mirabelles*, *biscuits*, chocolates, *dragées*, compotes, macaroons, and dried fruit, and in a giant bowl, the specialty of the house, a *crème de marrons*—cooked and crushed chestnuts flavored with vanilla and ambergris and liquor and served with whipped cream from portly brown earthenware jars. With the dessert went wine: not the light claret now, but dark-golden heady Oporto and Spanish.

Scarron was scribbling something on a paper, and presently he rose and read aloud:

> "*À la belle et charmante Ninon*
> *À laquelle jamais on ne repond pas non*
> *Je souhaite un mari bel et bon*
> *Et doux comme cette crème de marrons . . .*"

He was roundly applauded, and I myself—I must have drained my cup of the heavy Oporto too rapidly— heard myself humming, all in a rosy flutter: "*Crème de marron . . . Scarron . . . non, non . . .*

bon, bon . . .'' Through the agreeable warm confusion befogging my head I could sense the strongly erotic atmosphere of the place and of everyone in it but me. My impulse was to let myself burst into tears of loneliness and despair. Certainly I had no inkling then and would not on any account have beleived that before too long a time had passed I myself should help make one of those couples that disappeared in the grove or of those that unobtrusively withdrew—always the prelude to the drawing of a curtain at one or another of the windows on the floor above.

I was startled out of my abstraction by someone's calling out: "There is de La Rochefoucauld." I turned quickly and caught sight of a tall, slender officer with a proudly erect head, threading his way among the tables. And suddenly I could see in my mind the castle of Loches, the dusky armory where I had crossed swords with the boy prince, my moonlit chamber with him tiptoeing toward my bed in his long white nightshirt, the picture gallery immersed in an olive green light with the rain outside making soft music; and then I saw the white handkerchief waving and waving, and in my ears echoed his words: "Adieu, Ninon, and au revoir!" Yes, it was he, my boy of Loches, broad-shouldered now and tanned. He had the same high forehead, with bushy and close-knit brows over his extremely intelligent round black eyes. I thrilled to the idea that he might come to our table, might recognize me, might sit down by me for a chat about times long bygone.

"With Marion Delorme, of course," a lady said to her neighbor. "One look is enough: he is head over heels in love with her.'' It was disappointing in a way to see the exotic-looking woman with slanting oriental eyes walking possessively arm in arm with Rochefoucauld. Dark-haired, dressed in salmon rose, and of a most ravishing figure, this woman seemed magnificently capable of turning almost any man's head. ''She's capricious as the devil,'' I heard someone say. Scarron commented: ''So far, Rochefoucauld has played with women as with cards, but now it's the other way around: it is he who has to dance to her piping.''

Rochefoucauld had come nearer, and I recognized every feature of him, every movement. I cannot say that I felt for him in the old way, because Charles had taken and destroyed my whole heart; but I had got it into my head that Rochefoucauld must recognize me and have his chat with me in spite of the beautiful Marion by his side, and I turned on him a look into which I tried to gather all the melting sweetness of the *crème de marron*. But he scarcely looked at our table, and then only to bow to Madame de Senne-terre. To me he did not vouchsafe even a look, and, as when he had treated me *de haut en bas* on his arrival at Loches, I was stung to fury. I did not, however, run away as then: I only sent a forlorn look after him when he moved away and disappeared with Marion in a corner of the courtyard.

I turned to Coligny and said: ''As to your showing me Paris, I have changed my mind. Arrange for it with Madame de Senneterre if you wish.''

2

WHEN I GOT HOME I found Mother waiting for me. She had not a word of reproach because I had left her alone, but in her dear face there was a drawn look that worried me deeply. Her health was not good. Charles's desertion had come to her as a great shock. She didn't know, of course, the whole truth. I would have let myself be cut in pieces before I would have shocked her with the confession that I had lost my honor. I simply let her think Charles had had to leave me because he had failed to obtain his father's consent. On the afternoon when I told her about the break with Charles, Madeleine had found her unconscious in her room, on the floor at the foot of her big black wooden crucifix. Doctor Nompart, our old family physician, had opined that her exhaustion was due to the overstrain of her spiritual exercises.

"The good man," Maman told me when the doctor had gone, "does not understand that experiencing the presence of God cannot hurt anybody if it is done in the right way. I have learned to do it from the *Bonnes Filles*, who had it from the Rose Mystique if not from the Holy François de Sales himself. If I fainted, it could have been only because I made a mistake in my method of approaching the Lord.'' It was true. Hitherto Mother's states of trance had always left her with a rosy and perfectly contented face; but, mindful of Doctor Nompart, I dreaded her continuation of her practices. And she intensified them after Charles's desertion. Without doubt, she was praying her heart out.

On that evening when I got home from the Truffe Mother and I sat long together, side by side, holding hands, in silence. At last she asked me: ''I wonder whether going out with Madame de Senneterre can do you any good, darling.'' ''I don't know, either,'' I replied, guessing her disquiet. ''There is only One Who will never deceive you,'' she said tenderly and solemnly; and I felt that she was right.

At night, though, I had confused dreams, nebulous fancies about Truffe, its merrymaking, its door in the fence through which the couples disappeared into the grove, the shades drawn at the upstairs windows—all this strangely intermingled with fond childhood memories dominated by Rochefoucauld, my boy of Loches.

In the morning I was annoyed to the tip of my fingernails, and I made up my mind that if there came another occasion I must make Rochefoucauld recognize and love me in spite of all the Marions in the world. Before I went into the convent, I thought, the world owed me the satisfaction of that one small vindication.

I had thought this day would be a quiet one, but there was a regular invasion. Not only did Scarron come to pay his respects before going to Le Mans, but a flock of young men who had been introduced to me at the Truffe came swarming in, and finally Madame de Senneterre arrived and, waving aside all resistance, took me with her to the Palais, where she shopped in the salles and *perrons*, buying or ordering for me dresses, lingerie, and shoes and a wonderful mantle of black velvet with glossy white silk lining. "Count Coligny is madly in love with you," she told me, "and I don't mind making the arrangement for which he has asked me. He is a Huguenot, but as a direct descendant of the great Admiral Coligny he belongs to the *grands de la religion*. He has not much money, but his family has secured him the prospects of a rich mariage de convenance. He won't marry until he is back from the war, and between-times, and even afterward, you can have him if you want him. An affair with him would mean quite a good start for you."

Though, in my anger about Rochefoucauld, I had promised Coligny a sight-seeing tour, I cared little about seeing him again and still less about an affair. But when, one afternoon, Madame de Senneterre had her carriage stop in front of Notre Dame and Coligny, who had waited at the entrance gate, came to greet us, I didn't mind alighting and going with him. Neither did I regret it afterward, for sightseeing in Paris with him was a real pleasure. Out of inert stones, out of magnificent churches and palaces, out of forlorn and forgotten corners, courtyards, and hovels I could see, when these were illuminated by his enthusiastic comments, the picture of the real Paris take shape. I saw a living picture of glory and greatness and at the same time, of bitter and sordid misery; the mystical Paris of ardent faith, the pleasure-hunting Paris, and the city of the cruelest human passions and of all the passions. At first I had thought of his preoccupation with archeology as a playful aristocratic pastime; but I soon came to realize that the past was a genuine obsession with him, a part of him, and, carried away by his tales, I agreed to go with him again and again.

Toward evening of the last day of his furlough we stood together on the height of the Mont Geneviève, with Paris lying below in the flush of sunset. As always, he was talking about the past of Paris, her history, the Roman emperors who had loved her so much.

"Why is it," I asked him, eager to know, "that you seem to love the past more than the present?"

"Why would I not?" he burst out with sudden passion, "—I, a Coligny, heir to a name that was a glory in the past, and in the present a Huguenot and a second-rate man at whom they all look down their noses? We live in the shade. The great past is all we have."

I felt sorry for Coligny. Not until then had I realized that his haughtiness to others was nothing but a cloak to hide his inner discontent. How different was that haughtiness from the pride of Rochefoucauld, which came from fullness of endowment and a brilliant, superior mind! I groped for consolatory words, but he did not let me say them. Passionately he took my hand. "Yes," he said, "I love the past because I myself *am* the past. And, without your knowing it yourself, you too are the past. It is no mere imagining, but a certainty at the core of me, that in me King Henry IV, once also a Huguenot, lives again, and that you are his wonderful sweetheart Gabrielle d'Estrelle. I have a castle ruin deep in the woods, that was once the bower of King Henry and Gabrielle. Of her I used to dream in my lonely hours in the castle. Now I dream of you, because you are she and she is you. What is love anyway? Love is two pasts meeting each other. And now we have met again, after almost a century. And it is now as then. I love you."

I ought to have laughed at this bizarre historiographic declaration of love, but I could not. He was so earnest, standing with his tall dark figure against the paling sky as if in a magic circle cut off from the world! Also, by some indefinable quality of gestures and expressions he reminded me once more of Charles. I somehow did not mind when he took my hand and pressed it to his heart. A gleam of happiness shone in his face. What a dupe he was! He didn't know that it was Charles's hand and not his that I felt encompassing mine.

With a sudden jerk I pulled my hand away. He looked at me, incredulous and baffled. I said coldly: "Let me go." When, obviously persuaded that I couldn't mean it, he tried to seize me again, I pushed him back and said determinedly: "Take me home, please, and now."

When we parted that afternoon he said that it might be several months before he could see me again. With Protestant officers the rules about furloughs were strictly enforced; and they got leaves but sparingly.

To his last question before we parted, whether upon his return he could see me again, I answered only with a meaningless nod, because I really didn't care.

By night, though, when I lay in my bed staring into the darkness, I grew restless. Ever since Charles had gone my nights had been torture. Could I ever love again? The black void that Charles's desertion had left in me was like a malignant tumor, growing, ever growing, and increasing its pressure until I thought my skull and my breast must burst. With Colingny I could have attained at least a vicarious happiness—one that would have satisfied the hungry beast in me and kept its angry impatience from driving me mad. In the end I made up my mind that when Coligny returned I would be a little more lenient—perhaps even more than a little; and my mere dallying with the idea ended by somewhat relaxing my taut nerves.

3

AFTER COLIGNY had gone I stayed at home and put my mind on my mother again. She had visibly aged; and how frail she was! While she was in church for afternoon Mass I complained to Madeleine that Mother's health worried me, and Madeleine admitted that a few days back Mother had had another fainting spell. "I had to promise her not to tell you," she said, "but I think that you should do something to stop her goings-on. I am a good Catholic, too—eat only fish on Fridays, fast every Lent, make a novena every year, and once in a while bring Saint Mary a taper. But what Madame is doing is madness, and if it goes on I shall have to fetch the *pompes funèbres* for her."

I took fright at Madeleine's warning, and a feeling of guilt took hold of me. In the days that followed I tried to keep Maman quiet. I stayed at home, was more tender of her than ever, and went back to the caresses of my childhood, kneeling by her, letting her hand pass over my hair; or, sitting with my head on her breast, I would hold her hand. It made me very happy when I saw a flush of color and the old lovely calm come back to her face.

When, on one of Maman's good days, Madame de Senneterre came and urged me to go to the Palais to try on a dress that she had ordered for me, I felt safe in making an exception and going.

In the Palais she talked about the plans she had for me for the autumn season, when people of rank would have returned from their summer *séjours* on their estates or at watering places. She would take me to the Louvre, the Palais Rambouillet, and the other great salons then in fashion. "Your affair with Count Coligny was a good beginning," she said, "but I have much greater plans in mind for you." She mentioned a whole list of illustrious names. I ventured to ask demurely: "And what about de La Rochefoucauld?"

"Well, well!" she said, smacking her lips. "How dashing ma petite has become, how ambitious! Are you aware that the prince is not only Marion's lover, but also that of the Duchesse de Longeville, sister of the Prince Condé—one of the most beautiful blondes in the world? All the same, when I look at you I could wager that in this new dress, and with a little luck to help, you can snatch him away from the others." I felt myself flushing with pleasure. I explained to her how I happened to have known the prince from childhood. When she introduced him I should appreciate it, I said, if she did not mention my real name, because I was tantalized by wondering whether he would recognize me after so many years. "Certainly, that will be fun," she said. But then she dampened my spirits with the warning that it might be quite a while before the prince could get to Paris, because, despite his youth, he had been commissioned a general and now held an important post in the field army.

But, after all, it was not Madame de Senneterre who put a summary end to my enacting the demure maiden for Maman's benefit. One day a tall, elegant officer, tanned brown and flinty by the hardships of war, came to see me; and though we had not met for almost six years, I recognized instantly a dear friend of my childhood—Évremond. "Two pasts meeting each other"—the words flashed into my mind. In the sudden joy of reunion we rushed into each other's arms.

His smile still had the dash of *bizarrerie* that I had loved as a child, and it fascinated me now. And, as then, my kiss seemed to have touched him deeply.

"What a lovely young lady you have grown into!" he said when we had disengaged ourselves. He was taking me in from head to foot. Still searching my face, he went on: "But you have changed, too. Where is my wild and ever laughing little girl of the old days? What is worrying you?"

This was more than I could resist. It was as if Papa himself had returned and challenged me to make a clean breast. When we had sat down I poured out all my troubles upon him—my grief about Papa's loss, my anxiety about Mother, my drawing toward the convent; above all, my story of Charles, his love, his desertion, and—by implication—even my *pas fatal*.

I was glad that I had plucked up the courage to confide in this man only a few years older than I. He took my hand and looked deeply, probingly into my eyes. "Silly child," he said, "have you altogether forgotten your father? Don't you know what advice he would give you now?" When I shook my head, no, he went on: "Come, then, entrust yourself to *my* guidance. I do not know how long my stay in Paris will be; Richelieu is gathering a new army to stem the Spanish invasion, and they may call me up any day. But as long as I am here I will devote my whole time to you and try to lead you back into the way your father taught you, which you seem to have lost. In his philosophy there is no place for despair—don't you remember?—no foothold for a passion that could destroy one's bright spirit. Put all your thought of the convent aside. Come down to earth! Take down your Montaigne; learn to live your life by the wise precepts of Epicurus. Make the most of little pleasures—the playful, easygoing, superficial ones; and you will see how they will buoy you up on their glittering surface! You are young, beautiful, charming, endowed with wit and temperament. For girls of your kind the cake of life holds any number of raisins and other sweet candied fruits to be nibbled. Gather them! Gather them with both hands!"

It was as if I heard Father himself speaking. Of course I would entrust myself to Évremond's guidance! I did so without hesitation. From that very hour he was tireless in cheering my spirits and surrounding me with enjoyments. He showed me about Paris; but his Paris, unlike Coligny's, was a living city, breathing, bustling, young, full of color, whether on the Pont Neuf or in the Palais or in the Théâtre de Bourgogne and the Fair of Saint Germain. And when we were at home in my room it was like the old happy times with Papa. I sang to the lute, we read poetry, we had delightful talks about Life and art and philosophy.

To me one of the most important consequences of these talks was that my dilemma, marriage or convent, lost all its terror; because—so Évremond asserted—no such dilemma existed. I knew that my father had always been opposed to the very idea of marriage for me. He had thought marriage a bad bargain for any woman: it delivered her into a bondage not unlike that of slavery and unworthy of a self-respecting human being. It had always made my blood boil to hear of a man's beating his wife or imprisoning her for the most trivial shortcoming, and I had been stung with indignation when told that he had the legal right to do it. In connection with Charles I had overlooked those aspects of marriage, being utterly absorbed in anticipation of its bliss. But with Charles gone, I agreed wholeheartedly with my father and Évremond. Independence, which so well matched my freedom-loving and sensual disposition—independence should be my solution.

And so, presently, the shadows began to slip away from me and my old moods to return. I began to ponder Évremond's singular charm; I wondered if it were not, in some baffling way, linked to the disfiguring wen that exerted such a fascination on me. Perhaps that small defacement bothered him more than he was ready to admit to himself, and so drove him to lessen its importance to others by gathering up and projecting all the powers of his inner charm. If so, the result was superb. I could not help thinking how much good some little shortcoming like his would do to many persons who, fancying themselves perfect, disdained any effort to make themselves pleasant to others, thereby making themselves intolerable and incurable bores.

But, much as I enjoyed Évremond's company in the daytime, his most brilliant philosophizings did not avail to appease my nights and the suspense of my body. I had singled out Coligny and Rochefoucauld to allay it; but how long might it last before Coligny returned! and Rochefoucauld was still unconquered! Unfulfilled, nerves on edge, my body was an incessant ache of wanting—wanting and demanding. And there came a time when I asked myself why I should wait, why I should not season my friendship with Évremond with a little folly. What if I gave in to my irresistible desire—with him? Once conceived, the thought tantalized me again and again. And in the end I decided that I would make him my lover.

But would he want me? I had to find out.

One afternoon Évremond took me for a walk in that Elysium of enamored couples, the Tuileries gardens. We promenaded slowly through the woodland part and into an area of beautifully cultivated flower beds. These, Évremond said, belonged to Monsieur Renard, who sent the most exquisite of his flowers and a bunch of roses every day to the Queen. For this token of his loyalty he had been rewarded by the privilege of maintaining a restaurant on the terrace overlooking the flower parquets, with the grove as a background, and the Renard restaurant was now a *très élégante affaire*. We went to find a place at one of its tables on the terrace; but before we had seated ourselves Monsieur Renard himself came to greet us. He asked for the privilege of showing us, before supper, his whole establishment. We accepted his invitation; and I was delighted, not so much by the elegant dining room as by the many little chambers, their walls hung with red satin and embroidered with flowers and amoretti. "These *chambres separées*," Monsieur Renard said, "are reserved for small companies, or for those who prefer no company at all—to be just *en deux*." I whispered to Évremond: "Please, let's stay here," and I could see that he was glad enough to comply.

We had our supper. A hush had fallen on the little room; only a muted wail of violins reached us through the curtained doorway. "When I was racing with you on horseback a few years ago," I said, "I should not have imagined that we two would ever be sitting together like this." I mustered my courage and gave him a look intended to eclipse the candlelights from the table.

"True," he said; "who would have thought it? I and our pet—our petite Ninon." But he only laughed and did not go on.

"In this place—and like a couple in love," I persisted in my attack.

"Just so. Like a couple in love."

My fingers nervously crumbled a piece of bread, picked up a flower and played with it. In his mechanical repetition, had there been a bitter undertone of irony at his own expense? Perhaps his old shyness and the wen prevented him from penetrating my words to my feelings. I stopped being oblique and said: "*Like* a couple in love? Why do we say only 'like,' Évremond? Aren't we?"

I shall never forget the indescribable happiness that welled up in his face. My heart pounded with triumph: Évremond *did* love me. Yes, only his little blemish had made him fear that I wouldn't respond to his love. For a long while he could not speak; then he stammered: "I didn't know—— Of course I love you. I always did. Even when you were a little girl. But that you—yourself——"

I leaned over and tilted my face up to his. "Give me your lips," I said, "your bitter-sweet lips. I loved to kiss them then, and I want to have them now."

His lips grew hot under my kiss. For what followed we threw ourselves upon the discretion of the little room and of the admirable waiters, who came only when called. The room, though, lacked the piece of furniture that, by its mere presence, would have given the tête-à-tête a more decisive turn, and I was chafing at the delay. Évremond might be called to his regiment any day; there was no time to lose. When, with his arm around my shoulder, he cried exuberantly: "I would not have dreamed of such happiness!" I put my lips to his ear to murmur wistfully: "We must make it perfect—this happiness of ours."

My implication set his arm to trembling and his heart to pounding. My impulse was to take him to my room and give myself up to him this very night, without more reflection, but a kind of reluctance held me back. Too much of Charles's insistent presence still clung to my bed, and I feared lest my memories stand between me and Évremond. Yet I could not long endure the suspense, the longing. Another glass of wine gave my courage the needed push; in fact, it so went to my head that the flowers on the wall seemed to bloom and the birds to flutter. "You will drive me to the Truffe Noire tomorrow," I said, "will you not?"

He looked at me amazed. "Have you ever been there?" he inquired. "You know what kind of place it is?"

"Yes, I have been there with Madame de Senneterre and a whole company. But only at the table: not in the grove, and not in the inn. I do know what kind of place it is, and—I'm so terribly curious to know it better! But only with you, *mon cher*."

His eyes rested burningly on me for a moment; then he burst forth with a thousand, thousand thanks. I was touched almost to tears to see what happiness my surrender meant to my good Évremond, who had made so valiant an effort to cheer me in my desolation. But even stronger than my gratefulness and my pleasure in his joy was the tingling of my expectancy.

4

THE NEXT AFTERNOON, before my mirror, I found that my new yellow frock with the white lace collar and, around my neck, the narrow black velvet ribbon with the medallion suited me fairly well. It was just before two o'clock, the time for Maman to come down from her room with her missal and kiss me au revoir before she went to first afternoon Mass. But today she was carrying no prayer book, nor was she dressed for church. She did not kiss me good-bye, but only said: "Are you going out, darling?"

I wondered. She could see well enough that I was making myself smart, and that the new black velvet mantle with its white silken lining lay ready on my armchair. "Yes," I said. "Why, Maman?"

She hesitated, and in the pause I noticed a new worried line in her face. She said: "It is—because I want you to do me a favor. Please don't go out today. Stay with me, darling."

"But Évremond is calling for me. You don't want me to offend him, do you?" I said with a pretense of lightness.

"Do you think it right—this going out first with Coligny and then with Évremond, and every day, and not chaperoned?" she demanded gently. "Do you realize that our neighbors are making the most of it, darling, and that such things can badly damage your flawless reputation?"

Nettled by this encroachment on my freedom, I said: "Évremond is Papa's friend, and I cannot see why I should not go out with him. It is as if I were going with Papa himself. Just tell me who dares criticize our going out together! I will tell Évremond, and someone will certainly get a good thrashing."

My uncompromising defiance seemed to distress her. Suddenly she did something she had never done before. She came to me, took my arm, and pleaded, indeed all but wailed: "Ninon, dear, only this once, only today! You *must* do me this favor—stay with me. I have had such strange thoughts, such dreadful dreams. Last night I dreamed about you, and there was a great, evil multitude, and blood—oh, so much blood! I'm so afraid for you. Please stay at home."

"Dear, dear!" I said teasingly. "Such a clever Maman, and lets herself be frightened by night-mares! In no company can I be safer than in the good Évremond's. And as for my going out with him every day, you mustn't worry: he may be called back to his regiment any time now. Just a few days, and I shall be staying with you all the time. I promise it."

She made one more attempt to keep me with her; I heard Évremond's carriage.

First we drove to the Place Dauphin, where we intended to amuse ourselves with the droll perform-ances of a white-and-green-striped harlequin and of

Monsieur Tabarin, the most famous quack of the day, who entertained his public with witty speech and little comedies.

On our way to the Pont Neuf on the Place Henri IV we met Madame de Senneterre's coach. I felt guilty towards her because she had been at our house twice while I was out and had left messages that I was to call on her. Upon my request Évremond stopped our carriage.

"Chère Madame," I said when I stood at her coach window, "I shall be so glad to go out with you once again, but—while Monsieur Évremond is in Paris I have to give him all my free time. He was such a dear friend of Papa, you know, and Papa would certainly want me to do that."

"Brava, ma petite!" she said with a twinkle in her eye. "You must certainly honor your father, as it is written." But then she told me that the Spaniards were so alarmingly near to Paris that if our army didn't deal them a decisive blow quickly, they would be before our gates within a week. "If it were only the raping," she smirked, "I shouldn't mind, because they are said to be such superior lovers. But they are expected to kill and plunder, too. We're preparing to leave Paris and to go to our estates, and if you and your mother care to, you're welcome to come with us." To stress the seriousness of the situation she pointed to a crowd of wretched, weary-looking people who were being herded by soldiers along the bank of the Seine toward the grain mills. "Those are refugees," she said, "and there are so many already that the government doesn't know what to do with them. Lest their lamentations and their tales about what is going on at the front alarm the populace, the city keeps them herded together behind ropes. But, *voilà!* your Papa's friend is popping his eyes out of his head for you! Run back to your filial duties."

"Where next, ma petite?" Évremond asked, when I was back in his carriage. "To the Fair of Saint Germain or the Tuileries? I'll take you wherever you like."

"Then take me to the Truffe as we planned."

He looked at me with great eyes. "If it is only for my sake," he said, "then you shouldn't worry and force yourself, ma petite."

"It's for my sake, too," I whispered, leaning my head on his shoulder and dropping my eyelids in a way that the most innocent maiden couldn't have managed better. "I had not a wink of sleep last night, dear. I could hardly wait for the morning."

"I was thinking of you at night too," he said, "and wondering whether you are still in love with your first lover."

"Perhaps I am," I said. "But let us not speak about that. Let us simply be happy together."

He kissed my hair tenderly, and I knew that he was aware of the role I had devised for him—that of a mere stopgap—and that he accepted it and was actually grateful for it.

In the Rue Franc Bourgeois we met empty carts returning from the market, and Évremond directed the coachman to go through the Place des Halles. When we got to that square we could make but slow progress, and presently our carriage came to a complete halt, blocked by a solid mass of excited, murmuring, sometimes bellowing people. In the intervals there were hideous hair-raising screams.

"Please, let us turn around," I besought Évremond. I knew about the pillory in front of the Halles, used for "small excutions." The great ones, in which criminals were put to death by rope or wheel or sword, or by boiling in hot water, were performed on the Place de Grève; but the small ones here were horrible enough. Blasphemers' tongues were burned out with red hot pincers; minor criminals were "only" whipped. I had once unwillingly witnessed the whipping of a man who had stolen a faucet. Tied to the pillory and with the stolen faucet hung about his neck, he had received fifty lashes. I did not want to look at so dreadful a spectacle again. But with the crowd hemming in our carriage we could not move. It seemed to consist of a motley—guttersnipes, a scattering of servants, and also respectable burghers and their better dressed wives. All faces were fevered, all staring toward the pillory.

Évremond leaned out the window. "They're going to whip a courtesan," he said.

The people were craning their necks. Some of them, to see better, had climbed on to the empty market stalls. "Please tell the coachman to force his way out of here," I pleaded. "I cannot stand it."

"I'm afraid we cannot get out and must wait until she's had her hundred lashes!"

"One hundred?" I exclaimed, terrified.

"That is the law—and once in a while they enforce it, to bolster public morality."

I could not help thinking about what Charles had told me about Miossens—how he had threatened

Yvonne with a whipping in this very square. Indignation welled up in me at the manifest inequality of what was called justice, and I said tartly: "I see. Men need them. Men tolerate them. But it is never anyone but the girl who is whipped. Why, pray, not the man? At least, why not both?"

Suddenly a murmur went through the crowd. Someone shouted: "Attention! Make way! Here she comes!"

I looked out. Against the somber slate-colored structure of the Halles, on a small platform raised about five feet from the ground, stood the pillory, a simple rough post with an iron ring around it and a heavy iron chain hanging down. It was bespattered with dried blood. A morose elderly man with a tired bearded face stood beside it and with the bored air of official routine drew a paper from beneath his outworn coat. Another man with a red, dirty, and unshaved face stood with legs spraddled, holding a knotted leather whip in his coarse hands. He looked like a butcher waiting for the next head of cattle. A black-robed nun now stood by her side.

The crowd was swearing and jeering, and now it burst into song:

> *"To the Madelonettes!*
> *No meat, no wine, no beds;*
> *Only blows on your posterior*
> *By the gracious Mother Superior . . ."*

"The Madelonettes," Évremond explained, "is the institute to which the courtesans are turned over when picked up by the city patrols. The Visitandine

Nuns that run the place have the privilege of assisting if there is a public whipping. If a girl decides to go with them and stay in their institute until she's restored to virtue, execution of the sentence has to be stopped."

Two city sergeants with a girl between them ascended the platform. The girl wore a light green, badly crumpled summer dress. Her hair was glossy and fiery red, and the thought "It looks like Yvonne's!" struck my mind. Heart faltering, I leaned out the window. I could still not see the girl's face. She stood turned to the elderly official. "Yvonne Floraison?" he asked her in a matter-of-fact tone. I felt myself trembling. "Yes," the girl answered defiantly, in the voice that, from the darkness of Charles's garret, had screamed at me with concentrated hate: "Get out of here, get away out of here!"

"Judgment of the Châtelet," the old man said tonelessly. "You are to receive one hundred lashes. After the execution your hair will be shorn and you will be expelled from the city, under penalty of death in the event of your return."

Until now Yvonne had stood unmoving and silent. But when the two city sergeants seized her hands to tie her to the pillory she gave a shrill scream. "Let me go!" she pleaded. "I have not done anything. The dirty pig! That fat Miossens—he wanted me to sleep with him, and because I wouldn't, he denounced me." She slipped from the sergeants' grip and turned around; her eyes, their whites unnaturally exposed, searched the multitude. Then she pointed with arm and finger. "There he is, the stinky, filthy

154

hellhound!'' The city sergeants seized her. She struggled, kicked, and thrashed around, screaming: ''That swine, that swine——'' They tied her hands to the pillory. Now the Visitandine nun was by her side. ''For Heaven's sake,'' the nun entreated her, ''be reasonable! Do not let it come to the worst! You won't stand it, my poor girl! Entrust yourself to me. Come with me!''

''To you? To the Madelonettes? That stinking hole? With nothing but filth and hunger and drudgery? No! Not one girl ever came back alive from there.'' The Visitandine protested that that was not so. She made one last effort, but Yvonne spat in her face. With a despairing gesture the nun withdrew. The city sergeants ripped Yvonne's dress and chemise open. In the glaring sun her white back shone like silver. The crowd stared at it with feverish faces. ''Don't let it happen,'' I begged Évremond, my voice panicky and tremulous. ''Do something, please!''

''What can I do?'' he said. ''I am an officer of the royal army. The city watches jealously lest any royal officer interfere with its autonomy. Nothing that I could do would be of any avail. Only a public scandal could come of it.''

A numbed helplessness took hold of me. How cruel, how abominable were men! Their injustice seemed to me to cry to Heaven in the terrified scream that Yvonne let escape her when the whip swished and cracked in the air.

The first blow fell. A bloody wale sprang out on the silvery skin, and the scream went on, long-drawn, high-pitched. Her feet, left free, kicked and flailed frantically around. "Singing and dancing to the cadence of Monsieur the Whip," a woman sneered, hoarse with excitement. "In the academy of the god *amour*," another feminine voice chimed in. A third woman was exhorting the executioner: "Just go merrily ahead, monsieur, one, two, three——" This one, an old wench, beat the air in time as if she held a whip in her own hand, and spittle ran down from her black and yellow teeth. Doubtless she grudged Yvonne her beautiful body; obviously she gloated on seeing it mutilated.

"Are you not ashamed?" I cried at the woman. "Have you not a spark of pity left in your heart?"

"Hush, young lady!" protested a fat, motherly looking matron. "We are virtuous women. But she is a whore, and every whore should be whipped. One hundred lashes? Too few by many! One thousand wouldn't be enough. In olden times they used to throw them into the Seine!"

On the platform the executioner was continuing his bloody business. He did it dully, bringing the whip up and down in an inexorably regular rhythm. The spectators watched every detail with popping, lecherous eyes. Every time the lash snaked high, every time it whistled down on shoulder or back or arm, every fresh cut that opened on the white skin, with blood oozing forth, brought them to a sort of rhythmic frenzy. While the girl performed her grotesque dance under the whip, nervous and brutal laughter rang out, and every time the executioner—rather from fatigue than for pity's sake—missed Yvonne's body, they would cry out and admonish him that that stroke did not count.

Évremond must have seen the agony in my face. He stood up. *"Ma pauvre petite,"* he said, "I'll go and do something." He alighted and elbowed his way through the crowd, reached and climbed the platform. The executioner had just brought the whip high, but Évremond caught his arm. "Stop it," he ordered in a tone of military command. A general silence fell. The man, intimidated by Évremond's martial appearance and address, let the whip sink and looked to the old official. Yvonne turned and stared from red, swollen eyes, dazed and mystified.

Évremond had stepped to the bailiff. The old man looked utterly surprised at this unusual interference with his official duty. "I am sorry, Monsieur le Capitaine," he said apologetically, "but here is the sentence." He reached under his coat and again produced his paper.

I saw Évremond wink at the bailiff and the two men retire behind the pillory. In a minute the bailiff called to the Visitandine nun. The crowd gaped, tense with curiosity about the outcome of the consultation. At last the three reappeared. The bailiff stepped to the edge of the platform. "The execution is ended," he said. "The good sister will take the culprit to the Madelonettes."

For a moment the multitude accepted the announcement. Then a murmur arose and spread. It grew into a massed growl, then split up into curses and menacing clamors: "A fine business!" someone shouted at Évremond,—"a royal officer siding with a whore."

Évremond wheeled toward him. "Yes," he cried out in a ringing voice, "I have the honor to be a royal officer, and I am just back from the battlefield where I am fighting for your lives and your freedom. If it entertains you to see blood, then come and enlist in my regiment and shed the blood of men who are our enemies. Who of you wants to enlist? You, perhaps, or you, or you? Come on—come on! Our King and country need men not afraid to see blood flowing!''

The men shrank back. The growling kept up, but it was low-pitched and subdued now, like that of a dog that would like to bark but dares not. "Poltroons!" Évremond said contemptuously, and turning his back on them, he ordered bailiff and executioner to lift Yvonne from the floor. No sound issued from her swollen lips. Her head sagged sidewise. Blood was still escaping from the gaping cuts. Preceding the two men with Yvonne and the nun, Évremond made way for them through the crowd.

They carried Yvonne to the carriage and laid her on my new mantle, which I had spread on the back seat with the white silk lining outward. I sat in the corner with Yvonne's head in my lap. Évremond and the nun took the opposite seats. At Évremond's order to drive to the Madelonettes and to lose no time about it, the coachman cracked his whip.

Though the carriage bumped and clattered on the uneven cobbles, Yvonne did not come out of her swoon for some time. At last she moaned and moved a little. I leaned over her. Recovering from her stupor, she opened one of her eyes and squinted fearfully at me from the side. A glimmer of recognition passed over her face, "Oh, it is you," she said. "Yes, I, Ninon, and I am your friend. You are safe now, and we will take you wherever you wish." But when she caught sight of the nun she jerked herself upright with a scream of horror and struggled frantically to the door, ready to leap out though the carriage was dashing on at full speed. Évremond and I caught her in time. When I cried to her that the mob was following, and that if she sprang out they would catch her and take her back to the bailiff, she gave in and let herself fall back on the seat. "Are you sure," she whispered fearfully, "that they won't take me back to the bailiffs?" I was glad that I could set the unhappy creature at ease on that point. Évremond, I knew, had slipped some money into the bailiff's pocket and arranged with the Sister that she should be satisfied to talk with Yvonne in the carriage and not report the girl if she failed to win her over. Overwhelmed and disregarding her agony, Yvonne bent down and kissed my hand passionately. "I do not deserve your kindness," she whispered hotly. "I've been mean to you—so mean! I knew that Monsieur Charles would have married you. I can still see him pacing up and down, swearing that marriage is hell, but that he had to have you whether or no and that if he could not get you otherwise, then he must swallow the bitter pill and marry you. I should have gone and warned you, because I knew you were a fine lady. Instead, I was glad that he got the better of you and possessed you. What a vermin I am!"

Her words came to me as a great shock. In a sudden flash I saw how little had stood between me and a perfect happiness that I had destroyed by letting my gross carnal impulses overmaster me.

When the carriage stopped at the Madelonettes on

the Rue des Fontaines the nun tried once more to persuade Yvonne. "It's of no use, Sister," said Yvonne. "I am what I am and what men have made of me. I wouldn't give a fig for this life if I couldn't make love." She used a gutter expression that visibly shocked the nun. Before alighting, though, the nun blessed Yvonne and gave her a medallion with the picture of Mary Magdalen, begging her to look sometimes at the beautiful penitent saint, that she might become aware of the perishableness and worthlessness of the flesh.

"Where shall we take you?" asked Évremond when the nun had disappeared into the poor and gloomy building.

"Out of the city, please," replied Yvonne, "through the Porte Saint Antoine. Outside the gates they can't do anything to me. Two or three miles beyond the gate there is a *bordelle* where I can find refuge." The expression was new to me; not until later did I learn this name for a house outside the city borders (hence the name) in which whores expelled from the city could find accommodation and receive customers unmolested by the Provost of Paris.

We had driven scarcely a mile outside the gate when our carriage was suddenly stopped. A dark, unkemptly bearded face showed at the coach window. Évremond pulled out his pistol, but Yvonne sprang up and cried: "Don't shoot! These are friends."

With a leap she was at the coach door and opening it. There stood out against the faintly discolored sky a wild-looking troop of men tanned almost black, clad in rags and armed with clubs and knives. These they dropped at sight of Yvonne. Falling back with her, they listened to her story with stunned, incredulous eyes. When she turned to take leave of us, one of them, a dangerous-looking giant, stepped to the coach with her. "Thank you both," he addressed me and Évremond, "for what you have done for this girl. At last there are some of the fine people who have a heart for us, the canaille. What you have done for this girl, demoiselle, we shall especially remember, always. Don't look so amazed. We are not so powerless as you think. We are more powerful than the king and all the nobles together, because we are the people."

We did not reach the Truffe until after nightfall. The moon-faced innkeeper received us at the gate, volubly regretting that refugees unable to make headway on the roads north of Paris, and trying to reach the city in roundabout ways, had invaded his inn and eaten up almost all his provisions. But for Monsieur le Capitaine and his lady he would still have *"pas de grande chose* but still something" to eat. It was not the pleasures of the table on which I was intent. I was satisfied when I overheard the innkeeper promising us a fine room afterward.

We had dinner served at a table behind lilacs, by flickering candles. Though it was not a *repas magnifique,* the *"pas de grande chose"* seemed to be enough for a whole generation of gourmets.

At first I could not take a morsel. My mantle lay thrown over a stool, and I could not avert my gaze from the bloody pattern imprinted on the white silken lining. But Évremond turned the lining inside, and to divert my thoughts he made small talk about the newest books and plays, and particularly about Corneille, who was now such a sensation in Paris. He was satirical about Richelieu, who wanted to be a playwright himself and was blocking Corneille's way into the Académie Française because the great dramatist had commented on one of his manuscripts in terms that disappointed his expectations. And meanwhile Évremond made me eat. He cut meat into little bits and fed me as if I had been a stubborn child. And with the wine that he gave me the warmth of well-being began to flow back into my cheeks. Yet after a time my eyes strayed back to the mantle, staring and staring at it, and I could see the ghastly red pattern dancing before me in fiery lines just as if it had not been hidden from my eyes. "Put the girl out of your mind, do," Évremond besought me. "By this time she will have shaken off the whole affair as a dog does the water when he comes out of the river."

"It is not just the blows and the cries and the pain," I said, my stare still fixed on the mantle. "I cannot stop thinking and thinking that it was *I* who was tied to the stake and whipped under the stare of the rabble."

Évremond looked at me with deep understanding. It was clear to both of us that the way of independence that I was choosing, in acceptance of his and Papa's advice, must bring me into conflict with the prejudices of the great world. If I, unmarried, were going to live by Epicurean maxims, they would throw stones after me and call me a courtesan, and Yvonne's lot, perhaps in some different but not less excruciating form, was bound to be my portion.

"I wonder, *ma chère petite*," Évremond said gently after a thoughtful pause, "whether I ought not to make you a proposal that I would never make to any other girl. I love you dearly; I am anxious to see you have protection against this world of imbecility, meanness, and cruelty. I promise that if you accept, I won't abuse my advantage—that you shall have every freedom you want. Would you marry me, Ninon?"

I was, of course, deeply touched. I took his hand, pressed it warmly. "I don't know how to thank you, *mon chéri*," I said. "But I cannot accept your great generosity. You may wonder why. True, I am a freethinker like you and Papa; but, even so, I have a strange dread of the violation of a sacrament. I could never bring myself to commit the frivolity of using the sacrament of marriage as a cloak for license. I feel strong enough to dare the fools alone. But, married or no, let us enjoy to the full this evening and the rest of your days in Paris."

After dinner, then, a door closed behind us. Its closing somewhat sobered me, for our room looked quite different from the cozy bower that I had fancied. It was a prosaic and unattractive place, without carpets or tapestries, and its scanty furniture consisted mainly of a bedstead without canopy, a Spanish paravent, and an armchair. The curtains were drawn, but they failed to close tight, and the glare was bright enough to reveal all the drab inelegance. It occurred to me that all this would not have mattered if I had come here with Charles. But Évremond, in a state of high excitement, seemed to notice neither the unsavoriness of the place nor my disappointment, and began at once to disrobe me with impatient but obviously experienced fingers, until I stood there in my chemise. I told him then that he had seen enough for the moment, and slipped away from and into the bed under the covers.

When I lay stretched out, a strange feeling took hold of me. At the same time that a sweet warmth surged in my vitals and every nerve yearned for fulfillment, it was to me as if my mind, sobered by my disappointment about the commonplace room, were detaching itself from my body. Resolutely, to escape the disillusioning sight, I closed my eyes to wait patiently, trustingly. I had not to wait long. Abruptly my bed cover was pulled aside. The next moment the bedstead was creaking under Évremond's weight, and I knew that he had stooped over me. My eyes flew open, and the first thing they met was Évremond's chest, all grown with curled dark hair. I could not help summoning up Charles's chest, hairless and smooth as that of a Roman god.

Passion overwhelmed me, and I abandoned myself to him.

On our way back to Paris we sat near each other, passionately revolving plans for the morrow, exchanging kisses and intimate caresses. They might have grown even more intimate there in the cozy dark of the coach with the curtains drawn; but we were interrupted by cries outside, and noises of carts and cattle, and at every other moment our carriage was stopped. When Évremond drew the curtains aside and opened the coach window we learned that the people who jammed the roadway were new refugees. They said that they came from communities south of the Somme, which the enemy had forced at two points, and that a great decisive battle was going on. The thunder of the distant cannonade, to which the lightminded Parisians had recently become used, seemed to have drawn ominously nearer. There was also a red reflection in the sky, as if from bivouac fires or burning towns. "It looks critical," Évremond said. "They might call me now—perhaps by tomorrow."

When we arrived in the Rue des Trois Pavillons there was a light shimmering through the trees, and when we drew nearer I discovered that it came from my own room. Mother had stayed up waiting for me the whole evening, and now she would plague me with her presence and her questions. She was spying on me! I was stung to fury.

When we had parted for the night and I entered the house I was seething with anger. This could not go on any longer, I decided. I must have it out with Mother once for all. When I reached my room and saw her coming to meet me I felt that the glitter in my eyes was defiant and evil.

For what followed, what I did and said that night to my mother, the fine, selfless woman whom I loved above everything in this world—for all that paved the way to such tragic results, I have only the excuse that it was not I who was to blame. It was that mad, insensate, and insatiable longing within me.

But there was nothing but love and relief in her kind eyes—not a hint of disapproval or reproach in her words when she said: "Thank God you are here!"

"Much too early," I replied, throwing my mantle over the nearest chair. "It's really a pity to waste such a night in sleep."

She did not seem to notice the impertinence of my answer. "My dreams have haunted me the whole day," she said anxiously. "Even in church and in the midst of my prayers, the blood—— The many evil faces—— And then I heard cries——"

"Silly fantasies!" I tried to dismiss her visionary fears, but she got sight of my mantle and of the bloody marks on its lining. "Oh, there has been something terrible!" she cried out. "Something terrible. Don't conceal it from me, darling. Tell me, for the Lord's sake, tell me—what has happened to you?"

I submitted to the inevitable and told her of the whipping of the Place des Halles and how Évremond and I had freed poor Yvonne.

Had she only contented herself with my story and, knowing me safe and sound, gone to bed! But she did not go. She too seemed rather ready to speak her mind, to bring to a definite close the silent struggle that had been going on all the time between us under the surface. She let herself sink into my armchair, and after a long moment of thought, and this time not without a gentle hint of reproach, she said: "I wonder whether it was right—what you have done. You have exposed yourself to a danger, and Monsieur Évremond to a great embarrassment. And even to the girl you have rendered no good service. Yes, if you had persuaded her to go with the good Sister, that would be different. She would be taken care of by the good Visitandines and be led to a right way of life. What will happen to her now? She will go on living in sin and end in the gutter.''

At her ever so hesitant reproach my anger sprang up again. ''I am glad that I helped her from the pillory,'' I snapped back, ''and I take great satisfaction in having freed her from the nun, so that she could go on loving.''

But Maman only smiled, shook her head, and said: ''Oh, no, Ninon, dear. I know you don't mean that. I know that all you did, you did out of your noble, good heart and not because you approved of an easy woman.''

I threw my head back. If she wanted an argument she should have it. ''I completely agree with the 'easy woman,' '' I said bitingly, ''because I am not any better than she.''

''Oh, *mon Dieu!*'' my mother exclaimed, lifting her hands entreatingly. ''How can you say such a terrible thing about my wonderful little Ninon, the best and finest maiden on this earth? Not for one moment do I even dream that you would do anything evil and sinful. I have an unflinching trust in you and your virtue.''

''How naïve you are, little Maman,'' I said with a malicious and provocative smile. ''What do you think I am made of—clay, or coral, or ivory, or wood, or stone? Or that I am a ghost? The guardian angel of chastity knows better of what stuff I am made, because he was discreet enough to close his eyes at the right moment. And Charles knew how to seize a proper and oh! so thrilling opportunity, and *voilà*—gone was my so-called virtue. Yes, Maman, gone, like that pair of white gloves that I mislaid last year and could find never again.''

I looked eagerly for the hurt in her eyes, but there was none. For a moment her features were drawn, bewildered, but the tenderness was still there. ''My poor child!'' she murmured. ''Oh, what has Charles done to you?''

''Done to me?'' I brushed this aside with a laugh. ''Do you think I regret it or reproach him for it? Quite the contrary: I am only grateful to him. Love-making is such a superior pastime, and it costs so little!'' And when my mother lifted an arm in dismay, I decided that this was the moment to have the matter finally settled. My words came torrentially, and in them I gave vent to all my passionate need for independence, my indignation about the prejudices of the world, my incorrigible will to defy them. ''And that is how Papa would want me to live,'' I ended, ''and how I am going to live; and please, Maman, don't try any more to interfere with my pleasures and to spy on me.''

I had achieved what I had meant to. Now at last her eyes clouded over. The corners of her mouth sagged; her face looked defeated. To me it was as if I had spoken for the whole generation of the young and, with my mother's defeat, had broken their shackles. I enjoyed, gloried in, her humiliation. ''Oh, my Lord,'' she mumbled falteringly, ''where will this lead?'' and I could see her hand go up and press against her heart. As I watched this gesture a faint stirring of conscience warned me that she was a

sick woman and that I should stop hurting her. But I
could not stop the onrush of my cynical triumph, and
my mockery went on: "Where will it lead? I will tell
you." Dancing around the room, I broke into the
song that I had heard on the Place des Halles:

> *"To the Madelonettes!*
> *No meat, no wine, no beds;*
> *Only blows on your posterior*
> *From the gracious Mother Superior . . ."*

While I sang and danced I watched her standing
there, for a moment steadying herself with a hand on
the edge of the table. Then, with a look that I shall
never forget, she wished me good night. With head
bowed she walked slowly out of the room.

The moment the door closed behind her I stopped
my foolery. I listened. How tired her steps as she
dragged herself up the stairs! The gesture of her hand
going up to her heart flashed back into my mind.
Should I hurry after her and be kind and appease her?
I held the doorknob in my hand. But I did not turn it.
To go after her would be to spoil all that I had
achieved, would mean submission and promises that
I was not able to keep. I had to make love, I told
myself aloud with great firmness. Only I did not say
"make love": I used the vulgar word that I had heard
today from Yvonne. The very sound of its brutal
carnality hardened my defense against tenderness,
against conscience.

But long after midnight, when a dull sound like
that of a fall made me start up from confused and

sleepless dreaming, I sprang out of my bed and ran up the stairs. On the upper landing I opened the door to my mother's room very slowly and cautiously. But at the very first glance inside I caught my breath. My mother's narrow bedstead was empty.

5

THE ONLY REAL horror of the soul is consciousness of guilt. When, scarcely daring, I had entered my mother's room and caught sight of her on the floor, her dear face, thin and hollow, turned upward toward the Christ on the wall, and when I saw her rosary slip out of her powerless hands, I stood stock-still. I knew instantly that this was no fainting spell—that the cold wings of death had swept through the room. "Oh, my Lord," I moaned with my hands over my face. "What has possessed me? What have I done? Oh, Lord! oh, Maman!"

When the first impact of the shock subsided I threw myself down by my mother, kissing her cold face as if my belated outburst of love and hot tears could bring her back to life. Poor little Maman. How weightless her body when I carried her over to the bed! It was like that of a little dead bird with its broken wings hanging down. But when I had laid her down and listened fearfully with my ear close to her breast I became aware of an ever so slight stir of breathing. I would not admit to myself that this could be no more than the last flicker of a dying flame. I let myself be seized by a new and keen hope. "Yes, Maman, breathe, do breathe," I kept calling to her. "I love you. Do you hear me? I love you." And when the faint vestige of life did not vanish, I vowed to myself that from now on nothing on earth should matter but the struggle for the life of my mother, and that into it I would throw all the forces of body and soul.

In the meantime, alarmed by my cries, Madeleine had come upstairs. "Now I can go and fetch the *pompes funèbres*," she wailed; but even while she went on chiding my mother about her crazy religious practices, large tears came rolling down her coarse cheeks. Though she doubted that anything could be done for my mother, she obeyed me at once and went to wake Perrot to send him for Dr. Nompart.

It seemed hours before Perrot returned, and then not with Dr. Nompart, who, so Perrot had been told, had gone to Amiens and not yet returned. But Perrot had hunted up another physician and had brought him. He was Dr. Tabareau, a spindling, affected young man who, even at that advanced hour, was very carefully dressed. He examined the still unconscious patient with all the circumstantial elaboration that professional punctilio required. At last he gravely pronounced: "It's too late. The heart—*domicilium vitae*, as our science calls it—is strangled. I am sorry, but I must declare her dead."

I felt the floor give way under me. But at that very instant my mother opened her eyes, though but in a narrow, staring look, as if she saw nothing. Quickly the young doctor altered his tactics. "You are fortunate, demoiselle,'' he said, ''that you sent for me, a man who by his mere presence and touch has succeeded in bringing many a patient back to life. To keep her alive, of course, will require a steady medical supervision and daily administration of many and carefully selected *excitantia*, and such treatment is very expensive. But in view of the austerity of this chamber I will content myself with a hundred écus.''

I told the young charlatan that I would let him know in the morning. He had hardly gone when our good Dr. Nompart arrived. He had been delayed on his way from Amiens because the roads north of Paris were jammed with refugees and their carts; the whole situation, he said, looked critical. When he had heard my report and examined my mother he growled: ''Heart failure? Nonsense. That is a cerebral condition, and one not rare in these days when every other fool wants to become a saint.''

''Will she live?'' I asked anxiously.

''That depends entirely on the will of God,'' he said, ''on her will to live, and on the vigilance of both of you. She must lie absolutely still, without any motion whatever. If she wakes, you might infuse her.—No, Madeleine, no *eau-de-vie* and no Oporto either: just a few drops of lemon water. If you'll follow my instructions strictly, Nature *might* play a trick and keep her alive. But—one single move or the slightest excitement, and you had better call for a doctor of another Faculty.''

Not since my prayer before the moonlit white statue of the Holy Virgin had I really prayed. But tonight, when Dr. Nompart and the others had gone, I knelt by my mother's bedside; and when I saw the agony and the sagging flesh on the beloved and now, alas, so shrunken face, I burst out into a heartfelt ejaculatory prayer: "Oh, God, my God, don't do this to me. I know that what I have done was shameful and wicked and horrible. But I will never do it again. Never again will I give sorrow to my mother by being a bad girl. I will make up for everything that I have done. I will begin a new life, I swear it. But do forgive me. Don't punish me. Don't take her away from me!"

All the while that I prayed, I was aware that I did it out of emotional need, the child's animal fear of harm to his mother, and that the barrier of disbelief still stood between Him and me. But my disbelief received a perceptible shock. For—and it seemed like a miracle and an answer to prayer—at that precise moment my mother opened her eyes; and this time it was not only for the fraction of a second. They stayed open; and at the same time a smile overspread her face, as if for joy to see me praying. And from this moment on I was firmly convinced that the only way to save my mother's life was to keep my promise to God and to pray for her.

In the morning Maman rallied remarkably. When she awoke she looked at me with a look so full of tender love that to my guilt-stricken conscience it was hard to bear. Her lips moved in inarticulate syllables. Mindful of Dr. Nompart's order, I told her that she must neither speak nor move. Towards ten o'clock Madeleine and I managed to coax a few drops of lemon water between her lips. Swallowing them seemed to cost her a great effort; but she opened her mouth for a second spoonful, and after she had taken it she again fell asleep. Her sleep seemed relaxed now, her breath deeper and more regular; and when Perrot came up to tell me that Évremond had arrived and was waiting for me in front of the house, I did not hesitate to leave my mother alone with Madeleine long enough to go down and tell him that mother was ill and that we must forget about our rendezvous.

I had not dressed: I was still in the state in which I had hurried upstairs in the night—that is, in my nightgown, with only my mantle wrapped about me. For that reason I did not go out of the house, but spoke to Évremond through a window in my room. He had come, not in his carriage as usual, but on horseback and in full field equipment. He called up that he had only come to bid me farewell. I motioned to him to come up; and, having no time to dress, I slipped into my bed.

"Things look rather bad at the front," said Évremond as he sat down by my bedside. "The Spaniards have thrown the élite of their veteran troops into battle, and the German hordes under Werth and Piccolomini are veritable devils. If there isn't an eleventh-hour miracle, they'll get Paris in a week or two, and there will be pillage and massacre and such cruelties as Paris has never known. I strongly advise you to accept Madame de Senneterre's offer and leave Paris with your mother as soon as you can."

Of course, he was talking about the impossible. It was out of the question to move my mother—and it was all my fault that I could not take her to safety.

Poor Évremond! He was dreadfully worried for us

and upset by my tears and my swollen eyes. He tried to cheer me by saying how much he did love me; he would think of me in the field all the time, and upon his return we would make up for all that we had missed. Then he kissed me goodbye, not once, but a hundred times; and I could feel how excited he had become—not only by the stress of parting, but also by my nakedness under my nightgown. At one moment I thought he was going to lose his head and take me. I even wished that he might. For—would it not be the last time that I was ever to know a man? Had I not a whole lifetime to be virtuous? But Évremond, excellent fellow, must have felt that, at a moment when my mother was lying sick unto death, I should cringe from the very thought of making love. Later I felt grateful for his chivalry, for when I got back to mother I found her worse. Beholding her wan and stricken face, I recoiled from the thought of how much worse she might be if my good Évremond had been less disappointing.

In the first days after his departure I spent almost all my time, day and night, at my mother's bedside. There was no opportunity for temptations, and the very atmosphere of her room excluded frivolous thoughts. It seemed pervaded by spirits from a higher world, and there came to me luminous and uplifting moments when I thought to hear their whisper in the stillness. I felt myself drawn nearer to God, and I even wished that I might feel His touch upon me. "Let me believe in Thee," I would pray; and when I saw Maman on her bed, full of poise and grace and with that lovely smile of hers, all for me, I felt greatly rewarded.

While there went on in our house the struggle for

my mother's life, and, mysteriously coinciding with it, the struggle of God with the Devil for my soul, between the Somme and the Oise another battle was being fought over the fate of Paris and of France. Dr. Nompart, the only one from whom I had news about the war situation, was more pessimistic than ever; he insisted that only a miracle could save Paris from invasion and bloodshed. The government was organizing a new army, but he doubted that it would be ready in time or strong enough to stem the enemy's advance.

La Capelle, Câtelet, and Fouraques, the fortresses in the north, had fallen. La Corbie, the key stronghold and the last before Paris, was still untaken. But how long it would hold out, Dr. Nompart did not know. "And if La Corbie falls, too," he said, "there is nothing more in their way. Paris herself cannot be defended. Our antiquated works of crumbling brick will totter at a flourish of trumpets. If these Parisians knew the whole truth, there would be a panic."

By day our little street would lie peaceful and still except for one two-o'clock interruption. At that hour Richelieu would pass in his carriage, and people would gather to admire the beauty of his horses and the scarlet cassocks of his guards, gallooned with white silk. Remembering my experience with him in the Palais Cardinal, I refused to let myself believe that he had chosen this roundabout route with me in mind. Yet why else should he have altered his usual course? And whenever, in passing, he saw me standing at the window he would look up and give me a friendly wave or a smile whose ulterior meaning escaped me.

But soon the quietude of even our little street came
to an end. Refugees had begun to invade the Marais,
and finally our neighborhood. Cadaverous of cheek,
bodies little more than skeletons, and eyes wide with
horror, these poor wretches would knock at our door
and beg for a crumb of bread or a shred of cloth; and
as long as we had anything we gave it to them. But
our meager provisions quickly vanished, and so did
our money—the faster because prices in the Halles
had soared. I had finally to consider going to see
Monsieur Breux, our old notary, and asking him to
raise some money on a mortgage. But I put off this
errand from day to day: I did not want to leave
Maman's bedside until she had regained some
strength. Though, as Dr. Nompart insisted, she
showed distinct improvement, she still seemed to me
frightfully weak. At last one day Dr. Nompart admitted that he had kept her too long on a mere lemon or
Oporto-and-water diet, and that if she were to survive she must have some real nourishment. He
would have recommended a beef bouillon, but he
knew that for days there had been no beef on the
market. I was to try to get a chicken and give her
some broth or hashed chicken meat.

The next morning I sent Madeleine to the Halles,
and, knowing that the prices were going up by leaps,
I gave her a whole gold écu. But she returned without
any chicken. "There is nothing but rotten cheese to
be had," she reported, "and spoiled fish and moldy
bread. There were a few emaciated hens, too, but
they wanted three or four écus apiece." Seven écus
was all I had in the house. I gave them to Madeleine,
telling her on no account to return without a chicken.

But when she came back her basket was empty again. There was a terrible hubbub in the streets, she reported, and when at last she had managed to get to the Halles the market had been closed. And it would not reopen the next morning.

But mother was so pale, her chin so pointed, her head so pitifully sagging! She must have her chicken, or she would die of starvation. I had to act, and I decided to leave mother to Madeleine's care and to go myself.

"You cannot go out alone," Madeleine protested while I changed my dress, downstairs in my room. "They've all gone out of their minds in the streets, and——"

"Well," I said, "I'll take an armed knight with me. Perrot has to report to the Hôtel de la Ville, and we can go together." A recent *ordonnance du roi* had required that every lackey and male servant be equipped by his master with lance, sword, or musket and that he register in the recruiting office of the Maréchal de la Force.

It was long after two when I left the house with Perrot. The good Perrot looked rather funny under the big helmet and with the large sword that we had dug out from Papa's armory, and had I been in the mood to laugh, I should have shed tears over the *"Parbleu's!"* and *"Mordieu's!"* and rolling eyes whereby he tried to show that he was a man and a soldier. An oppressive sense of approaching calamity overcame me as I walked through the streets. There was no sound or movement in the little houses; they seemed pressed down under the weight of the livid, overcast sky. From beyond them there was a continuous buzz and an intermittent rumbling that might mean either thunderstorm or cannonade.

As we advanced toward the inner city the buzzing grew in intensity, and we found the Rue Saint Honoré a bedlam of shrieks and curses. All the shops were closed, but in the street there was dense congestion of people, horses, and carts. The whole city seemed to have taken to panic-stricken flight. People with strained and bewildered faces were carrying housewares, furniture, birdcages, rugs, or whatever they could snatch up in their blind haste. Children whined, drivers shouted at their horses, dogs howled calamity after their masters. And to compound the confusion a stream of refugees, barefooted, in foul and stinking rags, lips cracked, eyes dilated by recent horrors, flowed in the opposite direction and stemmed the flood of those pressing forward to get out of town.

The refugees' news was frightening indeed. They had seen the Spanish guns shoot the defense works of La Corbie to pieces, and they were sure that La Corbie must fall this very day. Their news spread fast, and it was spreading the frenzy.

I could not help observing details in strange contrast with the general misery. I caught sight of a couple closely entwined in a shadowy doorway. On a cart, between heaps of piled-up furniture, a boy and a girl lay kissing and exchanging intimate caresses. In the crowd men squeezed themselves against women in the most obscene way; the women either let it pass, as if they noticed nothing, or else actually responded. All this, and much else of the same sort, on the very brink of the general doom!

We reached the Place de Grève. On the steps of the massive, turreted Hôtel de la Ville, from across the immense plaza, and as far as the bank of the Seine, people were now one massed herd of terrified cattle penned together in common anguish.

6

IT BEING IMPOSSIBLE to cross the plaza, we tried to pick a way beneath the arcades of the houses on either side of it; but there, too, we forged ahead but slowly. At last we decided that Perrot should try to make his way to the Hôtel de la Ville alone, and that I should await his return in one of the wooden market stalls attached to the stone pillars of the vaulted arcade. To my left in the wall of the arcade, the door of a wineshop stood open, and from its shadowy interior came a reek of sour wine and the brawling of men mingled with high-pitched and bawdy feminine laughter.

The crowd on the plaza, like that under the arcades, stood with faces turned toward the Hôtel de la Ville in frightful suspense. A stentorian voice was speaking in the plaza, but I made out only the comments of those near me. "Who is it?"—"Some monsieur de la Ville."—"What is he saying?"—"That we should not lose our heads."—"That La Corbie won't fall."—"That the government has brought all available cannon to La Corbie."—"And

Sieur de Soyecourt, the commander, and Monsieur René de Mally have put into the king's hand a solemn written oath that they will hold La Corbie whatever happens and to the last man.''

Even from inside the tavern came drunken cheers of ''Vive Soyecourt!'' ''Vive Mally!'' ''Vive le Roi!'' and ''Vive Richelieu!'' A fat man with a drooping mustache that dripped wine came staggering out of the shop, an unsavory-looking black-haired strumpet by his side. But when his goggling rheumy eyes caught sight of me he pushed the strumpet aside and came reeling toward me. A moment later his evil breath was in my face, and, leaning heavily against me, he backed me toward the pillar and his arms encircled my hips.

I cried out, but none of the bystanders paid the slightest attention. I kept on struggling and screaming for help. Suddenly the pressure of the heavy body against me relaxed. A pair of giant red hands had seized the man by his short neck from behind and was pulling him away. My savior was a powerfully built but very young lad of perhaps fourteen, with a ruddy face and ginger-colored bushy hair sticking out from under his little black cap. He looked at me with lively black eyes. ''Aren't you pretty!'' he blurted out. ''I never saw such a fair one in my whole life. I bet you're a princess.'' I said that I was no princess, but that I thanked him for his chivalry. ''No thanks necessary,'' he said; then, after a brief hesitation, he begged candidly: ''But I'd like to kiss you. I'd like to know how it feels to kiss such a fine person.'' He seemed noticeably aggrieved when I declined to be kissed. At that instant I caught sight of a hen fluttering on one of the neighboring market stands. I told the lad that he was too young to be thinking about kissing strange girls; that it would be more to the point if he caught the hen for me, and that I would pay him well. He made off at once and came back with the hen, but he would not take any money. He insisted on his kiss; and I, in dire need of the hen and perceiving no harm in letting this big stubborn child kiss me, assented. He bound the bird's feet and stowed it in my basket. I held out my cheek. With an air of triumphant bravado he pressed his full, fresh lips to it. It was to me as if a girl were kissing me. But I could not help noticing that it was very different to him. He stood there, face scarlet, licking his lips and stammering a thousand boyishly awkward thanks. Then a voice called: "Michel! Where are you, Michel?" It was he who was being called from the inn. He was the innkeeper's son, and he had to go to his work now. He advised me to climb on to the trunk, where I would be safe from molestation. I agreed, and he helped me up; then he cried "Coming, Coming!" and darted into the wineshop.

From my perch I could overlook the whole sea of bobbing heads, and I could see that time-honored structure, the gibbet used for the "great" executions. A tense silence descended on the square when a man climbed the rostrum to speak. After he had said a few words, the whole plaza was reverberating with the substance of them: "La Corbie has fallen!" "La Corbie surrendered this morning!" "Colonel Rivière is still holding the south bastion, and that is all." There followed a chorus of panic: "We are lost."—"They'll be here tonight."—"They'll burn and plunder Paris."—"Not one of us will be left alive."

Another man in rich attire, patently a high "monsieur de la Ville," ascended the rostrum and pushed the first speaker aside. He besought the multitude to keep calm; there were still the defensive works of Paris. And if the Spaniards did enter Paris, the populace should be dignified and maintain law and order. The Spaniards were cavaliers—*caballeros*—and would not eat them. "They won't eat us?" an angry voice shouted. "Don't you know what they did to us thirty years ago, when they were here as our allies and friends? What can we expect when they come as enemies?" "Just have a look at what they did to me!" exclaimed a pale and haggard monk in a brown cassock. He lifted both arms, and the sleeves fell back. There were no hands—only bloody stumps, covered with pus and dust. The sight wrung a gasp from the multitude. "And this they did to all our holy community," the monk cried mournfully, "to three hundred of us. Every friar had to walk to the altar, and there stood the German savages of Piccolomini and hacked off our hands with their swords. Our blood flowed in torrents, but they only laughed and went on hacking, hacking. And at the last they quartered our Prior and threw his limbs over our heads." Overwhelmed by the ghastly memory, he stopped and choked. But others climbed the rostrum to volunteer their own experiences, and endless chain of horrors. In the Champagne the *Landsknechte* of the German general, Werth, had locked the nuns of a convent into a church, raped them, and then decapitated them. In a village in Normandy the

Spaniards had pinned babies to their mothers' breasts with swords, and other babies had been nailed to the church door.

"In Dannemarie," wailed an old man, "there were sixteen hundred of us, good folk, God-fearing folk. But then came the Landgrave Otto Louis and massacred us. I was the only one that escaped. And all the others had to dig their graves before his men killed them." Another man stood up. He had no face. The invaders had cut his nose and ears off. While these gruesome tales were being told from the platform I could see many of the crowd making their way out to join those that were leaving Paris. Others vomited, and some even fainted; a few tried to choke down their nausea with ribald jokes.

I finally decided that I could wait for Perrot no longer. I jumped down with my basket, thinking to make my escape by the bank of the Seine and hurry home to Maman. But when I had elbowed myself through the throng in the arcades to the corner of the plaza, another frenzied mob came swirling like a wild river from the opposite direction and carried me with it. I came to a stand, tightly wedged into the crowd, on the Place de Grève.

The mere fall of La Corbie had been disheartening enough, but what people heard from those newcomers brought home the imminence of catastrophe. "The enemy has reached the outskirts of Paris."— "German cavalry in the Faubourgs."—"Pillaging and burning in the Faubourg Saint Victor." Others were trying frantically to extricate themselves from the crowd to throw themselves into headlong flight; but other cries demolished this last hope: "No use running away. No one can get out. The government has closed the city gates.''

"Closed the city gates!" The words ran like wildfire through the square, spreading indescribable panic. "We are trapped!" But no one dared to cry out the name of the one who, as everybody knew, was responsible for this war and its outcome. No one dared call: "*À bas* Richelieu!" Even in this hour of obvious and tragic defeat of his policy they feared the "mailed fist of France."

I turned my attention to the rostrum, on which a great tumult had risen. "We want the truth," cried the crowd at the monsieur de la Ville on the rostrum. He was struggling with another man who had a paper in his hand, and he was crying: "You won't read that. That's high treason, you wretch!" He tried to snatch the paper from the frantically resisting man. Two halberdiers rushed up to help the city official, but the crowd invaded the rostrum, swept official and soldiers away, and set itself up as a solid protecting wall at the back of the man with the paper. "Read it! Read!" the multitude adjured him. He stepped to the edge. "Listen, my friends," he called down to the multitude. "This is a paper that refugees have just brought in from the battlefield—a battlefield that is now before our very gates. It is an appeal of the enemy, addressed neither to the King nor to the government, but directly to us—the people. Do you want to hear it?''

"Read, read!" the plaza shouted in unison.

" 'Proclamation,' " the man read. " 'Proclamation of His Imperial and Royal Highness the Cardinal Don Fernando, Governor of the Spanish Netherlands and Commander of the Spanish forces in France. To the noble and beloved people of Paris——' "

The crowd applauded. "Read on," they cried, "read!"

" 'Beloved people of Paris,' " the man on the rostrum continued, " 'we have not come to conquer or to destroy, but solely to compel your king to keep the peace with us. Our monarch, His Majesty the King of Spain, our father and father of our beloved sister, your Queen Anne of Austria, knows well that your King Louis XIII is a prisoner of ill advisers. It is only these ill advisers that prevent your King from yielding to the pleas of your Queen, who desires nothing more dearly—and how could it be otherwise?—than that the subjects of her father and those of her husband live in peace and friendship together!' "

"Vive la reine!" the crowd echoed frantically. "Peace!" "Peace!" Hope swept through them. If they clung to their Queen, even if it were against the will of their King, there was hope, there was salvation, and mercy could be expected from the victorious Habsburgs. "Read on!" they cried.

" 'But we know,' " the man on the platform continued, " 'that neither our King nor your Queen can attain their noble design until your King has removed from his council those ill advisers who maliciously disturb the peace of our two countries and of Europe——' "

"Richelieu!" someone called out.

At the very utterance of the name a gasping silence fell, as if everyone on the plaza were struck with fear that merely to have listened to the ominous outcry might draw the vengeance of the dreaded man upon his own head. But, the impulse once given, other voices, at first scattered, but fast multiplying and uniting, shouted "Richelieu! Richelieu! The Red Spider! The Red Fox!" and all the other epithets and curses hitherto only whispered in dark corners or in the privacy of home. They broke out now in an explosion of mob fury. He, the tax-grinder, the warmaker, had started this war—started it frivolously, for no reasonable cause, against a country that wanted to live at peace with France; with the fatherland of his own Queen, whose sacred person he had even dared involve in a criminal investigation for treason. Richelieu had challenged the most formidable military power on earth, and now its army was at their very gates. It was *he* who had brought doom upon their heads. *He* was guilty; he alone. *He* was the greatest criminal of all time.

"He is the one the Spaniards hate," exclaimed a voice from the rostrum, "not we. Let him, not us, pay for what he has done, and the Spaniards will let us alone."

"*À bas* Richelieu!" bellowed the crowd.

A woman had appeared on the platform. She lifted her skirt, took off her red petticoat, and handed it to the men. "Here he is, the Red Rascal!" she screamed, and cackled hysterically. "Here he is! Have him burnt." The crowd applauded. Some men brought on a wooden pole and dressed it with the red petticoat. In no time a pyre had been built up of other poles and benches and stools kicked to pieces. The stake was set afire, and the petticoat went up in flames; and men and women spat into the fire, whistled, laughed, yelped, swore, and danced singing around the blaze.

They were a mere uproarious mob now, and the whole plaza appeared to me a hellish place filled with the uproar of crazed devils. The sky had a macabre aspect, too. Half of it was covered with a heavy blackish fulvous cloud that hung down clear to the Seine; the other half had a greenish-yellow pallor, and the reflection of this together with that of the red flames was ghastly on hundreds of twisted faces.

The dummy on the pyre had burnt to ash; but not so the paroxysm of the crowd. Some few moderate men, mounting cornerstones or hoisted on others' shoulders, advised prudence. Even a refugee, a man from Picardie, warned: "Don't believe the manifesto. It's a fraud. They always work with such manifestoes. Before marching on the town they want to take they send in spies or *avant-gardes* with just such manifestoes promising friendship and peace, but when they get in, there is nothing but plundering and burning and death. Don't believe them." But the counsels of prudence went unheeded. They had found a scapegoat; they needed an outlet for rage and despair; and, not satiated by the burning of the dummy and the satirical songs, they shouted: "We will kill him!" And with war cries of *"Allons!"* "To the Palais Cardinal!" "Death to Richelieu!" and singing frivolous street songs the fanatical mass set itself into motion.

Like a river in spate they swept me along. I looked for a way of escape. I did not want to witness their attack on the Cardinal's palais. I knew, too, they would be scattered into wild flight by the first volleys from Richelieu's musketeers. Blood would flow. But more than anything I wanted to get home to Maman with her hen. I tried desperately to keep myself close to the houses; but not until I had been dragged on through a good part of the Rue Saint Antoine did I succeed in turning into a side street.

On leaving the Place de Grève I made my way between the old hunchbacked houses through dark and unknown streets. I could see that I had got myself on to extremely hazardous ground. Here was the same atmosphere of uncleanness and doom; but here were no limits to the obscenity and the frenzy. Night had fallen swiftly, and in the darkness, illuminated only by rare flashes, I saw things going on that beggar description. I saw women sprawled on the ground fling their legs high or assume other lewdly provocative attitudes, and men throwing themselves on them like hunting packs. And those were about the least revolting of the sights that at once nauseated and fascinated me. And sometimes I had to hurry to escape men that pursued me, snatching my hand or skirt or trying to stop me to demand favors that, they said, the Spanish *caballeros* would have anyway before the night was over. Several times I was able to jerk myself free and run off. Then, at a narrow lane that I thought deserted, I slackened my pace. Without warning a shadow, huge in the darkness, emerged, darted at me, and stopped across my path.

A hot breath of garlic, tobacco, wine, and foul teeth reached my nostrils, and through the darkness I was aware of a hairy and coarse-jawed head with ears set low and a pair of ugly-looking eyes. "Where are you going, little chicken?" the man asked in a

191

drunken voice interrupted by gulps and belchings. I tried to fight down my disgust and fear and told him politely "Home, monsieur." Seeing him squint at my basket, I covered it quickly with my mantle, for at no price would I have parted with Mother's hen. But he jerked the mantle away. "Oh, a hen," he mumbled, "a hen, a hen," uttered an imbecile laugh, and added an imbecile obscenity.

He seized my arm and held it tight. "Please let me go," I protested, but he roughly ordered me: "Lie down, chicken," and tried to drag me to the ground. Feeling the tremendous power of his pull and his determination to violate me, I was seized by a strange feeling of weakness and dull passivity. Idiotically, I thought of Madame de Senneterre's remark that it would not be so terrible, after all, to be raped. But, with nausea uppermost, I dropped my basket and struck the man in the face. Completely oblivious of the blow, he leaned heavily against me and, by the sheer weight of his massive body, backed me toward the wall. And this time there was no good Michel at hand to save me. "You are no human being but a beast," I screamed at the man. His veins stood out like thick cords, and he snorted like a bull, with yellow spittle between his teeth and his eyes rolling.

I bit and scratched and pulled his hair; I struggled frantically to twist myself out of his clutch. But it was a hopelessly unequal fight, and when he seized my skirt I knew that the next moment he would have pulled it up or torn it off, and that I was lost. Some innately shrewd feminine instinct came to my rescue. Suddenly I pressed against my attacker. He had made a few quivering, undulating movements. It was a terrible moment. The man gave off a savage grunt of pleasure. It was followed by a noisome excremental sound, and he was reeling. It was now easy for me to push him. He lost his balance and fell. I snatched up my basket and made off.

Trembling with horror, the blood still thudding in my temples, I ran on, away from the man, away from the clamor raging in the distant streets, away from every moving shadow. And when, on a small square, I came on a church quite unknown to me and saw the vaulted door open and a mild reddish glow filtering through it, I fled straight into this sanctuary.

No service was being held, and no priest was at the high altar, but in the reflection of the sanctuary lamp that hung before it I could see people kneeling in deep silence, heads bowed. Here and there a devout voice murmured a prayer in a tone between speaking and chanting. It was as if I had entered another sphere—one in which, as sometimes in my mother's room, everything seemed immaterial and of the spirit. Spirituality flowed over me like a marvelously cooling breeze. Never before had I been in so great a need for the touch of it. Holding my breath, I tiptoed along the side wall of the nave and knelt in the shadow.

Intent on praying to God to let me make my way home safe and find my dear mother alive, I folded my hands and raised my eyes to the Christ on the high altar. But at the very sight of Him my head turned away in shamed realization that I was not worthy of His grace. How could I dare address Him in such a state? My dress was soiled and torn and loathsomely befouled. Far worse, what had become of my promises to Him that I would free myself from my unclean obsession? I had watched and experienced sex today in its most hideous degradation, devoid of love, wallowing in mire; and yet I had felt my flesh incited to a thrill of lust. To what had I sunk! I deserved nothing but God's punishment. And by reason of my great guilt my good mother was going to die. I had become a mere heap of sobbing misery.

Suddenly the hen in my basket began to flap its wings and emit loud cackles that pierced the holy quiet. I tried vainly to calm the wretched bird by stroking its head, and then I threw my mantle over the basket to muffle the sounds. But the disturbance had been noticed. I heard steps re-echoing on the pavement, and when I looked up I met the eyes of a young priest with a long, waxen face, half stooped over me. Wide eyebrows were drawn up in questioning disapproval, and a tapering white finger pointed at the heaving mantle.

Still on my knees, I apologized to the young priest and told him how difficult it had been to get the hen and how my mother's life depended on it; I had had to flee into the church to escape pursuers, and I could not have left the hen outside without losing it. He nodded; and when he saw me rising he extended his hand, which I saw was not only white but also beautifully aristocratic, and helped me to my feet. "You are a good daughter," he said, "and the Lord will love you for it." His large, dark eyes were upon me in a kind of stern gentleness; and now I saw that his face, with its long, classically straight nose and high-domed forehead, showed nobility.

Suddenly his nose crinkled; his nostrils widened. He was surveying me from head to foot, and from his frown I knew that he had noticed my torn and dirtied dress and was aware of its meaning. I was smitten with chagrin, and it cost me some effort to stammer: "Excuse me, Reverend Father, but a man attacked me just now in the street."

He asked me if the man had done me any violence; and when I told him, weeping hot tears of shame the while, that I had been able to escape in time, he put his hand on my shoulder and said: "My poor child, you must not worry: it was not your fault. You are free from sin."

His words only made me even more miserable. "I am not so good as you think," I said in a low voice. "I am deeply in sin."

He motioned toward a confessional. Frightened lest I commit myself to something in the sanctity of which I did not now believe, I shook my head. "Not now," I said. "I have much to confess and to be forgiven, but I must get to my mother." I picked up my basket with the hen. "Could you tell me, please," I asked, "where I am and how I can reach the Marais? We live in the Rue des Trois Pavillons, near the Place Barbette."

He pondered for a moment; then he said: "You cannot go alone on a night like this. I will see you home."

We stepped out on to the little plaza. Beyond it the city was still full of clamor, and sometimes the clamor sounded like flourishes of trumpets and beating of drums.

"The Spaniards must be in the city already," I ventured timidly.

"They will never get into Paris," the young priest said with a calm certainty that amazed me.

"Don't you know that La Corbie has fallen and that the Spaniards entered the Faubourg Saint Victor hours ago?"

"That may be so, but God will never suffer them to take the city. Our community has been praying from morning to night, and, as you saw, they are still praying. Neither they nor I believe that our prayers can go unheard or that God will forsake our city and France. At the worst, He will work an eleventh-hour miracle."

After what I had seen and heard in the course of the day I could not share his faith. But I was much swayed by the words that fell from his beautifully mobile lips and by the fire and zeal behind his deep-set, noticeably somber eyes. While he was conducting me through dark alleys entirely foreign to me, he told me that he was Father Chersay and that he had been ordained as recently as June; that his church of Saint Damien dated from the fifth century and the times of the Merovingian kings. Remembering my sightseeing tours with Coligny, I told him that I knew almost all the ancient churches of Paris, with a little of their history as well, and that I wondered how I could have missed his church. He invited me to come and see it some day.

At first his attitude, though kind, had been that of unapproachable dignity. But when, in the course of our talk, we got around to my troubles, for the first time in my life I felt an actual and urgent prompting to confess them to a priest, and I told him something of the stress of my sexual obsession. His reserved attitude, after a first little shock, turned into that of warm and wistful compassion.

"You burn, my poor child," he said, "and of those who burn it is written that they had better marry. But as you say that marriage is closed to you, you must face the facts and not try to find satisfaction for a lust that can never be satisfied. It is a hard task, but if you fight the Devil with every one of God's weapons, you will see that the spirit can transcend everything and that a wonderful peace will come to your heart."

I did not know that he had quoted Saint Augustine, of whose youthful struggle against the clamorings of his flesh and its obscure raptures I came to learn only later when I went to live in the Ursulines' convent. But from the great unction with which he spoke of the ever-lurking danger of sensuality to an unsettled temperament, I could see that he must at some time have been burning himself, and have gone through struggles not unlike mine; and I was glad, because only someone who knew the hunger of sex in youth could understand me. Perhaps he could impart something of the spiritual strength that had helped him overcome the tyranny of his own flesh. It was like having a common ground of sympathy. "When I go to your church," I said, "I will make my confession to you."

As if this were a matter that he must consider some more, he gave me no answer. But he repeated his warning that I should not look for any love but God's. While he was speaking, and I watching him sidewise, it occurred to me that his own struggles must have been very cruel, for, being conspicuously handsome, he must have been exposed to many temptations. Were he not a priest, I admitted to myself, I should certainly not remain cool to his charm.

At last we got to the Place Barbette. When he stood facing me to take his leave, the contours of his black-gowned figure were clearly visible against the white wall of the Tour Barbette, and I saw that he was slim-waisted, narrow-shouldered, and of an extremely winning grace. In spite of myself I was seized by an almost irresistible desire for contact with his slender body. At that moment I no longer minded at all his being a priest. Indeed, I realized with a little stab of conscience that precisely his sacerdotal quality was what added a peculiar and indescribable thrill to his attractiveness. I leaned ever so slightly toward him.

How strangely red were his full curved lips in the beautiful waxen face! Only with difficulty could I refrain from putting up my face to be kissed by them. "I shall come soon," I whispered, and, regardless of my own will, I gave him a look that I should have done better to hide.

I saw him wince from it. A flame shot up in his cheeks and a glint in his eyes. He drew his lips in, set his face hard. For a moment the glint yielded to a rigid stare and the flame to pallor. The blue shadows under his translucent eyelids deepened to black. But glint and flame returned to him. And from the panic on his face I knew with unmistakable feminine instinct what was going on beneath his priestly garb.

"Do you know how evil you are?" he whispered hoarsely, in a voice in which fascination struggled with dismay and righteous anger. The he burst forth: "Oh, you! Whatever you see and feel and touch becomes lust and filth, and your lewdness does not shrink even from sanctity." When I lifted my hand in a gesture beseeching forgiveness he shrank back as if my hand were very hellfire. The last vestige of gentleness had now been swept from him. "Do not dare touch me!" he cried at me, shaking a vehemently forbidding finger. "And never dare defile my church with your presence. I should have known. You are marked by God as a fornicator and a whore. It is visible on your face and all over you. But mark my words: you shall not escape His wrath and His justice. His punishment is suspended over your head. He will crush you in a whirlwind of scourges."

He fled and was gone in the shadows.

7

THE NEXT MORNING Maman had her chicken broth, hot
and strong—a whole big bowlful of it. Happily unaware of the turbulent outside world, she had slept
deeply throughout yesterday and the night, and when
she awoke she was rosy-cheeked and bright-eyed, as
if her illness had miraculously fallen from her.
"Soon after you left the house yesterday,"
Madeleine said, "Dr. Nompart came and brought
Madame a few biscuits. They were so hard that you
could break stones with them, but we dipped them in
undiluted Oporto, and Madame was able to finish
them in to the last crumb. She fell asleep right away.
And there you are! The pure Oporto is what has
cured her. Had you followed my prescription and
given her some of my *eau-de-vie*, she would have
recovered long ago."

Dr. Nompart came in the forenoon and, extremely
pleased with mother's condition, lifted some of his
restrictions. We could change her bed linen and
dress her in a fresh white gown; and he even allowed
her to speak. "But only a little," he said. "You

might even say a short morning and evening prayer; no harm in that. But by no means any mystical exercise. No excitement at all. If you will strictly obey my instructions, she will be restored to full health in a week or two.''

While these wonderful things were happening to Maman and to me, I could hear echoes of martial tunes, drums, and trumpets outside the window; but when I looked anxiously at Dr. Nompart, he said there was nothing to worry about. ''Quite the opposite,'' he assured me. ''I told you that only a great miracle could avert the fall of the city. Well, the miracle happened. It happened last night. The Spaniards are marching north; they are on the run.''

From what Dr. Nompart told me that day and later, and from the swaggering reports of Perrot, who appeared the next day, behaving as if he personally had preserved the city, I learned what happened after I had disengaged myself from the mob as it set out from the Place de Grève, fiercely intent on murdering Richelieu.

When they reached the front of the Palais Cardinal they found the entrance gate closed, but from inside they could hear the iron-shod stamp of marching detachments, the clinking of halberds and hoofbeats, and the sharp command: ''Load your muskets!'' But they went on clamoring: ''Death to Richelieu!'' and men with heavy iron bars moved to the fore to ram the entrance gate. Suddenly there was a flourish of trumpets, and a moment later the men dropped their iron bars and drew back from the gate, which opened outward. The mob, expecting a volley of musket shots, recoiled and looked for cover.

But then they all gaped open-mouthed. There was no charge; not a single shot was fired. Instead, slowly and quietly, with no cavalry or halberdiers in front or behind, the Cardinal's coach came rolling out. Only one old lackey was on his stand in the rear. Then the gate closed with an emphatic bang.

In the first moment of stunned surprise the crowd yielded impassively and let the carriage pass on. But presently the murmur and the cries of *"À bas* Richelieu!" and "Death to Richelieu!" rose again, and clenched fists were brandished. The carriage stopped. The lackey jumped from his stand, lowered the carriage steps, and opened the door. Slowly Richelieu emerged. Slim-waisted, small, but erect and unafraid, he stood on the footboard and faced the crowd. On how he vanquished the menacing clamor, opinions and reports varied. Some ascribed the outcome to the sustained energy of his pale tense face, others to the invincible occult power of his dark gaze, and still others to the dignity of his cardinal's purple or to the admirably modest and easy way he raised his cap to the crowd. Then he spoke.

"What did you want of me, my friends?" he asked gently. "You have only to tell me. That is why I have remained with you while all the nobles have closed their palaces and taken to their heels." Having thus undermined their fury, he began to appeal to them not to let themselves be deceived by a promise of a Spanish peace that could mean only enslavement—men to be pressed into the Spanish armies and sent to the Devil's colonies, wives and daughters given over to the debaucheries and the loathsome diseases of the Spanish *caballeros*. "We

202

need no Spanish oranges, coiffures à la Infanta, and laces from Valencia," he harangued the crowd bitterly; and everyone knew what high-placed persons he was referring to. "You want to remain French women and girls and drink our French wine yourselves and enjoy in freedom everything that God makes grow on our lovely French soil? Well, then, to Hell with this Spanish plague!"

It was a simple speech, but a stirring one, and when he invoked the heroic spirit that the Parisians inherited from their great Salic ancestors, he not only succeeded in hammering confidence and pride into them, but also in swinging them to his side.

"Every one of you, my friends," he cried, "will go and assemble at the Hôtel de la Ville. There you will be given arms, and you will be marched out to the Oise. Whoever cannot bear arms, let him help on the earthworks. All of us know what we owe to our King and to ourselves, and we will show the foul Spaniards, God helping us, that the people of Paris can subdue the Devil himself."

"Vive le Roi!" "Vive Richelieu!" The clamor was now one of martial zeal and fierce resolution. The booming roar followed Richelieu through the whole city and surrounded him at every corner where he stopped to kindle the masses. Before day broke there were fresh earthworks bristling with arms along the whole line of the Oise. The rising sun glittered on massed helmets and halberds, and one could see the Spanish vanguard falling back. Afterwards we learned the reason for this sudden withdrawal. That the whole populace of a great city would rush to arms and throw up defense works overnight was an idea so inconceivable to the Spanish and Austrian generals that it had never even crossed their minds. They had assumed that they were facing a newly organized French army. In fact, they plumed themselves on extricating their troops from a fatal trap just in time.

Thus the miracle for which the young priest and his whole community had so confidently prayed had come to pass. And in my small way I too had been blessed with a miracle. After my night of shame, remorse, and nameless fear my mother was given back to me, though I had not deserved it. How generous was God, how many times more gracious than His young priest! Instead of punishing me, He visibly showered me with the fullness of His love. Though I had known only fear of Him hitherto, it was His love that drew me to Him now; because I could resist everything else, but never in my life could I resist love. I gave myself up completely to this newly discovered emotion.

I was happy to see my mother aware of my growing faith in God, because it contributed so much to her speedy recovery. If I had only been able to wipe out the memory of that hideous night on which I had behaved so spitefully and vindictively to her! But, knowing that any excitement must still be spared my convalescent, I did not dare mention that night, even to ask her forgiveness.

But one day she broached the subject herself. "I know I was very unwise and rash in trying to impose my views on you, my child. Please forgive me."

This was more than I could bear. "Please, don't speak that way, Maman; it is I who have to ask for forgiveness———'' And after that neither of us could say another word. My arms were around her, and we kissed each other in tears before I thought of the doctor's warning and coaxed her head back on to the cushion. It was only a few days later that I told her: ''You have always been right, Maman. I have nothing to expect from this ugly world, I know. I shall follow your advice and enter the convent.''

Mother was enormously cheered by my words, but reluctant to accept them as a final decision. ''If I only knew that you will do it, not just for my sake, but because you feel yourself being drawn to God, my last great sorrow would be lifted from me.''

I well knew the kind of sorrow that was weighing on her. Though she seemed convinced that I had found my faith in God, she realized that I still did not see Him through the eyes of His church. ''I know you are on the road,'' she told me one day when we openly discussed this common distress, ''but how am I, a simple and unlearned woman, to know whether you will reach Him? If I could only present you to Vincent de Paul before I die! Like François de Sales, he has the mystical gift of recognizing by immediate intuition for whom the Kingdom of God is open.''

In these days the thought of Monsieur Vincent seemed to be uppermost in her mind. She told me a great deal about this saintly man. He would visit the gallows and the tomblike prisons of the Conciergerie and the Châtelet, where prisoners devoured by vermin and maddened by starvation were chained to the walls. He would go among lepers and other plague-stricken people, disdaining the leather coats, masks, gloves, and other precautions that the doctors and nurses used in approaching such unfortunates. With nothing but his faith in God's love, and proving thus that the spirit is mightier than the flesh, he would kiss them and dress their wounds and their sores. Through his angelic goodness he had brought the light of God into many an inferno of horror and suffering. More, his influence was sweeping the whole country, enabling him to organize charity and care of the sick on a hitherto unknown scale; the King had appointed him *grand aumonier des galères*. "I know it would be pretentious to ask him to come to see me," my mother told Madame de Moussau, our neighbor and a Friend of the Bonnes Filles de Madame Arcarie. But secretly, I knew, she hoped that her wish might reach him and that he would come to see me.

One afternoon, at the approach of an evening gloomy with rain and low-hanging clouds, I heard a murmur from the street and, looking down, saw a crowd in ragged clothes following a dark-garbed man of medium height and stocky build. He was coming toward our house in direct, sturdy strides, and though I could not see his face, but only his snow-white hair shining out from under a black béret, it struck me at once that this must be Monsieur Vincent.

A few moments later he was in my mother's room. Though he was the King's *grand aumonier des galères*, there was neither a bishop's violet nor a cardinal's red on his dark worn-out garb, and he carried no crozier, but only a crude wooden staff. His strong round head with its big flattened nose and bushy

vershadowing brows could have been called physi-
ally unattractive, even plain, but the merry sparkle
f his dark eyes was so deep and warm that one knew
t once that the love of God was speaking from them,
nd this light seemed to pervade the murky shadows
f the whole room and to illuminate it.

Monsieur Vincent walked to my mother's bed. I
tepped aside, overcome by an emotion so strange
hat I could not explain it. When he had exchanged a
ew words with my mother he turned and invited me
with a gentle gesture to come forward. He looked at
he long, and my heart sank when I saw him knitting
is brow as if in great sorrow and pity. It was a
reathless moment. From beside us I felt my mother
watching with fearful tension. Then his smile re-
urned. "Let not your heart be troubled," he said.
'There *is* a cloud about you, but if you will be
atient it will be lifted. For there is a human kindness
a you that can come only from God, Whom, indeed
I can see in your face. Yes, God loves you, my child.
'ou will hear His call."

His hand was extended. Irresistibly I felt myself
rawn down to my knees, and when he touched my
ead a shock went through me, and I felt as if
ansported to an invisible world and blessed with an
neffable sweetness.

When I awoke from this state I knew that he was
one, and that instead of kneeling before him I was at
he feet of the cross, looking up to the Saviour with
n inexpressible desire, as if I had fallen in love with
lim. And then I saw that I was not praying alone.
1y mother had left her bed and was kneeling by my
de, her hands raised in ecstatic prayer. Her face

was glorified and beautiful as I had never seen i before. But when the doctor's warning came back to me it was too late. I could see Maman swaying, and when I caught her in my arms she collapsed.

As I had done on that ominous night, I picked he up and carried her over to her bed. She lay there scarcely breathing. All color had gone from her face and though she tried to tell me with a smile that she was happy, she sank into a deep coma.

She came to when Père Luc arrived to administe extreme unction; but she could no longer say th Confiteor, and I had to recite it for her. A faint smil had stayed on her face all the time, but it did no reach its full lovely radiance until the priest mur mured: " . . . through the most sacred mysteries o man's redemption, may God open to thee the gate of Heaven and bring thee the life everlasting." The the smile went out like the dying of a candle, and knew that with its dying the flame of earthly life ha left her. Père Luc's Apostolic Blessing: "May Al mighty God bless thee, Father, Son, and Hol Ghost," she did not hear. I fell sobbing to my knee at her bedside.

8

MY SEVENTEENTH SUMMER ended a chapter of my life, and its close seemed like the end of life itself. In the four months past, life had blessed me with its sweetest gifts and dealt me its cruelest blows. But worse than the smart of their pain was the dull weight on my own guilt. It had all been my fault. Through my uncontrollable passion I had lost my lover, without whom the world seemed an empty and loathsome place. My selfishness (for so it seemed to me) had caused the death of my mother; and that was a monstrous sin for which I knew no other atonement than to fulfill the wish of my dear dead Maman by withdrawing among the Ursulines and taking holy orders.

But when I told Père Luc about my design he was greatly upset, and he warned me solicitously that in the sight of God the reason I had given was no reason at all. I told him about Monsieur Vincent; I said that I had had an inner change and was aflame now with an honest desire for the religious life. He remained unconvinced and assured me that he knew his little

Ninon better than she knew herself. We finally com
promised. I was to go to the Ursulines' convent as a
pensionnaire and not apply for the veil until my
vocation had been established beyond any doubt a
clear and true.

And Madeleine? She was opposed to my going to
the Ursulines at all, even as a pensionnaire. "Wha
will Monsieur your Papa say," she insisted, "when
he returns to Paris and finds his house gone and hi
petite in a convent?" The good woman still believe
that my father had been the victim of some injustic
or misunderstanding, and, not knowing the ways o
the world, she refused to believe that any hope of hi
return was chimerical. Not wanting to deprive her o
all hope, I told her that she and Perrot should remai
in the house and keep it in order. And she could vis
me, of course, in the convent as often as she wished.

Three days later, and at once after I had put m
dear mother to rest, I hired a fiacre and made for th
convent. From the noise of the city, which wa
resounding with deafening cheers and peals o
bells—for a great victory had been won over th
Spaniards—I drove into the stillness of the Faubour
Saint Antoine, past its many monasteries and othe
pious institutions and its gardens and vineyards
until the familiar friendly roof of the convent and it
symmetrical octagonal turrets emerged before me
and I entered my island of shelter, peace, and obliv
ion.

The room into which I moved, long and narro
like a monastic cell, was not unlike my mother's
The bedstead was comfortable; the washstand in th

orner plain, but provided with a big jug of water. A
small writing desk, permitted only to pensionnaires,
stood near the window. But there was no mirror, and
neither were there curtains or carpets or any other
kind of luxury to beguile the senses.

Through the first days I was shy and reserved, and
all I wanted was to be alone with my God and my
grief. But everyone in the convent, from the Mère
Très Révérende Sainte-Étienne de Soissons down to
the youngest novice and postulant surrounded me
with as much love as if they had known me from the
beginning and I were already one of them. I could do
no less than respond and begin to take part in the
routine of the community life—to be present at the
Holy Office and other devotions and to share in the
common meals in the refectory.

Though the Rule forbade forming close friend-
ships among the sisters, I saw various groups habitu-
ally gathering around some of the nuns; for instance,
Sister Beatrice, a very young novice of tiny stature.
Her charmingly naïve ways made her the pet of the
older nuns; her little blue-eyed, heart-shaped face
peered out from under her white veil, they said, like
a angel's head out of a cloud. And Sister Marie
Tower of Ivory, another novice, gathered a circle of
her own. I wondered what could be so especially
attractive about her. She had a dark, pinched face
and an almost masculine voice, and there was always
something abrupt in her manner. Sometimes her
little shifty eyes would fix themselves on my person,
and I felt that she was watching me. When she
invited me to sit beside her I did it, but out of
politeness and not because I cared particularly. But I

loved Sister Sainte Ursule Double Martyr, an old
wise nun who had a shaggy face but lively eyes an
was vivid in movement and speech. She was th
mistress of the convent school in which the Ursuline
educated younger girls; she was incredibly learned i
history, and, hagiography being her special *attrai*
she would entertain us with innumerable and some
times very grotesque stories of saints and devils.

There were also a few postulants who were prepa
ing themselves for the novitiate, and these, not bein
clerical persons as yet, were exempt from the Rule
But one of them whom they called Suzanne alread
displayed so perfectly monastic an attitude that bu
for her postulant's dress of black serge with dar
blue apron I should have thought her a nun. Hand
piously folded before her, always holding the rosar
between her fingers and telling her beads, neve
raising her eyes, she would sit in her place demur
and silent. When I saw her for the first time he
narrow, angular face, small snub nose, and he
rather large but well-shaped mouth seemed some
how familiar to me, but her evident reluctance le
me no opportunity to ask whether we hadn't me
before. When, later on, she made confidential ac
vances, I could see that Sister Marie Tower of Ivor
didn't like it; she always called her back to her side

But one day Suzanne addressed me. "I know wh
you are," she said, "because our house is in the Ru
Barbette not far from yours, and I used to see yc
sometimes." And when she revealed to me that sh
was Suzanne Tillier I could not believe my own ear:
She was, then, that long-legged slim girl with the sl
gray eyes full of mischief whom I had seen so ofte

n our street. What a profound change had come about in this turbulent, willful girl, once so impudent and full of life, to have made her forget and so completely abandon the material world and its sensual pleasures! What an alembic was this convent, that it could convert even such a creature into a soul given to humility and spiritual concentration! I must say—I was still very gullible at that time—that her striking example contributed much to my ever-growing desire to take the decisive step and commit myself to the life of the spirit forever.

But though I threw myself with passionate ardor into prayer and ritual and drew increasing comfort and solace from doing it, to my youthful impetuosity my spiritual ascent seemed to me to be not half fast enough. I had brushed aside Monsieur Vincent's warning that I must be patient. All I wanted was to hear what he had promised me: to hear the call of Christ now and then, and soon.

On the fifteenth of September, a mild, clear autumn day, three of the novices, Sister Beatrice, Sister Marie Tower of Ivory, and Sister Marie des Anges, were to be regularly admitted into the religious order in the Ceremony of Perpetual Profession. The church looked lovely in its virginal splendor, with all the candles alight in silver candelabra on the decked and shining altar. It was not a large church—just spacious enough to hold the sisters of the community and the few pensionnaires. It had graceful clustered columns and lofty, beautifully pointed arches. Beneath the great rose window and over the richly decorated tabernacle hung a great painting of the Annunciation by van Mol of the school of Ru-

bens. There were still other beautiful paintings along
the walls, and stone and wood statues of saints. But
my favorite devotional piece was a wooden crucifix,
gift of the founder of the convent, Madame Sainte
Beuve. Black, massive, tragic, the cross rose from
the elevated sanctuary directly behind the iron railing, and when I looked up to it and at the Saviour it
was as if He had followed me from my mother's
room to this church.

With all the bells pealing and the organ resounding, the procession entered the church. The bishop in
whose hand the three sisters would have to lay their
vows ascended his chair. The nuns filling the whole
nave stood with their heads bent. Before the bishop,
still in their white veils, stood Beatrice and the two
Maries.

Then the organ stopped, and the ceremony of the
profession began. "Send forth Thy spirit and they
shall be created," the bishop prayed, and blessed the
black veils and the wedding rings of the three young
brides of Christ. The Mass of the Holy Ghost followed, and then, while the three lay stretched out at
the bishop's feet like a white flower bed, the community prayed in chorus.

I must confess that in the moment when I heard the
community murmuring " . . . that Thy servants here
may persevere in chastity to the end of their lives,"
felt a little inward shock. But I fought it down, and
thrust away my lurking uneasiness when I heard the
three brides of the Lord singing: "For Thee my flesh
and my heart hath fainted away." The last remnant
of that uneasiness fled from me when the three, now
with the black veils on their heads, broke into full-

voiced song: "I am a spouse to Him Whom the Angels serve and at Whose beauty the sun and the moon stand in wonder. . . ."

There was such a rapture of love, particularly in the clear young voice of Beatrice, that it made the nuns weep with happiness. I too should have liked to give way to my tears, but I dared not, because they would have been the bitter tears of jealousy. The enchantment of everyone present had driven my desire for Him to such an intolerable pitch that I thought I could bear the suspense no longer. Why was I not already like these three and the rest of them? Why did He not call me? Over the heads of the kneeling nuns and across the whole church I looked at Him on His black cross, tearfully and with ineffable yearning.

"As it was in the beginning, is now, and ever shall be, world without end. Amen." The choir's last cadence had swelled to a fortissimo, and with it the organ and the bells. The three brides of God turned their faces. In their midst Beatrice, suffused with the light of inward exaltation, really looked like an angel.

The procession formed again. Slowly and solemnly they left the church. But I did not go with them. I hid behind one of the pillars at the back until the last nun had gone.

I now stood alone in the church. The candles had been blown out. A solemn dimness reigned in the magical silence. Light smudges of incense and the sweet fragrance of flowers hovered in the air. A shaft of clear red light fell through the many-colored side window upon the black cross. In the red glare His pink painted body seemed living flesh, His wounds a dark purple glow.

Across the church I gazed at Him, and my lips kept whispering: "When—when?" And then it was to me as if His body were stirring; if His eyes, burning and radiating a warmth, were answering my gaze—drawing me to Him with a gentle but irresistible urge.

I advanced toward Him. My silent steps were impatient, yet timorous. But the nearer I came to Him, the stronger became my sense of an imminent, an inevitable consummation. When I reached the railing—I cannot explain how it had come about—I felt suddenly uplifted. I mounted to the narrow upper edge of the railing. And there—for I could restrain myself no longer—I flung my arms around Him and kissed Him on His beautiful lips.

At the very instant of the contact a poignant thrill went through me, and with laboring breath I whispered to Him in an outburst of passion: "Oh, Thou my Beloved One! Now Thou hast called me. I am all Thine."

"Christ has called me," I told myself over and over as I descended from the railing and walked back through the vaulted silence. That meeting of lips had been a foretaste of Heaven. Nobody was lovelier than He was. And I was His.

Overflowing with ecstasy, I felt I had to speak to someone, to confide my marvelous experience. And so I went to see our confessor, Father Latonne. He was a jovial man with a broad, homely face, and he was all friendly understanding—the perfect priest. But the door to his office was closed, and no answer came when I knocked. At that moment Monsignor Guillaume, one of the ecclesiastic supervisors of the convent, came down the corridor. In contrast to the rather portly Father Latonne, he had a tall, lean figure; his face was ascetic, narrow, flint-hard. Father Latonne, he said, had gone to town with the bishop, but he would help me himself.

The office into which he invited me was spacious, but the abundance of books that lined the walls and lay on the table made it seem to me very homelike. How happy I should be to read them! Père Guillaume smiled and bade me sit down and tell him what I had on my mind. At once and in a flood of words glowing with inner exaltation I told him of my rapturous experience; and when I had ended I looked at his face. I had to look up, because he was standing bolt upright now, and I thought he was going to praise or bless me—at the least, to do or say something extraordinary and memorable. Instead I met a pair of eyes full of dismay and with a look in them of burning anger.

Taken terribly aback, I caught my breath, anticipating an outburst. But he turned away from me, walking around in circles, hands twisted together behind his back, head bent and concentrated in thought. At last, much calmed, he sat down facing me and, his eyes searching my face, began to interrogate me, asking matter-of-fact questions about the date of my birth, my family, and so on. Soon I noticed that those questions were following some artfully contrived pattern whereby this great doctor of theology meant to penetrate systematically to the very heart of my story.

"You must summon up all your courage," said Père Guillaume when he had finished his questioning, "and bear with humility what I am going to tell you. I am sorry to say that what you experienced just now in the church was not God, but the Devil. From the circumstantial way you describe your act—throwing your arms around our Saviour and clinging to Him, with your feet on the narrow edge of the railing—I can see that you must have been very near to His sacred body; so near, indeed, that I hardly dare let my mind dwell on that fearful moment. For what you did was savagely obscene—an act of the incubus of concupiscence—a sacrilege that might lead to damnation."

"Oh no, it wasn't like that!" I started up impulsively. But in my mind there suddenly appeared the young slim-waisted priest, Father Chersay, whom I had seen for the first time and the last on the night of La Corbie, and I heard once more his words: "Whatever you see and feel and touch becomes lust and filth."

"I dearly want to believe you," said Père Guillaume, "and I will assume that your intentions—at least, those of your mind—were pure; that you became the victim of a delusion to which postulants and even novices sometimes succumb—though I have never experienced so excessive a case as yours, my poor child. No, my dear child, loving the Heavenly Bridegroom is quite different from loving a man, and, as the examples of all the great saints and mystics prove, there is no easy road, no short cut, to the experience of His presence on a higher plane. The way is arduous, narrow, thorny—a way of unceasing toil and prayer, self-denial, sacrifice, heroism. If you honestly want to attain spiritual life and to become a nun, then content yourself with Christ's love as it comes to you in the mysteries of His holy sacraments.''

I sat motionless and speechless. Under the priest's words my exaltation and all the beauty of the world collapsed into ash like a burned-out fire. A chill ran down my spine, and I felt my lips tremble.

He said more, explaining why I had no need to despair. But, though I listened eagerly, his words failed to have any effect on my great disillusionment. I had put all the ardor of passion of which I was capable into that one kiss, thinking it divine. Now, with my rapturous sense of God's presence and love exposed as the fantasy of a delirious and pitiful fool, even a crime—for how was I to disbelieve a priest who was himself a mystic?—the blaze of light had faded out, and I was left to shudder in a frozen solitude.

9

THERE FOLLOWED long weeks of cold darkness in which every leaf in the garden that fell to rot in endless drizzle seemed to me a symbol of my perished joy, and the icy fog that shrouded the convent not only chilled my bones but also penetrated the innermost recesses of my soul.

Père Guillaume did not desert me in these times. He often had me called to his office. Besides meditation and prayer, he recommended plenty of work, and I owed it to his intercession that the Mère Supérieure ordered Sister Rosaline, the choir mistress, to take me under her wing, as she did with much zeal. I became acquainted not only with modern church music, but also with the plain Gregorian chant, whose higher meaning as *musique de la prière* I learned to understand. I had previously found it monotonous and cold.

But the vitality of my faith failed to return to me. Old doubts reappeared to haunt me; and I think my soul would have disintegrated completely had I not been cheered up by a kind of friendship quite new to me—a friendship with a girl.

The moment Suzanne Tillier noticed my depression she began to draw nearer to me. At first she did it in a cautious, even a sly way, taking care not to be observed by Sister Marie Tower of Ivory and trying to give our encounters the appearance of mere chance. Once, when she knew me to be alone high up in the choir studying the manuals and antiphonics, she followed me. And there where nobody could overhear our conversation she opened her heart. In many ways, I found with rising pity, her fate was akin to mine. As the dowerless youngest daughter of Monsieur Tillier, a high official in the Parlement de Paris, she had been destined to a convent life.

"I never wanted to be a nun," she said frankly, "and I was still playing with my dolls when I discovered that I was made for *amour*. There was Guy, a minstrel who sings in the streets to a lute. He would often come to our house and sing of *amour*, and we would always throw some food or a coin down to him. I found him much nicer than all the men who paid court to my elder sisters. I fell in love with the boy; oh, Holy Marianne, Agathe, Hildegarde, and Euphrosyne, did I fall in love! I could not have him come to our house, of course, but I used every opportunity to slip out and meet him. You don't need to be told that we weren't saying Ave Marias together. But then my doings were discovered. Father raved like a madman and took me to our estate in the Auvergne, where he imprisoned me like a criminal. It was the blackest time of my life. The cold, the darkness, the solitude! I thought I should go mad. One day when I was just about to jump out of the tower, Father came and brought me here to this convent. His coming seemed like a miracle. And so here I have been for over a year, waiting for my novitiate. And that's the end of my romance.''

"You are not so happy here as I thought," I said sympathetically. I tried to find out whether she doubted her vocation. She gave a queer laugh. "Never mind about my vocation," she said with a quiver of bitterness in her voice. "I am going to be Sister Agathe Hildegarde. She was the saint who jumped from a prison tower and received no injury. She must have protected me when I was about to jump out myself—and maybe I shall need her the next time I try it."

She looked out the window high in the wall, staring at the melancholy gray sky and the rain. A shudder passed through me at her expression, which was blankly fixed, haunted, and touched with derangement—an expression utterly at variance with both her usual serenity and her former eroticism. It seemed to me that both influences were still struggling within her, and that the poor girl knew no way to harmonize them but to jump to her death. "You must not talk like that," I said sympathetically. She gave me a grateful look, and I had a flash of insight into her repeated efforts to draw nearer to me. "Do you think it would help," I said impulsively, "if we became friends, and should you like it?"

She seized on my suggestion. "You don't know how much it would mean to me!" She took my hand and pressed it so hard and so long that I wondered if I were ever going to get it back safe and whole.

From that day we were together whenever the

occasion offered; mostly in the garden, now bald and ragged and nearly always deserted. There we would forget Rule, spiritual concentration, and prayers and be like children at play. She would make me laugh as I had not laughed for a long time, and later on, when our attachment had become even closer, we would walk with arms around each other's waist or even fall to kissing and other endearments.

In the beginning I could not see any harm in such expressions and mutual affection between girls, and though there was a stormy impetuosity in Suzanne's caresses that might have suggested to me that they were not so innocent as I thought, I didn't become suspicious even when they grew a good deal more intimate. But one night I was forced to realize what a dangerous game I had let myself in for.

Every evening after the recreation hour, when the night prayers had been said, Suzanne and I parted, I retiring to my room and she to the dormitory of the postulants. One night, already asleep, I felt the soft pressure of two hot lips on my mouth. I thought I was dreaming. Then I heard Suzanne giggle; and when I opened my eyes, I found her crouched at my bed. ''I couldn't get a wink of sleep, darling,'' she said. ''Do you mind my stealing here to you for a chat?''

Still unsuspicious, I welcomed her, and we chatted for a while in the dark. When she said that she was shivering with cold and should like to crawl in with me to warm herself I told her to do so. We lay side by side, somewhat separated, and the nearness of another human body made me feel pleasantly cozy. It seemed entirely natural to me when we moved closer and kissed as we were wont to. Nor did

I sense anything improper in our fondling. But then Suzanne's hand crept under my nightgown, and her fingers passed gently over my bosom. "Do you know what lovely breasts you have?" she whispered hotly, "—two sweet little morsels, and so firm, though so soft! And what wonderful shoulders— arms—hips! oh, I have never touched anything so alluring as your body. Ah, how I do love you!" Over the caresses that she lavished on me I had better throw a veil, for they went to extravagant lengths and finally attained a pitch that shuns specific description. All this, from a girl, was quite new to me; it took me by surprise and rendered me defenseless. My head reeled, and when I became aware that my friend's body was sturdy, muscular and slender like a boy's, I myself did not remain unresponsive. We ended panting with mutual pleasure.

When Suzanne had gone I became painfully aware of the sinfulness of what we had done, and I was shaken by bitter remorse. When I met her the next morning in the refectory, though, she showed her usual pious attitude, avoiding my eyes; and when, later, we met in the garden and chatted as usual, we abstained from caresses and even from a too tempting nearness. I assumed that she, too, was stricken with shamed regret and wanted to forget our doings in bed. But the next night, feeling lonesome, unable to get to sleep, I heard her soft footsteps and realized that she had slipped into my room again. I could not resist. Without protest I let her crawl into my bed; and on that night and many following ones we let ourselves go in unheard-of abandon.

"I never dreamed," Suzanne told me once as I lay

in her arms, "that I could love a girl as I love you. When I first came to the convent I could think of nothing but my boy—how I had to have him and make love with him. I even made plans for eloping with him. With the help of a girl in the convent school I succeeded in sending him word, and I got an answer that on a certain night he would come and take me away. But he never came, and I could not get word to him after that. You can imagine how desperate I was. I have to make love, or I shall go mad or kill myself. But then Sister Marie Tower of Ivory told me the secret of what girls can mean to each other, apart from men. I didn't like her particularly, but I was glad of what she had taught me. Then you came to us, darling; and from the moment I saw you I knew that I should never care for Guy or any other man if I could only have you. With you I am perfectly happy." She kissed me from head to foot, lingering at certain places.

It was quite a disillusionment to me that Sister Marie Tower of Ivory was pursuing sin under a cloak of sanctity. "Are there other nuns of this kind?" I asked Suzanne. "Not many," she said. "With the exception of Marie Tower of Ivory and a few whom she has let into her secret, they are all saintly women. True, for most of them it is not very difficult, because the whole subject of *amour* leaves them cold. Others, though, have to destroy their fleshly lusts with mortification. Most of them pray and pray until they succeed. But I never could."

"Pray and pray until they succeed." Suzanne's words struck me. I drew away from her with an impulsive jerk. Suzanne laughed. "Don't defend yourself against your own nature, darling," she said, "because you can't escape it. More than anyone else I have ever known you are made for amour."

But that night I made up my mind that if I wanted ever to be delivered from my spiritual desolation I could not go on with Suzanne, for I knew our relationship would absolutely cut me off from the grace of God. I was not, to be sure, in love with Suzanne as she was with me; but our doings were a poison to which my body would become gradually accustomed, and I should again be under the lash of its tyranny. I decided to be absolutely frank with her and to tell her so; and the next morning when we met in the garden I asked her with all possible gentleness not to come to my room at night any more. She visibly winced.

"Don't you love me any more?" she cried, and so loudly that I had to look about to make sure that no one had overheard us.

"Certainly I love you," I said, trying to soothe her. "I love you very dearly, and I want us to keep on being friends—only as it was before, like sisters." She was chewing her lips; her hand went up in a fretful, distraught gesture and pressed against her heart. I asked her not to make it so hard for me, and she said chokingly: "I cannot. I cannot part from you. You are mine and I am all yours." And she flung herself on my breast and wept convulsively.

When I had finally freed myself from Suzanne I was terrified of my own weakness, and, feeling that my own strength was but frail, I decided to seek help from our confessor, Father Latonne. But then a certain reluctance suggested that I might do better to confide first in a woman; and, encountering Mère Clothilde, Mistress of Novices, I asked if I might consult her on a personal matter. There may have been signs of my recent agitation still on my face; anyway I saw, by the way she looked at me and by her very friendly and compassionate voice, that she understood what kind of help I was expecting from her. "I shall be glad to have a good long talk with you," she said. "Let us both excuse ourselves from the recreation hour. Come instead to my office."

Night was coming on and the gentle light of the *heure bleue* already melting the room when I entered it. Mère Clothilde, sitting at her desk, received me with the sign of the cross. Her narrow, pallid face had always interested me. A sharp profile with a steep forehead and severe, deeply furrowed lines contrasted strangely with her dreamy, pathetic, and profoundly mysterious eyes. Tonight the softness was more in evidence than the austerity.

I told Mère Clothilde about my struggle against the flesh. I did it trustingly, though, of course, guardedly, so as not to incriminate poor Suzanne. She told me at once that she was glad I had addressed myself to her. "It was my own tragedy," she confessed, "to be a slave to my insatiable temperament, like Sainte Clothilde, my patron saint, whose youth was filled with *épisodes romanesques et quelquefois très violentes*." Before asking me to sit down she had me turn around and take a good look at the painting to the right of the door.

It was a huge painting in violent colors representing Mary Magdalen, the Sinner, in the traditional

scarlet garment, its folds hardly veiling her voluptuous rosy limbs. She lay on a fur, surrounded by jewel
cases and flasks of perfume. Her hands, themselves
plump and soft, were clasped around a gray-green
skull; and out of the skull, ghastly to behold, were
crawling worms and insects of all kinds. Mère
Clothilde did not need to say a word to make me
aware of the frightful symbolism of the scene. For a
long while she had me stand before the picture in
silence. Then she had me turn back to her, sit down,
and listen.

"My own words," she said, "are too poor to
convey what you need to hear; therefore let me read
to you from the Confessions of Saint Augustine,
who, like both of us, was a great sinner in his
youth." Then, in a subdued whisper and with a deep
gravity, she began to read to me from the book, not
continuously, but turning the leaves back and forth,
while a flame rose and quivered in her cheeks.

Mère Clothilde's voice had risen to high, clear
tones exalted by passion. Her face seemed beautiful
and young when she spoke of the grace of conti-
nence, which, she said, was no barren thing, but a
source of joy beside which all the so-called delights
of the flesh were worthless and repulsive.

Spellbound by her words and by the glow that
radiated from the pages of the Confessions, I was
seized by the desire to be like Saint Augustine and
Mère Clothilde and all the hosts of maidens who had
found their joy in chastity. I listened eagerly to the
Mère's counsels about inward concentration and
constant prayer and other ways of nurturing my
reliance on God.

That night I bolted the door of my room. I heard Suzanne scratching at the panel, imploring me in a smothered voice to let her in for just a moment, and then whimpering and whining. I pitied her, because I loved her, and there were moments when I was tantalized by the image of my own body molded to her long thighs, her longs legs, her hard little breasts. But I fought the temptation; I pretended not to hear her; and our struggle went on until the convent bell called the community to Matins, and she had to leave her place at my door.

I wanted to give Suzanne the companionship of our first days, but it meant nothing to her. Instead she pursued me with protestations of love, and I had to make a study of avoiding her. Weeks passed. One day I met her in the corridor and was about to whisk past her as usual, but she tugged at my skirt and, holding fast, implored me: "Don't be afraid, Ninon; I won't annoy you. You will be rid of me very soon. I am going to leave this place, and I need you. You are the only person in the world who can help me." Then she confided that she had at last had word from Guy. He was going to come a week from today and carry her off. He had a ladder prepared and hidden near by; and she had to let him know to what window he was to raise it.

I agreed at once that she should select the window of my room. I was relieved both for her and for myself, and I saw nothing unfair to the convent in the plan, for I knew that the nuns abhorred the thought of its being regarded as a place of imprisonment.

When the critical night arrived I let her slip into my room with a little bundle. This she placed near the window; then she sat down on my bed. I was sitting on the one stool. I had not undressed, because, though Suzanne had promised to let me alone, I dreaded an outburst of her passion at the hour of parting. But she was keeping her word: she sat on the edge of the bed, looking toward the window and listening, though with no sign of joy in her exploit. "If you were to say one single word," she said, "telling me that I should stay and that you could love me, I wouldn't go with him." But I told her that I had made up my mind. I proposed that she get up from the bed, stand near the window, and devote herself to listening and watching.

She obeyed, and in a few minutes I saw her waving toward the street. "There he is," she said, and hurriedly took up her bundle. I let her kiss me goodbye, and there would have been no end to the kiss if I hadn't freed myself from the embrace. "Must I really go?" she said chokingly, her eyes on me in a last supplication. "Of course you must go," I said, and pushed her gently toward the window.

She looked out. But the next moment she shrank suddenly back. Outside was a barking of dogs, a confusion of voices. Suzanne said, white as a sheet: "My father has found out. They have caught him. Now I am lost."

Through the following days I felt even more worried about Suzanne. When I met her and she looked at me out of haunted eyes in hollow sockets, I saw how her cheekbones stood out, and she implored me: "Have mercy on me, Ninon, or I'll kill myself." I could not help remembering the day when we had been together in the choir and she had stared rigidly at the melancholy sky through the high window with a touch of madness in her eyes. I did my best to persuade her that it was better for us both to remain just companions, but she would only stare at me dazed and perturbed, and her eyes would turn misty or fill with tears. Though I knew her to be unconvinced, I could not help her.

One day the news spread about the convent that this very week Suzanne was to receive the white veil of a novice. It came to me as a relief, because Suzanne, once received into the novitiate, would move to the convent proper. She would then have scarcely any occasion to enter the pensionnaires' wing.

The taking of the white veil was not the occasion of a "great" ceremony, though the prioress wanted it always to be impressive and solemn. She ordered Sister Marguérite and me to have the altar decorated with flowers from the conservatory. My hands were trembling when I put the fresh green and the virginal white lilies into the vases, for I knew that to Suzanne the white veil was the symbol of an imprisonment from which she could hardly hope ever to escape; yet, near now to Marie Tower of Ivory, she might become a source of trouble or of scandal. Poor Suzanne!

But no sooner had I left the church and entered the courtyard than I heard a confusion of wild voices from somewhere in the upper part of the church. And then, to my supreme horror, I saw Suzanne appear at the window high up in the choir, swing herself out, and pitch head down straight to the ground. Half crazed with shock and foolishly imagining that I could catch her in my arms, I had started running across the courtyard. But when I got there she lay with her head crushed against the cobblestones. After a few grotesque twitches she lay without the slightest move. Her blank, fixed eyes, still open, with all the blood, made the world turn black to me, and I was tottering. I knelt by her side and broke into sobs. The prioress and the two priests came hurrying out of the church. They arranged Suzanne's body decently and Père Guillaume examined her for a sign of life. When he declared her dead they knelt by her side and recited prayers. I tried to join in, but I was too stupefied with terror and with a pang of guilt for my part in this tragedy.

The winter was exceptionally hard that year. Suzanne's little grave, in a remote corner of the convent cemetery, lay buried under a high shroud of frozen snow. The icy cold gales from the west penetrated the thick convent walls and froze the water in the jug on my washstand and in our cups in the refectory. But, like anyone else in the community, I could stand the adversities of the long winter. Concentrated completely inward, I drew warmth from the glow of prayer, from Saint Augustine, and from the holy passion of chastity, which under Mère Clothilde's guidance I was learning more and more to value and enjoy. And if sometimes my old senseless fleshly longings returned to try me, I had only to look at the church window high in the choir or at the death's head in Mary Magdalen's hands to make the temptations take flight.

Then a warm thawing wind set in. Clumps of frozen snow slid from roofs and fell from trees.

Slender twigs stuck out, aglitter with melting ice. Quivering drops pattered down from swaying branches and mingled with the soft swish of the rain. Selective imaginings intruded into my very dreams, most of them with my lover Charles at their center; and I found it constantly more difficult to deafen my ears to the mysterious voices calling me back to the life of the world. I would lie awake by night and stare into the darkness.

One night I started out of my sleep and found myself screaming, and I knew that my flesh had revolted. It did not want to be mortified. In the morning I looked for help from Mère Clothilde. "I have no desire for the delights of voluptuousness; I do not grieve for the pleasures of the flesh; I despise them. But how can I stand this agony, these headaches, this nervous prostration?"

"How lucky you are!" said Mère Clothilde. "If you despise the flesh, never mind its torments. Only set your will against it and call God and all the saints and angels of Heaven to your assistance. If you won't give in, it will yield, and you'll be rewarded with pleasures in which there is no bitterness."

In this period Madeleine came to see me often. She had been satisfied with my health in the first weeks, but now she was dismayed, and she protested that it was high time for me to return home. Madame de Senneterre came to see me every week and never failed to admonish me that it was a shame to throw away the best years of my life; that I had played the little saint for my mother's benefit long enough. "Rochefoucauld is in Paris now," she would coax me, "and it is high time that someone finally got him out of Marion's snares. Scarron and Coligny and many others are asking about you, too. The season is in full swing; there are parties in the Rambouillet and balls in the Louvre; and all this you are missing, you stubborn little light-minded ninny!''

But one day, well along in the spring, she neither scolded nor coaxed me, but only inquired minutely about my prospects for the novitiate. When I explained that I should have to wait for at least a year she said: ''Splendid!'' and smiled slyly. Knowing nothing of any changes in my prospects that might be impending in the outside world, I took her smile for irony. I felt her attitude as a challenge, and it made me redouble my strivings to attain sanctity.

One morning, though, when I looked out the window and saw the chestnut alley outside the convent walls in full bloom, I was seized by a sudden desire to go for a walk. Since entering the convent, though my freedom was in no way restricted I had never set foot outside its walls. I struggled with the temptation throughout the forenoon. But after the midday meal I could resist no longer, and I let myself out. When the gate of the dark entrance hall closed behind me I stood dazzled by the light and space. The sky over me, ardently blue, was filled with a thousand merry little voices. The whole faubourg was overflowing with sunlit greenery, golden laburnum, and pink and white hedge roses, and breathing in their perfume, I stretched my arms in an inexplicable yearning—for what? Was it for Paris, whose rooftops and turrets shimmered hazily on the milky horizon? Even if I gave in to my present blind longing, where could I go, what could I do?

The chestnut alley was a lovely sight. Walking on, with the ocean of its green foliage surrounding me and the white and pink clouds of its blossoms overhead, I found myself carried back to another May day in another chestnut alley; and presently I was whispering, then calling audibly, the name of my faithless lover. If he returned, I wondered, would I leave the convent and go with him? Would I go! Why, I would run wherever and toward whatever fate he offered me; for, I now realized, I had never ceased to love him and never should cease.

It was foolish, of course, to indulge myself in such sentimental longings. Charles had not, like me, withdrawn from the world. He had crossed many seas in the past year, seen many ports, loved many beautiful and exotic women. What would make him think of an insignificant girl like me? Nevertheless I kept on playing with my fancies, and they grew upon me so vividly that when I walked back to the convent I had an irrational but powerful intuition that I should find him waiting for me in front of the entrance gate and was quite disappointed when I didn't.

But my hope flared up again when the lay sister in charge of the gate told me that they had been looking for me everywhere, and that I should go at once to the parlor, where a visitor was waiting for me. She could not tell me who it was, because she had just come on duty; but to my impetuous question "Can you tell me at least whether it is a man or a woman?" she replied that the visitor was most certainly a monsieur.

With heart beating wildly I flew up the stairs, and I was out of breath when I opened the parlor door. I stopped at the threshold, blinking across the sun-filled room. The tall figure of a man stood silhouetted against the window. He stretched out both his hands, came forward, came towards me.

"Ninon, ma petite!"

With a cry of joy, sobbing and laughing, I rushed into his embrace. "Oh, Papa! My dear, dear Papa!"

And with that cry all the beautiful and desperate efforts I had made to feel holy came to an unexpected and instantaneous end.

PART THREE

1

HOW WONDERFUL he was, my dear, dear Papa! He had
got a little gray at the temples, and there were a few
isolated white strands in his rich brown hair. But
otherwise he was as though he had ignored those
long intervening years. He had not a wrinkle in his
lean ruddy face, and there was the same flash of
vitality in his merry black eyes, the same inimitably
elegant movements. And he was perfectly fresh and
well-groomed after his long journey. I knew how
deeply stirred he was by our reunion, and in the
carriage on our way home I told him what a comfort-
ing atmosphere of relaxation and *savoir vivre* he
imparted. He was talking vividly and caressing me
the while.

"It has been exciting to become acquainted with
all those foreign lands," he said enthusiastically,
"because the world is interesting everywhere. But
none of it was Paris, and it all meant being deprived
of you, ma petite, and that was the worst. For years
all hope seemed lost, and I should never have got
back but for my good Madame de Senneterre and her

special ways of settling the most tricky matters. There is a certain Bourdonnaux at court, a baby-faced young man who is a favorite of the King——''

I could see from Papa's ironic smile what kind of favorite the young fellow was to the King, though what such a relationship between men might signify escaped my knowledge. ''And on this Bourdon-naux's face,'' went on Papa, laughing, ''His Majesty loves to sprinkle perfume. And every time the youngster endures the procedure he is entitled to ask for a special favor and it is always granted. And thanks to Madame de Senneterre's lavish bribe, he made me the subject of one of his special requests. A few sprinkles of perfume in the right place—we may as well say it was a face—and my affair was settled once for all.''

''Was it really, though?'' I said, suddenly anxious; for, having just got Papa back, I did not want to lose him again.

''It most certainly was. I came to Paris under a royal *sauf-conduit*; the conclusion of my suit will get an official polish in the Palais; and with Chaban thoroughly dead there is no one likely to feel my damascus blade in his precious entrails.''

I remembered what I had heard in the years of Papa's absence: that not Chaban, but another man with whose wife Papa had been madly in love, had been his actual enemy and the cause of all the trouble. ''And Riberolles?'' I said timidly, watching Papa sidelong.

''Oh, Riberolles,'' Papa laughed. ''A coward—a nonentity. One look, and you won't be afraid of him any more. No one does another man's dirty work without money, and Riberolles has not a sou. He financed Madame Chaban's murder charges because he expected a share in the indemnity that she hoped to get out of my estate. But with that hope gone he won't even get back his expenses. He is utterly ruined. So you see there is nothing to worry about."

But I was worried. "And what about Riberolles' wife?" I ventured, clutching his arm. "Is it still a great passion? Are you still in love with her?"

Now Papa too was suddenly sober. He turned and met my look squarely. "Oh, I know what you mean," he said, "and I won't keep anything back from you. Yes, I am still in love with Lucrèce. But I have paid enough for yielding to this unfortunate passion. I have lost home and Maman and, above all, you, ma petite, my darling, my life—not to speak of my work and my pride. The Devil take me if I ever meet that woman again!" I could detect an undertone of nostalgia and suppressed emotion in Papa's words; but he had said them with a resolute firmness. I knew that he would stand by what he said. I felt mightily relieved, and I smiled at him gratefully.

Thrilled by Papa, and his fascinating ways and the whole sudden change he had brought into my life, I felt youth and warmth returning to me. I let myself drift into a state of lightness and indolence. I listened, I chattered, I laughed.

When we had driven for about half an hour my ear caught the far-off pealing of a bell; and, though other bells were sounding throughout the Faubourg Saint Antoine, I made out clearly the bell of our convent calling the nuns to the Angelus. Involuntarily I lowered my head and folded my hands, and then I heard myself whispering: *"Angelus Dei nuntiavit Mariae et concepit de Spiritu Sancto, Ave Maria gracia plena . . ."* My closed eyes saw the sisters gathering in long rows with calmness and piety on their happy faces. Then I felt a hand on my shoulder, and I looked up and saw Papa watching me with suspense and pity.

"Ninon!" he said. "Do you hear me, Ninon? Wake up, wake up! What have they done to you in the convent? Do you want to go back to them and dry up in the atmosphere of soured virginity of those unhealthy spinsters?"

For a moment I could only stare back at him; I was still half bemused, and comprehension returned to me but slowly.

"Have you forgotten," he went on passionately, "all I taught you? The churches and convents have crippled Nature long enough. They have despised and warped Reason, imprisoned it, and burned it at the stake. But those times are over now. Nature and Reason have become the sources of life. There are rebellious expectancy, creative expansion, and new ideas everywhere. We are breaking free, Ninon. The old fetters of the human spirit are being shattered. Would you turn away from this freedom and live on in blindness?"

"You need not be afraid, Papa," I said with conviction. "There will never be a Sainte Ninon."

"Apropos of Sainte Ninon," Papa said, "it will surprise you to hear that there is one." He told me about a girl in Compiègne who had come from Paris wearing on her bosom a medallion with a miniature that she said was the image of Sainte Ninon, who had been sent from Heaven and had miraculously saved a little courtesan from the whipping stake on the Place des Halles, and all the little courtesans in Paris had been wearing her picture as an amulet ever since. When I confessed to Papa that it was I who had performed this miracle, he seized me, folded me to his heart, and kissed me, laughing as he had laughed long ago in Loches when told that I, a seven-year-old girl, had slept with a boy. And he burst out, very much as he had done then: "My flesh, my blood, my golden darling—the Holy Saint of the whores!"

"You must not think," Papa said soberly when we were almost home, "that I want you to give yourself to excessive licentiousness the way I have done all my life, or that I would have you degenerate. No, I want you to be on the summit of life, a sovereign queen in a realm of beauty and culture and all the pleasures of body and mind. A great courtesan! Not like the Queen of Navarre, or like many a duchess and countess in Paris, but a courtesan in the finest Hellenic sense of the word—like the great Aspasia of Athens, who was beloved and adored by the best men of Greece and was able to inspire a Pericles, a Phidias, an Anaxagoras, a Socrates to great thoughts and deeds. I would have you the modern Aspasia—the greatest and happiest woman of any age."

I aspired to no such high goals as Papa was so enthusiastically defining for my future, but, carried away by his zeal and his affection, I felt like fully entrusting myself to him.

A cool evening breeze brushed my forehead. The little clouds overhead had caught fire and were sailing with us through an emerald-green sky toward Paris and its innumerable thrills. It was good to feel the strong arm around my waist and the powerful chest against which my head rested.

It was late at night when Papa and I parted, not without many kisses and caresses. He went upstairs, and I lay down in my own bed, which Madeleine, in the seventh Heaven over my return, had prepared with the finest linen in the house. I stretched out my limbs and gave myself up to the bed's spacious softness. But it was not long before the memories that clung to it set my blood to running wild, and its very spaciousness became first a discomfort and then a torment. Without Charles's body to snuggle up to, I felt terribly alone.

In the morning we went to the Palais, seat of France's administration and supreme justice and at the same time a focus of both business and lounging idlers. There was nothing one could not buy in the hundreds of multicolored *boutiques* and stands that had established themselves in the passages, court-yards, and galleries. They dispensed not only silks and brocades, but also artificial flowers, perfumes, gloves, books, paintings, and musical instruments, and of course a vast variety of the three things Parisians were said to be unable to exist without: ribbons, mirrors, and laces. But our errand was to the president of the Parlement, Monsieur Nicolas de Verdun. It was obvious that he had expected Papa's visit, for we were admitted without delay.

No one would have known that the overworked-looking, drab, simply dressed man who received us was the bearer of the ancient sovereignty of French justice—a justice equal to the King's and entitling him to purple and ermine and a golden royal circlet on his head. With hardly a look at Papa's *sauf-conduit*, he told us at once that the *procureur du roi* had dropped all the charges against Papa, and that he was now free to manage his property again. At first the old man was very rigid and dignified, but by and by his reserve melted and he launched into nonofficial conversation. "The sympathies of the court," he assured Papa, "were on your side, and it is a pity that your business abroad prevented you from presenting yourself to the *maître des requêtes* long ago. You would have spared your family a great sorrow." With great solicitude and in a warm, fatherly tone he counseled Papa to be more careful in the future about his courtship of ladies, and he especially warned him about Riberolles. At this name Papa made a disparaging gesture, but Monsieur de Verdun said that he must not underestimate one whom he himself considered to be a malicious and very dangerous person. "Even though he had lost the protection of Chaban and his men," the president said, "there are hundreds of other ways if a man wants to hire someone for promoting anyone to the other side. Right in your own neighborhood, in the Rue Franc Bourgeois, there is the very headquarters of the *cours des miracles*, which all the government's efforts have so far not been able to smoke out. Be, then, on your guard."

The president's words sent a shiver through me. I knew about that corner of the Rue Franc Bourgeois and the dark, narrow lane that was said to lead to the uncanny place. All passers-by made a wide circuit around that corner, for no one who entered the lane ever came out, and not even the armed city archers dared invade that capital of the underground *royaume des Argots*—the ancient and powerful organization of beggars, vagabonds, thieves, and robbers of all France. Anyone who made contact with them could carry out any murder he wanted; they provided the killer.

Alarmed by the president's warning, I begged Papa as we threaded the *boutiques* to take his words to heart. Papa only gave me a quick look as if he resented my mentioning a matter thoroughly discussed and closed. He merely conducted me to the *galerie des marchands,* where we did some shopping for books, a new lute, and a new saddle for Papa, and for me a green velvet riding dress and a small but exquisite pistolet, the butt of chased gold and inlaid with ivory and light blue enamel. Walking with my faultlessly elegant Papa, his head erect and towering over the crowd, the green feathers on his head fluttering, and his sword and spurs clinking, I felt reassured again and decided not to mention Riberolles in the future.

On our way to the art gallery beyond the *salle des pas perdus* I saw a man stop and lift his hand to his hat in a gesture of surprise and embarrassment. He had a commonplace, flabby face, and his mouth was twisted in a wry and ugly grimace. "The filthy dog can't think I will answer his salute," Papa said, loud enough for the man to hear.

"Who was that, Papa?" I asked, for the look of hate had shocked me.

"Can't you guess, ma petite? Our good friend, of course, Riberolles." Wasting no further words about the encounter, he took me to the *buvette*, the famous restaurant of the Palais, where one could get a "quick déjeuner" that was supposed to take not more than a single hour. Papa's courtly attentiveness was delightful, and when young men darted fiery looks in my direction it was only with utmost caution. No one wanted to affront so imposing a cavalier as Papa.

After the déjeuner we descended the great staircase to the inner courtyard. Papa was just buying me a perfume from one of the dealers of the Provence, when an uneasy feeling made me turn my head. For a moment I thought that I had got a glimpse of Riberolles' face staring at us from the shadow of one of the high-arched pillars, but when I told Papa about it he was merely annoyed.

"Listen, ma petite," said Papa. "Before you came into the world I wanted you to be a boy. When you turned out to be a girl my firmest wish was to spare you all the trouble that our idiotic society has imposed on your sex. Your body was that of a girl, but your mind, I decided, was not only to sparkle with all feminine charm, but also to acquire all the traits that men have arrogated to themselves: love of independence, honor, sincerity, loyalty, friendship, consistency, courage. That is why I taught you fencing and riding and shooting and why I bought you that pistolet today. Don't disappoint me, darling.

247

Don't be a milksop, and don't look for ghosts." I promised Papa with a handshake. Just the same, I used all my coquetry to wheedle from him the promise that on his honor he would never meet Lucrèce Riberolles again.

2

ONE OF OUR FIRST concerns when we settled down to the happiness of being together was the remodeling of the house. The shrubbery had become dense in the years of Papa's absence; we had it thinned and pruned. The white pilasters on the red brick walls were repainted; so was the vestibule, which we had frescoed with birds and garlands and flowers. Mama's former cell on the upper floor became a comfortable *chez-soi* for Papa, and the curving outer staircase that descended from his hallway directly into the garden was repaired. The most care of all was lavished on my room, which Papa decided must be the loveliest in Paris.

From an oriental dealer on the Pont Neuf he bought me a golden yellow carpet of rich and intricate figures. The hangings for the salon windows were of the same warm golden color. We ordered them at Monsieur Poquelin's in the Rue Saint Honoré, the finest upholsterer in town. The most impressive piece that we acquired was too large to be moved into Papa's music room, and it too was there-

fore set up near the alcove window in my salon—
new harpsichord, not only a masterpiece of instru
ment building, but also a work of art, for its exteric
was painted in pink and blue with shepherds an
lambs and nymphs and fauns among green lawns an
groves and soft hillocks. In short, the whole house
which Papa had meant to be just a *logement conven*
able, was turned into an affair of consummate grac
and luxury. With these changes came a troop of nev
servants, valets and stableboys and maidservant:
but no cook, for Papa, won over by Madeleine'
cuisine, left her in command of the kitchen that sh
had defended so bravely for so many lean years.

I was soon deep in my new life with Papa, wh
devoted all his time and thought to the molding of m
mind to his pattern. Following the Roman mott
Mens sana in corpore sano, he put much stress o
physical exercise—riding and walking in the park
and outside the city walls, fencing, shooting. And h
taught me one thing hitherto unheard-of for a gir
which for the sake of avoiding evil gossip we kej
secret: behind a partition he had set up for me
wooden tub, and in this, every morning, I took a fu
bath in fresh cold water.

Between the bodily exercises and the dancing an
the music lessons we would read together, as fo
merly, from the poets and from Montaigne an
Epicurus. Interpreted in Papa's fascinating way
these authors gave me a stirring summary of huma
wisdom derived from Nature as the first principle c
all practical morality and therefore true to life
Against this philosophy all the arguments I coul

propound in defense of Church and religion fell
short, being more emotional than logical. (I took
great care not to betray to Papa that, following a deep
nostalgic urge, I was still saying my morning and
evening prayers every day.) We had company, too.
When there were no guests for dinner, we would go
out and have supper in the new, fashionable eating
places or to the theater, in which I took an ever-
growing delight.

Of all the pieces we saw, the one that impressed
me the most was Corneille's *Cid*, played in the
theater that Richelieu had installed in his Palais Cardinal. High-ceilinged, beautifully frescoed, and
spacious, with an amphitheaterlike elevation of the
parquet, it was said to hold about three thousand
spectators; and it was praised as the most perfect
theater since antiquity and the best in the whole
world. Corneille's *Cid*, a work of pure and intuitive
genius and full of spontaneity, was quite to my taste;
and when I said so to the author, whom I met at a
party in the Hôtel Senneterre, I didn't take it amiss
when he replied, with his big dark eyes flashing:
"Yes, I know who I am, and I believe what people
are saying of me." This young lawyer of Rouen was
then basking in the glory of his literary fame.

Mostly, though, we went to the Théâtre de Bourgogne, where the *comédiens du roi* played Sopho-
cles and Euripides and also modern dramas of lesser
merit, such as *La Captive Égyptienne* and *Le Mort
d'Alexandra*. We rarely went to see comedies, for
Papa and I, though we loved merriment, felt that the
comedies and their actors lacked the kind of humor

that would have found a genuine echo in our hearts
French tragedy had found its genius; that of comedy
had still to come.

One day, after an early morning ride outside the
Porte Saint Antoine and on our way to the famous
ham breakfast in the Renard restaurant, Papa and I
and our small company of Papa's friends made a stop
on the Place Dauphin near the Pont Neuf. We loved
the *"grand bruit"* that Scarron had so vividly described in his poem—the cries of hawkers and *marchands ambulants*, the song of street *chansonnières*,
the pathetic recitals of the marionette theaters, the
cries of teeth pullers, *chirurgiens*, ointment sellers
and charlatans extolling nostrums that would cure
any illness in twenty-four hours. And here I discovered again the green-and-white striped harlequin
who had amused me so a year before on my strolls
with Évremond. Pretty, full-lipped, with jolly brown
eyes and an astoundingly sonorous voice, he was
inviting the public to stop at the tent of his master
the most famous of all charlatans of the day, Monsieur Tabarin.

"*Attention, messieurs, mesdames!* Stop here and
you'll hear and see hundreds of amusing farces,
extravaganzas, imbroglios, indiscretions, dia-
logues, paradoxes, *badinages* and *reparties*, all
full of piquancy and esprit and every word a tidbit or
a pearl." And as soon as a large crowd had gathered,
Monsieur Tabarin in person came forward, fat-
bellied, in cloth of gold and festooned with
thousands of glittering sequins. The harlequin, still
turned away from his master, changed his tune to

unhappy whimpering and whining. But when Monsieur Tabarin put his hand on his shoulder and asked him: "What, at it again? Do you always have to be pestering me with your exasperating problems?" The harlequin raised his eyebrows and peered helplessly at his master and with an incredibly comic idiotic grimace exclaimed: "Thank God you are here, for you alone, *mon maître,* can answer the question that has had me racking my brain the whole night and is racking it now." Then, pointing a solemn forefinger and impersonating a profound thinker, he stated his problem: "What is the deep underlying significance of the paradoxical fact that dogs do, and we men do not, greet each other by nosing each other's posterior?"

The full-packed square burst into roars of laughter. I was completely captivated by the harlequin's mock seriousness. "The *plus grand comédien du siècle,*" I exclaimed.

"Here he is!" Papa agreed, laughing heartily, "—the one we're looking for, the genius of humor and comedy."

On our way to Renard's the young harlequin—he was later to be known throughout the world as France's great playwright, Molière—was the main topic of our enthusiastic conversation. Both of us regretted that he was not an actor or a playwright, but merely a lowly harlequin assisting a charlatan, and we talked about how much we could wish to help him along and make opportunities for him.

Though it was still early, almost all tables on the terrace at Renard's were occupied. The *jambon d'Auvergne,* not cooked but smoked to a rich black-

ness and imcomparably tender, was served wit
numerous sauces and with mustards that were not th
products of ordinary *moutardiers*, but had been pre
pared by Monsieur Renard personally and with grea
delicacy. The wine that went with the *jambon* wa
light and cool and the mood of the whole compan
cheerful. I myself was so animated that I climbed
chair and impersonated the harlequin of the Plac
Dauphin, and Papa promptly mounted another chai
and assumed the role of Monsieur Tabarin. For
long while we amused ourselves with funny ques
tions and repartees, earning hearty laughter an
applause from both our own group and the whol
terrace.

But all of a sudden I stopped. I had got sight of
lusty and florid round face with jolly blue eyes—
Scarron! I waved my hand in recognition, jumpe
from my chair, and went to meet him.

"This time I am lucky," he said, kissing both m
hands. "My first day in Paris, and meeting *you!*"

Scarron was no stranger to the company except fo
Papa, who, however, took an instant liking to hin
and invited him to join us. Scarron congratulate
Papa on having me as his daughter and me on a Pap
who looked more like my cavalier than my father
and he said how thoroughly our Tabarin-harlequi
act had delighted him. "I am daft about this harle
quin myself," he said, "and whenever I come t
Paris I go to the Place Dauphin and watch him.
could watch him for hours, but he always disappear
after a few minutes." When I asked Scarron whethe
he knew who the harlequin was, he said he didn't; h
too would like to know more about this ingeniou

buffoon. "But all I could learn in Tabarin's tent," he said, "was that they call him Moulière, or Molière, or something like that. They couldn't or wouldn't tell me anything more. Once I tried to talk to him in the street—out of costume he is a finely dressed and well-mannered young man—but he looked quite frightened, said apologetically that he was in a great hurry, and tore away."

The mystery of this Molière or Moulière excited me, and I decided that some day I must get to the bottom of it. No doubt, that genius of comedy needed help.

"What has happened to you, Monsieur Scarron?" someone in our company asked. "Have you given up your plans to become an abbé?" I too had noticed the absence of the *petit collet* on Scarron's gold-laced and embroidered *justaucorps*. Scarron put his finger to his mouth and said roguishly: "Sh! I am in Paris on the sly. I am no future abbé now, but an actual chanoine at Saint Julien in Le Mans." In a style no less clownish than the harlequin's he launched into a description of his drab life as a cleric, moaning about the twenty-three weeks' *rigoureuse* he had just endured, three ritual services a day, and no pleasures but the *capons rotis* of Le Mans. He was afraid he would become a fat capon himself, so heavy that he soon would need two altar boys to get him to his feet after every genuflection. "But now I have a few days in Paris to make up for all this vexation," and, seizing a glass of wine, he exclaimed in the tone of a mock Gregorian chant: *"Vinum bonum laetificat juventutem meam."*

Scarron's perversion and travesty of words sung at

Holy Mass shocked me. So did the thought that there were people to whose ardent souls the rites performed by this mocker and debauchee meant holiness and the presence of God. One could not serve God and Epicurus at the same time without becoming a hypocrite, and I felt much of my former sympathy with Scarron vanishing. Nevertheless I kept him by us, for I had been seized by a desire to speak to him alone. He had known a good deal about Charles: perhaps he would know where he was now, or at least if he were still alive and well. And merely to know that seemed to me valuable and momentous. For a while I revolved complicated devices for getting away from the others with him. In the end I just said that I felt like taking a little walk in the park, and would he care to go with me? Except for Papa, the others were a little startled at my boldness, but Papa, seemed to approve of it, and when we started off he told us to have a good time. Yet, when I looked back to the terrace I could see his eyes following us, and I felt that he was missing me already.

We crossed Monsieur Renard's flower parquets, which were set in lacelike patterns of garlands, vases, arabesques, and birds, after the latest horticultural fashion. The butterflies and bumblebees did not seem to mind the stiltedness of these artful designs: they hummed and fluttered lustily over the sun-drenched multicolored sweetness. Scarron, pluming himself on his presumptive success with me, was not slow to begin his advances. Unlike Évremond, who had taken me to the menagerie and the aviary, he piloted me to the Grotte de Palissay, which was enough in itself to give the park its name of a *vrai paradis des délices d'amour*. It was over-grown with ancient trees and ferns and moss, and its silence was disturbed only by the plashing of a fountain, the wooing of violins in the distant music pavilion, the whisper of swaying boughs, sighs, stammered words, and half subdued wistful cries.

I had put off my questions about Charles as if in dread of the answer; but when Scarron seated me on a stone bench beside him and took my hand, it was high time to muster my courage. "Have you not heard from your friend recently?" I asked him, "—from Charles de Beaumont?"

There was disappointment in his smiling face. He kept it smiling, though, and said: "I wonder why you didn't ask me about him right away? All the ladies who knew him have asked me the same question. I haven't heard from him for a year, and as he was a hot-blooded adventurer when he joined the *armée* brigantine of Monsieur de Courteville, I can't even tell you whether he has survived the daring sea battles he was in. The last letter I had was from Cadiz, from where he wrote that they were about to engage with the Mauresques, after which they were to sail to China and India. He was full of praise of Spanish women; he wrote that we French still have no idea how to make love, and that he expected even more exotic experiences in the Orient." I took all this in, but still I ventured to ask: "And didn't he tell you to give me his regards? Or didn't he mention me at all?"

"Indeed he did. He asked me in his letter to mention him to you."

A great and joyful tremor passed through me.

"Why didn't you tell me at once?" I said.

"Because you were just one of ten or twelve to whom he asked me to transmit his compliments. I thought you wouldn't or shouldn't care."

"Wasn't he a wonderful man?" I said. "I think you wouldn't have been his friend otherwise."

Scarron did not contradict me. He admitted that there had been unusual beauty in Charles—poetry and softness and at the same time a great elemental life force. "Nevertheless," he said, "you should do everything in your power to forget him. For mixed with all that was admirable in Charles there was a warped, vicious character—something self-centered, reckless, and capable of any crime." In his effort to influence me against Charles he enumerated misdeeds and crimes much worse than anything Richelieu had named. But I, still enraptured by the knowledge of one brief line from Charles about me, shook my head and repeated over and over: "I love him. I do still love him."

But then Scarron said: "I wonder what you will say to this:

"When we first met you in the Luxembourg Gardens and I warned him to leave you alone, he made a wager with me that he would sleep in your bed within a month. And on the last day of the month he wrote me for the twenty écus."

I felt myself grow pale. "Let us not speak of him any more," I said, rising. "Let us go back to the others."

Through the rest of the day I managed to ignore my heartache, though it was like a superficially healed wound reopened by a new blow. But when

Papa, before kissing me good night in my room, asked me whether I was not hiding from him something that worried me, I was glad to confide the whole story to him. "My poor darling," Papa exclaimed. "You—and unhappy! That cannot and must not be! You must be rid of this obsession, or you are lost." He sat down with me in my armchair facing him, and used all his eloquence to appeal to my reason and to talk me out of my love.

"There is no such thing as love," he said. "It is only an invention of poets and romantic fools. What they call love is in reality nothing but the desire of the senses—a delectable gift of nature if kept within bounds, but otherwise a dangerous poison. And we two, my dear child, have to be more on guard than others, because the gods have mixed *amour* with our blood in such generous excess that if we don't control it wisely it is bound to involve us in untold suffering and in the end to be the death of us. The most dangerous of all beasts, Plato says, is man. But I say that what is dangerous is sex—particularly mine. And, since you are like me—my flesh, my blood—yours, too, darling. If you don't learn to cage and harness the monster and lead it on silken strings and make it serve you prettily, I warn you that it will gnaw at your flesh, and you will live in suspense and terror of its threat your whole life long, and in the end it will destroy and devour you and everyone you love."

I was shaken by Papa's words. Never before had he spoken so dramatically and with so tense and genuine a grief for me in his face. Deep down, I felt that every one of his words had truth in it. But what could I do? How could I stop this love, this longing that was part of my very self? For a while I gazed helplessly at him; then, as if I could find protection against myself in his arms, I clung to him and wept. His caresses, his murmured endearments, seemed somewhat to appease my hunger of heart and of body. But when he suddenly stopped his caresses and pushed me gently away, I was seized by an appalling dread of loneliness. I looked at him forlornly, wondering why he had so abruptly let me go. He smiled at me and said: "High time, ma petite, for you to take a lover, and I see no reason why you should delay it. This is your room, and you are free to bring to it anyone you like. I shouldn't be in your way. On the contrary, any amour of yours has my paternal blessing in advance."

3

I WANTED, of course, to be an obedient daughter. But among the young men I knew there was no one whom I should have thought capable of making me forget Charles.

One day, though, Coligny returned. Once more he professed an ardent passion for me. And, remembering my decision that I would be a little more lenient toward him—perhaps even more than a little—I yielded. This time I accepted his invitation to spend the two weeks of his furlough in his little castle in the woods, which he said he had renovated on account of me.

There was a moist shimmer in Papa's kind eyes when I kissed him adieu and departed with Coligny on the next day. Feeling remorseful that I should leave Papa alone for so long a time, I had told him that if he wanted I wouldn't go at all. He would not listen. "I should be a vicious father indeed if I didn't let you go."

I had not accepted Coligny's invitation without conditions. He was welcome to me as a lover, for I still found in his gestures and his features those same indefinable reminders of Charles. But he had greatly changed. He was not resurrecting amorous historical parallels now: rather, he insisted that he was deeply in love with my person and that he meant to oppose his family's plans to marry him to Mademoiselle de Montmorency—one of the wealthiest brides in the ancient aristocracy—and to marry me. I rejected him, of course; and I said that, if he wanted me to yield to his pleadings, he must respect my wishes and keep completely silent throughout our love-making; otherwise I should leave him at once. On his jealous protest and demand for explanation I added the further condition that he must never again ask me for my reasons.

Finding me firm, he accepted my conditions at last, though reluctantly, consoling himself with his own explanation that woman had always been a riddle and always would be one, and that perhaps her very mystery was the prime source of her fascination.

At first he kept his promise and tried to fall in with my moods; and thus I, knowing how to accommodate my flesh to self-deception, could give full rein to my imaginings. He was not so potent a lover as Charles had been—no man in my life has ever equaled my first lover's gifts—and his approaches were too submissive. But when his hand passed tenderly over my bosom, my belly, it was Charles's hand, and when he kissed me it was Charles who made the blood in my veins burn and drove me to ecstasy. What bliss to imagine the impossible—that the body in my arms was my beloved one!

But there came days and nights when my pseudo-Charles resented what he called my strange whim and watched me with eyes of jealous suspicion. I loved going for lonely walks in the woods, and I was vexed to observe that Coligny would follow me on the sly. By night I felt him spying on my face and struggling with himself. The time came when he could control himself no longer, and once, as I lay in his arms, he burst out desperately: "Why do you keep your eyes closed? I will be silent, but open your eyes. I beg, I implore you, open them. I love you so!"

The enchantment was broken. He tried to hold me fast with pleas, with clutching arms and clasping legs; but I pushed him away, refusing to be touched. I left his bed and ran out into the night. I did not return until morning, and then it was to pack my things and go. But I finally gave in to his desperate pleadings and stayed on.

I regretted this reversal of my decision afterward. The fortnight of his furlough was long over. I longed for Papa and felt uncomfortable about leaving him alone any longer. But I was sorry for Coligny, too; and, clinging to the last poor remnant of my dwindling vicarious happiness, I delayed my going until one day the outer world in the shape of an army captain and a whole platoon of soldiers made an end to our *séjour* by arresting Coligny and carrying him off to the Bastille for "neglect of military duty and desertion."

I did not regret our separation for myself, but I was sorry for Coligny, who had got himself into trouble because of me. A sense of honor and a feeling of comradeship told me that I had to do everything in my power to save him, and I drove to Paris at once, resolved to see Richelieu and to ask him for help.

Day was drawing to a close when I reached the Palais Cardinal. Before I had waited long in the *rez-de-chaussée* salon I was told that His Excellency was just having supper in his garden dining room and that he invited me to give him the honor of my company. The dining room to which they led me through the broad alley of limes with white marble statues was simply a round space in the open, enclosed by artfully clipped trees and boxwood hedges. It gave the impression of a high-domed room, and its curved openings seemed like arched windows looking out on to the terraces and canals of an extensive and carefully tended park.

Richelieu, sitting alone at the table arrayed in white, stood up and welcomed me with a lighthearted smile such as I had never before seen on his somber face. He seated me opposite him, and at his nod two lackeys served me lobsters, fish, helpings of joints on golden dishes, and wine.

"I have had a lucky day today," Richelieu said. "A day of no things but lucky ones. Above all, your visit, of course. But great news from the army, too. Only a few more blows like the latest one, and the Habsburgs are finished. That army of ours! It is wonderful. Every man in his place. We can be proud of them."

"I am afraid," I said a little faint-heartedly, but resolved to begin with my petition, "that you won't be very proud of me, because I have come to ask you for a pardon for a young officer who has overstayed his furlough. Other officers are not arrested for such a fault: they are simply sent back to the army. Why this severity just for Coligny?''

"If it is Lieutenant Count Coligny,'' said Richelieu, "in whose behalf you have come to see me, than I am truly sorry, my child. I can do nothing for him. He was arrested on my express order.'' While peeling an orange for me he explained that he incurred endless trouble by his tolerance to the Protestants. In general he never heeded the attacks and never permitted anyone to be wronged because of his creed; but when there was a complaint that a Protestant was violating the law and was being unpatriotic—as Coligny was—he had to let justice take its course. And that, most unfortunately for this young man, meant two or three years in the Bastille. His face hardened.

"You cannot do this to me!'' I cried. I pleaded for a long time. Richelieu's face remained granite. I burst out: "Please, do it for my sake. I won't be ungrateful to you.'' He gave me a startled look, and I took heart and, looking him straight in the eye, said: "I am ready for anything. Tell me your price.''

Richelieu searched my face for a long while in silence. But when, to show that I meant what I said, I gave him an insinuating smile, he could not resist, and he smiled back. Then, after more thought, he said: "*Bien*, have it your way. I will give orders to have Coligny removed from the Bastille and escorted to the field army. But don't try to see him again. It might complicate matters. Are you satisfied?''

I nodded. "I thank you, Excellency," I said gratefully. Then, becoming slightly afraid, I hung my head.

There was a strange hush now about us both. Nothing was to be heard but the bubbling of fountains and the whisper of trees. The garden outside, with its long smooth canals reflecting the fading day, looked like a fantasy out of Arabian Nights. When the day dissolved into violet dusk the lackeys brought candelabra that cast a coppery glow upon the darkening walls of leaves. Upon Richelieu's gesture the lackeys withdrew and stationed themselves outside the hedges with their faces turned toward the Palais.

He took my hand. I did not withdraw it, not only because I knew what I owed him and was prepared to pay my debt of honor, but also because a peculiar little tremor passed over me—a kind of triumph to think that the mere promise of my favor had made a breach in the rigid principles of this great statesman. And as I kept looking at his small erect head with its high forehead and eyes that could be so autocratic— though now they betrayed a touch of tenderness, a subdued and gentle inner flame—I began to understand the *obsession mystérieuse* that he was commonly said to provoke in women; and I felt not at all inclined to repent of my offer.

He finally broke the silence. "You cannot imagine," he said, still holding my hand and pressing it warmly, "how grateful I am for your kindness. As for sinning with you, believe me, I should not mind a few more tortures in hell, which awaits me anyway. For, like my great colleague Cardinal Ubaldini, who sold his soul to the Ghibellines, I have sold my soul to France, and for that another Dante might place me in one of the lowest circles of the Inferno. I am more fond of you than I should be; indeed, extremely fond. And there is an aroma of *amour* about you that makes resistance an almost superhuman assignment. But I know what I owe to the prestige of my purple, and therefore—— Do not let yourself be deluded by all the irresponsible and scandalous gossip about me and women. Though I am sure I shall regret the sacrifice of my opportunity as soon as you have gone, you need not be afraid. I am glad that I could find a way to comply with your wish, and—for doing it I ask nothing.''

As if to prevent me from answering and himself from changing his mind, he rang the silver bell on the table. The lackeys came in and picked up the candelabra. Richelieu offered me his arm, and in the flickering light we followed them through the lime-tree alley, between blue-green shadows and white pools of moonlight.

Night had already fallen when I got home. Our house lay perfectly silent. As no one expected me—only yesterday I had written Papa that I might stay in the castle another week—and I didn't want to waken anyone, I let myself in on tiptoe.

My room was dark, but the curtains at the alcove window were drawn aside, and in the faint slanting moonlight I could see a figure hunched in my armchair. Stepping nearer, I saw that it was Papa, head on breast and asleep. At his feet lay my lute. Poor Papa, I thought, he has been lonely for me!

Feeling terribly guilty, I knelt and stealthily laid my head against his breast. When he still didn't move I moved my cheek gropingly upward until I reached his lips. In his sleep he gave off a sigh and lisped something that fortunately sounded more like "Ninon, petite" than "Lucrèce." Only when I pressed my mouth to his did he awake.

Our joy in reunion was as extravagant as that of long-separated lovers, and this time Papa did not disengage himself or push me away when I flung myself impetuously into his arms. When at last he relaxed his embrace, we talked of the weeks past. "Yes, I had a good time," I assured him after insistent and solicitous questioning, "but I have had enough of Coligny, and I shall never leave you again, Papa dear."

The next morning we resumed our life as if there had been no interval. And one of the first things that happened was that Madame de Senneterre drew me lovingly to her more than ample bosom and said: "Now I've got you at last, you would-be saint. At last I can go ahead and dazzle all Paris with you." The same day I had to go with her and Papa to the Palais, and there they ordered new dresses for me—one of them to be delivered speedily, for Madame wanted to take me to a tea party that the Queen was giving in the Louvre. When, a few days later, we went for a fitting, I was as delighted as she and Papa by this marvelous work of fashion. It was a wide-sleeved, long-wasted gown of shimmering thin light blue material with two skirts, the outer one the *modeste* of embroidered satin, the inner one the *friponne*, visible *en avant*, of white brocade trimmed with lace.

I had never felt any particular desire to be received at court, and on the day of the reception I could not get excited about the honor as I climbed the cold marble staircases and crossed the still colder corridors of the Louvre. Before being admitted to the state room we were led to an antechamber in which dressing tables with make-up pots, brushes, and mirrors were set along the walls. After I had been asked my rank a patch of rosy make-up was painted on my cheek. As I was a simple *de* it was a pale shade and the size of a pea, whereas a princess of royal blood beside me got a patch of dark Portuguese red as big as a fist. The state rooms that we entered after that were overpowering in size, but chilly as the Ursulines' convent in wintertime, and my breath seemed to turn to frost. The impression I got was of an indistinguishable confusion of brocades, laces, ribbons, and jewels, grotesquely stiff gestures, and elaborate and guarded conversation and courtesies.

On the arm of Madame de Senneterre, who, garbed in scarlet velvet and green satin and gleaming with diamonds, looked very regal and proud, I joined the row of those who were to be introduced to the Queen. We were admitted to the Salle de Soissons, a room decorated with sculptures and paintings with medallions on ceiling and walls. Queen Anne was sitting by the fireplace, dressed in a cloud of pink silk and white laces; and with her copper hair and her emerald green eyes she was lovely. When Madame de Senneterre introduced me to her and I curtsied to the floor, she turned to Madame de Senneterre and said: "You have not exaggerated, Madame," and then to me: "I take great pleasure in seeing you and hope to see you soon again."

An elderly lady by the Queen's side—she had on her sagging cheeks two Portuguese patches big and red as raw *filet de boeuf*–gave me a vicious look, for the Queen's expression of so much amiability to a girl of the lesser aristocracy with no jewelry had promptly won me numerous enemies among the court ladies. As Madame de Senneterre afterwards told me, this enmity was aggravated when, entering the ballroom, I was quickly surrounded and led to dance by the cavaliers with the greatest and most ancient names, and actually by His Majesty's brother the Duc D'Orléans, who had a bloated red face and in his multicolored and overlavish dress looked like a puffed-up turkey. He kept pinching my arm and my waist—forms of attention regarded as a tribute; ladies of far higher rank thought it a signal honor to be pinched by him on the buttocks.

Between dances we had tea, and then we went to a room set with card tables. Madame de Senneterre, though a passionate card player, did not take part in the games: she withdrew me for a little chat and a rest to a small table behind a potted palm. Near us a few elderly ladies were playing cards and gossiping in whispers. A young man with big black melancholy eyes who was just making his way across the room to the Salle de Soissons was now the object of their conversation. They called him Mazzi, and from Madame de Senneterre I learned that he was Mazarini, the former Papal nuncio and now Richelieu's protégé. Beautiful, a great diplomat, a great cognoscente of literature, a collector of art, himself a fine painter, this delightful young man (who in a few years, as Cardinal Mazarin, was to become Richelieu's successor) was the pet of all ladies of rank. "Do you know," murmured one of the elderly women, "that he is painting a portrait of the Queen and that she sits for this portrait for hours with him, quite alone?"

"I'm sure," Madame de Senneterre giggled in my ear, "it isn't only his brush that Mazzi has to wield when he is alone with the Queen. One of the gossips said: That would be real luck for France, for our dull Louis will never give us an heir to the throne."

Presently I discovered that they had changed the subject of their gossip to my insignificant person. "Every morning," said one of them, "the Lenclos servants carry four or five big jugs of water from the well, and she takes a bath in a tub—and entirely naked!" "Quite naked! *Que dégoutant!*" remarked the others, and "*Quel horreur!*" and "*Jamais de ma vie!*" When the subject of this unheard-of indecency was thoroughly exhausted they went on to say that I had been seen going out with men unchaperoned and behaving like a coquette. "To be sure, she is a coquette," one of the scarecrows said with a sniff of disdain, "and one who knows her business. Did you not see? She angled for our best cavaliers and caught them, and after them the Duc himself." A clucking sound of tongues. "And the Queen likes her." "Poor Queen, she's still so naïve." "Someone ought to warn her."

I should have liked to go on listening; I found it

great fun. What an inexhaustible source of banter would these ladies have been for my green-striped harlequin! But now our hiding place was discovered, and there was another rush of cavaliers. They escorted me back to the ballroom and would not let me go until the music stopped and the last guests were leaving.

"Is there any particular one you would like to meet again?" Madame de Senneterre asked me on my way home in her coach, enumerating to me illustrious names whose bearers had confessed to her how enraptured they were by my person. I told her that I thought them all uninteresting and terrible bores. "I know," said Madame de Senneterre, fondly taking my arm, "that you were looking all the time for the one who was not there and never will be. But never mind, and don't feel sorry. I have good news for you. The Prince de La Rochefoucauld will soon be in Paris. Oh, now you smile! I knew you would be pleased."

It was, however, several weeks before Madame de Senneterre could inform me that Rochefoucauld had come to Paris and was expected to attend the next Wednesday's gathering in the Palais Rambouillet, an event to which I looked forward with great impatience. To be received and to take part in one of those famous receptions in the Rue Saint Thomas du Louvre was considered an honor and a pleasure of the most distinguished kind. Thanks to the lady of the house, the spirited and elegant Madame de Rambouillet, these receptions had become the very center of French culture; to them the French language, once crude and awkward, owed much of its present brilliant refinement and gracefulness; and in them had been created the new art, "conversation."

But how much more thrilling the occasion would be if I met the prince there, and if—my heart jumped at the thought—he fell in love with me! That would be a fulfillment not only of old, persistent childish dreams, but of a dream that I cherished even now. I enjoyed in anticipation the moment of recognition, the surprise, and all the delights that I hoped would follow. I felt that I could love Rochefoucauld; and his love meant freedom from my obsession.

The longed-for Wednesday afternoon arrived at last.

Never before had I been so impressed by the mere aspect of a room as I was by the Rambouillets' *salon bleu*. It had what I would call an intimate spaciousness, thanks rather to proportion and arrangement than to area. There were high glass doors from ceiling to floor, opening upon a large terrace. The park, beyond the terrace, complemented the room, which had many vases and baskets filled with flowers. There was an esthetic unity of garden and room.

The hostess, the Marquise de Rambouillet, a lady of majestic stature, magnificent complexion, and, save for her aquiline nose, classic features, received me graciously. Then she invited me to apply my attention to the game in which the whole company was engaged. Among the guests I recognized the impressive sharp profile of La Rochefoucauld.

There was at first no occasion for an introduction, for the prince, surrounded by a whole crowd—more ladies than men, I noticed—was sitting far off. The game in which each participant tried to give the cleverest definition of a given subject was in full swing. The word that had been chosen was "love." The definitions were mostly based on the teachings of Plato, and they centered on the ideas of beauty and truth. Only Rochefoucauld's comment: "Love is like a ghost: everybody talks about it, but no one has seen it," rose above the average. But neither his nor the others' definitions suited me. When Madame de Rambouillet requested that I too should make my contribution I stood up and said: "I am sorry, but I don't think that I can find a definition. For definition means setting limits to an idea by a few words—but how can one confine Love, a mighty ocean, in a small pint measure?" My answer provoked immediate applause and sympathetic acclamations, and I could see that it had stirred Rochefoucauld, who at once left his place and made his way towards me. Seeing Madame de Senneterre by my side, he asked her for the favor of being introduced to this "delightfully clever and charming little person." Madame de Senneterre was glad to oblige him. She said, however, only "my little niece," and mumbled an unintelligible name, for she knew that I wanted him to recognize me by himself.

But he didn't, though he seemed to have caught fire at once. He ignored the company and concentrated his whole attention on me. I told him, when he asked, that I was in the Palais Rambouillet for the first time; and he requested and received from Madame de Rambouillet and Madame de Senneterre permission to show me about the Palais and its art treasures.

There was much to look at in the gracefully furnished chambers, alcoves, and rich stuccoed salles. They were crowded with wooden and metal sculptures, ceramics, paintings, and objects of the goldsmith's and the silversmith's handicraft that Madame had brought and was still bringing from her native Italy. The prince's glance, however, glided over them quickly, to return over and over again to me. I could see from his delighted and puzzled look that he was not only falling in love with me and that some hint of recognition was dawning in his mind, but also that he was at a loss what to make of me; and I enjoyed playing the mysterious stranger.

When we had done the ground floor he gallantly offered me his arm—the charmer knew how to press it to himself both softly and firmly—and we ascended the great staircase to enter the picture gallery. There were scores of Rambouillet ancestors looking down as haughtily as the prince himself had once looked down at me, but today there was no trace in him of that look *de haut en bas* as when he had said in Loches: "Quite a charming little niece, you have, Baroness," and I, stung to fury, had run away.

At last we came to a stand in front of a painting that represented a fiery red Vesuvius. Instantly another painting of the Vesuvio took shape in my mind—that before which we two had stood in that other gallery in the castle in Loches. I could still hear his words: "Strange, those fiery mountains, aren't they?" and with a hint of a smile I repeated them now. He looked at me with a peculiar intensity. Still not sure of himself, he said: "Why, pray, are you telling me this?"

"You said so yourself—but, of course, it was so long ago that you would not remember." A flash that lighted his whole face declared his final recognition; and we found ourselves smiling at each other for a long while, as we had smiled in the Loches gallery in the olive and hazel dusk, with the thin rain outside making a soft music while we stood absorbed in each other.

At last the prince broke the silence with his words of many years ago: "All right, little girl, when you are grown up——" He did not go on. Suddenly we were laughing in each other's arms and celebrating our reunion with a long kiss.

Forgetting the whole world, we withdrew to a little bower, and there we spent hours crowded with memories, caresses, reassurances, and proofs that neither of us had ever forgotten the other.

But unfortunately this happy meeting had to come to an end. Somewhere a clock struck five. The prince sprang up and said that he had to attend to affairs of the utmost importance connected with his army corps. I didn't believe him: I felt sure that the affairs to be attended to involved rather Marion Delorme than his *corps d'armée*. I was even more disappointed when he told me that early in the morning he had to go back to the front. But, observing that I was downcast, he said he would write me; also that he would soon return, and we would spend a long, happy time together. He kissed me not only adieu, but also au revoir; and his last words were that he loved me.

The next morning Rochefoucauld sent me flowers and a letter to let me know once more how happy he was to have found his beloved little girl of Loches again. In the following weeks he at once soothed and aggravated my impatience with other letters and delicate little gifts. Soon it was known to all Paris that he had broken off his affair with Marion, and that he had singled me out as her successor; and everybody congratulated me on my great success.

But most of all—almost as much as I myself—it was Papa who rejoiced. "You are a model child," he would say, "who reverently heeds an old father's advice. Go on this way, *mon bébé*—just one lover after another—and the last rashes of your infantile passion will soon be gone."

4

IN THESE WEEKS of my roseate if sometimes tantalizing anticipations I met with an adventure, quite apart from *amour*, that was nevertheless of great importance; and its outcome was to be of considerable moment to my future life.

Papa, noticing that my bed curtains were not blending properly with the golden hue of my room, ordered new ones; and one day Monsieur Poquelin came in person, together with a young man whom he introduced as his son, to hang the new draperies. The sight of young Poquelin, a handsome youngster with laughing brown eyes under thick eyebrows, a wide sensuous mouth, a well-proportioned big forehead, and exquisite movements and manners, stirred in me at once a sense of recognition, though I could not be sure I was right. Monsieur Poquelin was standing on the ladder giving the final inspection to his work and adding here and there a finishing touch. In the course of it he leaned back and, with one arm and one leg balancing each other, described a circling movement that reminded me, and obviously his son too, of a ropedancer. The young man, standing at the foot of the ladder, mimicked his father's movement in so droll a way that I could not help laughing and exclaiming: "Are you not——?"

It was too late for young Poquelin to put a warning finger to his mouth, for I had blurted out my whole question: "—the wonderful harlequin of the Place Dauphin?" At this Monsieur Poquelin turned about and came angrily down. "Is it not a shame?" he burst out. "The Louvre, the whole aristocracy, and all the distinguished people of the city are my clients, and this rascal here will inherit not only my whole shop but also my titles of *tapissier ordinaire* and *valet de chambre du roi*. And instead of taking care of our business and carrying himself with dignity he uses every occasion to slip away to help a charlatan sell drugs by making a buffoon of himself. Please, Mademoiselle, tell him what you think of such foolery."

Mindful of what Scarron had told me and embarrassed that I had given the young man away, I decided to turn the slip of my tongue to his advantage and to defend him. "I think he is splendid," I said. "I have seen him on the Place Dauphin several times, and I can only say that there is something exceptional about him—something very promising, which I think should not be discouraged."

Monsieur Poquelin looked at me quite amazed; but in the side glance that he gave his son I thought I noticed a little twinkle of admiration. "Do you really think so?" he asked me.

"Not only do I, but Papa thinks so, too, and so does Monsieur l'Abbé Scarron, who is a poet and was a man of the world. We all think that your son is not only a buffoon, but also a very great one. He is a born actor and a great comedian." "And what if he is? What does it amount to? Struggling with poverty all his life, living from hand to mouth, and being looked down on by everybody!"

At this point, visibly encouraged, the young man interfered. "You know, Papa," he said, "I don't care for titles or riches. If I could only become what I want to be! Uncle too says what the lady just told you." Turning to me, he explained that his uncle was the president of the Brethren of Passion, *concessionaires* of the Théâtre de Bourgogne. An ardent theater lover, he was always pleading for his nephew to be sent to the Collège de Clermont, where not only Greek and Latin and science were taught, but also rhetoric, the composition of plays, and the mounting of ballets.

"Don't bother the lady with that old story," old Poquelin reproved his son. "You know very well that it cannot be done."

Young Poquelin's face turned sad, and with a sigh he said: "Papa is right. It cannot be done, and without the proper background I can become neither an actor nor a writer of comedies and shall probably have to hang curtains until I hang myself." This remark earned young Poquelin a resounding slap and a pull at his ear; whereupon Monsieur Poquelin, apologizing for their having bothered me with their personal affairs, ordered his son to clean up, pack the tools, and fetch them right away to the shop. He himself had to hurry to the Louvre.

When the old man had gone I told young Molière

about Scarron and how interested he was, and how much all of us wished we could help. "I think your father wouldn't at all object to encouraging your ambitions. He only plays the *grognard* because something or someone forces him to oppose your plans, and he thinks he must make you practical. Won't you let me know your real secret? I am on your side."

Instead of a direct answer Molière stuck his head and neck forward, made a long jaw, and with both arms flung high and fidgeting he sent his jaw into rapid up-and-down motion. His pantomime was a vivid representation of a bickering wench.

"Not your mother, I suppose?" I said.

"Madame my stepmother," he replied. He confided to me that his father was under her thumb, and that she would not permit spending any money to send him to college, though Uncle had promised to contribute. "Besides being stingy," he said, "she belongs to that group of dull people for whom the purchase of a pound of cheese is serious business, but the composition of a poem or a play a waste of time."

"Have you written a play already?" I asked, and when he produced a small roll of manuscript from his pocket I snatched at it eagerly.

"No one has read it yet," he protested. But I paid no attention, held it fast, and withdrew with it to my armchair.

"*L'amour médécin, comédie en un acte*" by Jean Baptiste Molière," I read, and did not stop reading until I had finished it. To be sure, it was naïve, the spelling was bad, and the style, except for happy flashes, was awkward; but how full it was of movement and life! It breathed the true, the incomparable comic spirit, the harmony and grace and wit that I had learned to love in the comedies of Plautus and Terence—the very qualities that we lacked on the present French comedy stage. I felt my heart pounding with the thrill of a tremendous discovery, and at the same time I kept smiling to myself at the little play's humorous turns, until, at its extremely droll crisis, I broke into continuous peals of laughter.

When I looked at Molière he was staring at me with wide eyes, big tears dropping from them. "Excuse me," he apologized, wiping his cheeks. "But I am so happy! Your laughing was so lovely, so right from your heart."

"You will make many other people laugh this way," I said, "—scores of them, millions. I am sure of it. And if you would let me help you—let Papa and me give you the money you need for college——" Molière started, made a defensive gesture, and said that he could not possibly accept such an enormous favor. And even if he himself felt inclined, there was his father. "Don't forget, *Monsieur le tapissier et valet de chambre du roi* would surely never permit it."

But I didn't let myself be deterred. I improvised a little conspiracy whereby Papa would take up the whole matter with Molière's uncle and give him the money so that he could assume all the costs for college, and Monsieur Poquelin wouldn't know of our contribution at all. For a while I had to argue and plead, but when I insisted that we would do it not so much for him as for the sake of art and that he had no right to refuse, he suddenly uttered a loud, joyous cry and began to dance around the room.

There was nothing artful in his dancing; yet it was somehow beautiful, like the flight of a bird freed from its cage and taking to its wings to soar into freedom. When, all out of breath, he calmed down, I made him sit opposite me, relax, and tell me more about his plans and ideas. He launched into a rather incoherent account of what was still only a blurred vision of his future high comedy; but in it pulsed his love for people, to whom, he said, he wanted to bring God's most precious gift, laughter. He wanted to make fun of them precisely because he loved them, so that they might see themselves on a comic plane instead of a dreary or a tragic one, and thus become happier. And as I listened to his enthusiastic youthful outburst I kept thinking how he, little more than a boy, might eventually revolutionize our whole theater. In my imagination I saw myself sitting in a box and looking down at him on the stage, while the whole house rocked to storms of applause for this lovable genius.

At last I had to tell Molière that it was late; that, if he didn't want to get into trouble with his father, and in the interest of our conspiracy, he had better return to the shop. His tools he packed reluctantly, as if he had nothing to do with them any more, and then he took leave of me. "How shall I ever be able to thank you for your great graciousness?" he said, kissing my hand with his boyish lips.

"By letting me always know how you are getting along; by remaining my friend and always giving me your plays to read."

"No one will ever see or read them before you," he said. "And I swear that I shall always throw my whole being into my efforts to earn again that wonderful silvery laughter of yours."

It was not difficult to make Papa keep my promise, and there followed long negotiations with Molière's uncle. They ended happily when his brother, old Monsieur Poquelin, was let in on the secret and accepted our offer. On the eve of our young genius's entry into the Collège de Clermont we gave a great dinner in our house. All three Poquelins were present, and all of us were happy.

5

THE DAYS THAT followed were completely filled with the pleasures that my father was indefatigable in devising for me, and nothing seemed to threaten our joint happiness.

Then, one day, a stately carriage drew up in front of our house. Two elderly ladies alighted. They came in to announce to me that Her Majesty the Queen was summoning me, and that I was to accompany them to the Louvre at once. When I asked what the summons meant, the two old shrews refused all explanation except that Her Majesty was calling me in her capacity as supreme supervisor of the morals of all young girls of the French aristocracy and gentry.

This time the Queen didn't receive me so graciously. Perhaps it was her obvious pregnancy that made her so irritable. I should have been considerably amused had I known that the child she was carrying, who was to become Louis XIV, and whom, when he was a little boy, I was to dangle on my knee, would one day propose to make me the uncrowned Queen of France.

The silky white-haired dog seemed not to share her lady's displeasure. This uncommonly fetching creature with small pointed muzzle and pointed ears stood up on the Queen's lap, watched me sidelong, and wagged her tail amiably and gaily.

At Her Majesty's nod one of her elderly court ladies—I recognized in her the venomous scarecrow of the tea party—took up a paper and in a jarring voice, sarcastic at the appropriate passages, read me the charge—which, to my astonishment, had to do with last year's incident involving Yvonne, on the Place des Halles. But I didn't intend to let myself be intimidated, either by the Queen's presence or by the malicious voice of my accuser. I frankly admitted my interference and told the Queen what I had already told Évremond. "Why does it always have to be the woman that is the loser in every transaction? Why is the woman always condemned, and never the man? If what the law declares to be an offense to public morals must be punished by whipping, why are only the girls whipped and not the men? If either, why not both? It is unjust, and I could not then and cannot ever reconcile myself to it."

While I was speaking to the Queen the little dog was growling at my accuser, and when I ended it barked at her in a high-pitched little yelp. Then, as if to show its sympathy, it jumped from the Queen's lap, put its tiny paws against me, and wagged its tail some more, peering up at me.

"Just take her up," said the Queen, suddenly friendly again. When I did so and the little dog snuggled into the bend of my arm, the Queen laughed and, turning to the court lady, said: "I think the demoiselle is right, and my little Marcelle seems to think so, too. It is my express wish not to be bothered with this evil gossip about her any longer.'' Then she kissed me on the forehead and graciously dismissed me.

''You're a true saint,'' Papa said, when, laughing, I told him the whole episode, ''who knows how to stick to her worshipers.'' He praised me for the spirit I had shown, too; and in doing it his look was that of the artist who steps back, searches his work, and finds it growing into his ideal. As always when I became aware of how much loving and concentrated effort my father put into shaping me to his preconceived pattern, I experienced that chaste thrill of awe and gratitude that creature feels for creator.

Spring came early. It was a lovely season, but cruel to me and my restlessness. Sometimes, to make up for a sleepless night, I would slip back into bed after my morning bath and, with window shades and bed curtains drawn, sleep for a while. In the ice-cold water I forgot all the sultry imaginings of the night, but back in the warm bed they returned with double-force to invade my sleep and my dreams. Charles was still their center; but sometimes Rochefoucauld would creep into them and, for moments at least, he and Charles would coalesce into one person and make love to me.

On one such morning—it was a year since I had been taken from the convent—I dreamed that I was a little girl again, lying in my bed at Loches. I could hear soft footsteps approaching, and the prince, the impertinent boy, removed my bedspread and then—what effrontery!—lay down by my side, leav-

ing space enough between us not to awake me, and
murmuring: "What have you done to me? What the
devil is the matter with me, little girl? If I could only
kiss you!" I heard him whisper hotly in my dream,
"—closer than that, quite close, quite close." Then
he was no longer stopping at the wish, but drawing
me to him, and the dream became so keen and
stirring that it was no dream at all, but flesh and
blood and reality.

Was it, then, a dream? Were not those two hot lips
on mine, this arm flung about my waist, these glowing words "Ninon, ma petite!" a living actuality?
Wonderingly I opened my eyes. And there he was,
my prince, my saucy boy of Loches, naked by my
side, laughing and kissing me all over.

"I hope you're not cross with me," said
Madeleine afterwards, "for letting the prince in. But
he is such a beautiful cavalier! and I thought that our
little girl had not known such joy for a long time."

There followed weeks of a great happiness, splendid and full of life. Though the court and society and
many jealous ladies were laying claims upon my
lover, he devoted all his free time to me. In the
daytime we would ride or drive together, or he would
stay in our house, either alone with me or in the
company of Papa, who delighted in him. A good
observer, of more than average learning, drawing on
a fund of knowledge of people and innumerable
adventures, Rochefoucauld was a *bon causeur*, and
he knew how to epitomize his view of life—which
was astonishingly akin to Papa's—in adroit and brilliant maxims. The pearls and diamonds and other
treasures that the prince would have liked to lavish

on me, I refused—much to the dismay of Madame
de Senneterre, but with Papa's full approval—but I
was avaricious of the infinitely greater treasures of
his wit. And I had to admit to myself that my Charles
would have seemed, beside him, a comparative
boor.

Rochefoucauld's brilliance had, however, its disadvantage. I soon found out that his reflective propensity had taken such complete possession of him
that, with all his eagerness for Life, he could not
enjoy anything that he had not preconceived in his
brain. The climax of his happiness was rounded
more in his analyzing and summarizing afterthought
than in the actuality of experience. This cerebral
quality penetrated even into his love-making. My
love nights with Charles had been dominated by the
elemental surge of sheer passion. In Rochefoucauld,
stimulating, delightfully extravagant, and fantastic
as he was, I nearly always felt the touch of abstract
premeditation; and rare were the times when I could
abandon myself, to lie at last, wholly appeased, in
his arms. Yet how overwhelmingly much did
Rochefoucauld, my prince, my boy of Loches, now
my François, give me in those incomparable weeks!

When his furlough was almost at an end and the
claims of court and society and of a certain high-born
blonde lady had become too pertinacious, we decided to escape into solitude. My aunt Montaigu had
died the previous year, and Papa was now proprietor
of her estate. It was overburdened with debts and
barely kept itself going. For that reason Papa didn't
even consider taking the trouble to go and see it. But
its solitude was suited to my purpose, and with

Papa's permission and paternal blessing I invited
François to the castle in Loches.

But for my bed and the two old ladies
(Mademoiselle Amélie, too, had died) we found
Loches exactly as in my childhood. Recapturing our
moods of that time, we would stroll together through
the meadows and woods, explore the ivy-grown
battlements, the turrets and cellars, climb the oak
and the cherry trees (François' eyes still looked like
the round, sweet black cherries), and fence in the
armory full of rust and dust. He still remembered the
fulmine improvvisato, to which he owed no little of
his prowess as a swordsman.

On rainy days we would rummage, as of old, in
the heavy oak chests of the library. In the picture
gallery we discovered well-remembered old objects—the Vesuvius picture (we didn't fail to fall
into each others' arms and kiss in front of it) and
"Suzanne and the Elders." This time, though, he
admitted that he preferred my shapely slimness to the
plump excesses of that buxom biblical prude.

François moved into the same small room that he
had occupied in his student days, and I took my old
large chamber over the dining room. The great bed,
of course, wasn't there now, but the one that had
been moved in for me was ample. And that was well,
for when I now expected the prince for the night I had
no intention of falling asleep at his side. The old
bed's only shortcoming was that it was a little wobbly; but we grew used to that, and we found in the
end that the squeaking and cracking of a bed is more
exciting love music than harp or lute.

The park at the rear of the castle was even more

neglected and overgrown than before, but there was still the broad path on which I had watched François pace up and down with his tutor. Now it was I who, every day after supper and before bedtime, would stroll with him along this path, reveling in his reflections and comments—some of them so illuminating about my own self that I often had occasion to remember them in the future, even though I might not fully have grasped their truth at the moment.

On one of those evening strolls we passed a broad-shouldered stone faun. The strongly muscled torso pleased me, and I passed my fingers lingeringly over it. "It is still warm from the sun," I said.

"From the sun?" said François. He stopped and smiled at me. "Rather from the touch of your lovely fingers. I would not be surprised if he came to life under them." Then, with a long, thoughtful look at me, he said: "Everything you touch or even approach stirs to life, is fanned to desire. Every line of your body, every movement, every pore breathes *amour*. Even your dress, your stockings, your shoes seem to whisper 'Quick!—take me off, here— here—on the spot!' " After a little breathless pause he added: "What a delightfully dangerous woman you are, *ma chérie!*"

"Are you afraid of me?"

"Perhaps," he replied, deeply earnest and ignoring my laugh. "You may not be aware of it, but it seems inescapable, fated—this power, this mystery of your blood. Even your own father is in love with you. No, don't laugh. He is ardently in love with you. However restrained his passion may be, I can perceive it in certain ambiguous glances, in undertones of his voice. No, I am not telling you this for pure jealousy, but because I want to warn you to be careful when you go back to Paris and to him. And it is also fortunate that you decided never to marry. For your own sons, I wager, would fall in love with their mother.''

I wanted to laugh his words off, but a shadow had suddenly fallen across my bright mood. I had again a glimpse of the pale, deep-eyed face of the young priest Chersay, and I heard his voice trembling with subdued passion and anger: "Whatever you see and feel and touch becomes lust, filth. It is visible on your face and all over you. But you shall not escape His wrath and His justice.''

I could not help a little shudder. I was really beginning to be afraid of myself. Then François said: "I have experienced it myself, this power of yours. You would not believe it, but I felt it even when you were quite a little girl." At that I had to laugh outright. A quick glance told me that, *Dieu merci*, he had not changed since boyhood. I flung all my gloom to the lovely evening breeze and myself into his arms.

The highest pitch of our passion came on the night before our departure. It burst forth then in a voluptuous, tumultuous transport. Love-making had always suggested to me a gallop through the open countryside, with my horse rearing and pitching under me, sometimes tossing me up, and with me adroitly regaining my saddle, cheeks burning, hair streaming, and with exultant cries driving my steed impetuously onward, onward.

At last, in the opaque translucency of predawn, I lay quieted in François' arms.

Outside the crickets began to sing. "Now my time is up, and I have to go," he said softly, and smiled; and then for the first time he told me that as a boy he had slept here with me night after night until the wild cock in the wood had crowed and the day was breaking.

"I knew it." I smiled back at him. "I knew it all along, from the very first night when you, impetuous boy, came in, drew the bedspread away from me, and looked at me. And I remember, too, that I didn't mind—that I first liked it and then loved it."

The admission seemed not only to amuse but also greatly to flatter him. "It was always so charming, so thrilling, so beautiful between us two," he said, "from the very beginning!"

I didn't know why the words came to me, but as if I was stating something very natural and self-evident I replied: "Yes, my François, beautiful—beautiful—from the very beginning—to the very end."

His eyes, which had been drowsing beneath half-closed leaden lids, were suddenly wide, and in them I read not only the utter amazement of a conqueror at his first defeat, not only the genuine pain of loss, but at the same time the flicker of a great relief. "You are a great woman, Ninon," he said. "I myself should never have had the courage or the will or the power to leave you."

"We have sung a beautiful love song together," I said dreamingly, "and its melody——"

"—will always sing in our ears. Nothing shall be

resented, no false, no harsh, no discordant note ever remembered; only beauty, delight and joy.''

And then, from the woods beyond, came the strident crow of the wild cock. François leaned over me, gently kissed my forehead, my eyes, my hands; then he tiptoed out.

When we left Loches in Rochefoucauld's carriage we were going away as lovers no longer, but as the friends we had pledged ourselves to remain. Traveling slowly through the Loire valley, we reached Orléans late in the evening. In the Aigle d'Or we spent the night apart; early the next morning we set off to reach Paris before evening.

It was lovely, this traveling together and exchanging delightful small talk, confidences, and memories. (How we did laugh at the recollection of our bed, now a tumbledown structure that would need the services of a carpenter if it were ever to be called a bed again. Nor did I tire of Rochefoucauld's abstract speculations, which he knew how to season so inimitably with irony and subtle satire. Condensed and polished, I found many of them long years afterward in his celebrated *Maximes*.) And no less lovely was it to sit together in silence and observe the landscape—the undulating hillocks steepled with picturesque castles or chapels or solitary chalets from which slim threads of smoke rose peacefully to a crystal sky.

The climbing sun flooded the world with an amazing resplendence. I could see a lark shooting straight into heaven; her flight and her ecstatic warbling filled me with a keen sense of regained freedom. I had found in François a man whom I had loved for his own sake: might I not find others who would cool the burning of my insatiable desire with no memory of Charles between me and them? As if born into a new life I triumphed inwardly, swept by an incomparable exhilaration.

When the shadows were lengthening and the turreted and pinnacled outline of Paris was sketching itself sharply against a red sky, Rochefoucauld said: "Before we part, let your devoted friend, whom you will now not suspect of jealousy, give you a trifle of good advice for your future. Don't call your lover Charles—unless, of course, it happens to be his name."

"Oh!" I cried out, a little startled. "You didn't take it amiss, I hope, that mere slip of the tongue."

He looked at me earnestly. "No," he said, "I didn't take it amiss; but neither was it a mere slip of the tongue. For, whether you know it or not, you are still in love with the man whom you called Charles. Not only once, but every time when you were lost in your abandon, you were aware only of him. Your very pronunciation of his name brought renewed and violent passion to your face, your whole body. Your eyes looked at me in transport, but they didn't see me; they were seeing only him."

My heart pounded frantically. I made no reply.

"You should not worry about it. I could almost envy you such a love, of which I myself should never be capable. I believe that there *is* something like an eternal and unconquerable love. *Hélas*, it comes only once in a thousand years, and all our loves are but faint copies. So, I am not trying to tell you that you should forget the happy but obviously ungrateful object of your devotion. My only advice is that you should call your next lover, not by his first name, but just *mon trésor* or *mon aimé* or the like."

It was not difficult for me to accept Rochefoucauld's advice with good grace; and before I reached home his vocabulary had provided me with a list of pet names so long as to supply me for many years and for scores of lovers.

6

WHEN THE FAÇADE of our pretty house with the white columns and pilasters and red brick walls emerged from the greenery it was unlike the time of my return from Loches as a little girl with Papa. The day of my arrival was known, and there were my good old Madeleine and Perrot and all the grooms and kitchen and stableboys in front of the house to hail my homecoming; only this time it was not poor Mama's wide-open arms into which I flew, but Papa's. He welcomed me as if I had been separated from him for years. An exquisite *bienvenue* supper was waiting for me, and Papa displayed all the charms of his humorous hedonism, rallying me on my fresh, relaxed looks. "The good country air, of course, and the sun," he said; and then, knowingly: "—and above all, I suppose, true to Epicurus, you had your pleasure in movement and your pleasure in rest, each at its proper time and according to the occasion."

At supper I learned about changes that didn't please me. "I have taken my old company over again," Papa said. "It was decimated in the war, and it won't take the field again: it will just do guard duty in the city—in the Bastille and the like. But it won't take much of my time. My lieutenant is doing most of the work. I shall have to go only two or three times a week to inspect them. And it's quite near—in the *caserne des Haudriettes*."

I wondered. There was no particular honor in commanding a hinterland company. Even if he went only two or three times a week, it meant taking time that I thought should belong to me. In the course of the evening his humor sounded forced; there was a peculiar strain in his voice, and he had an absent look that suggested an *arrière-pensée*. The impression grew on me that some secret worry was hounding him. Was it his old obsession again? Lucrèce? Anxiety for him and at the same time a jealous resentment took hold of me. But before he left me for the night another explanation was to come to me—one that, though I had been forewarned by Rochefoucauld, had not entered my thoughts.

When he kissed me good night this time it was not, as of old, to make me sit on his lap: he remained standing, and his kiss on my forehead was one of infinite tenderness. But then he broke away from me almost roughly, and in a thick voice, scarcely looking at me, he said: "Sleep well, darling," and went out.

"Darling Papa," I thought while undressing, "shy and awkward as an enamored boy! Oh, I do not worry because you are in love with me. It even pleases me a good deal; I find it much better than if your thoughts were of Lucrèce, who could cause you only trouble and disaster."

I listened. Upstairs in his room Papa was pacing up and down with nervous and impatient steps, like a lion in a cage. Poor Papa! He was suffering. Oh, I knew, I knew too well the pangs of such suffering.

Then—a loud crash. Poor, silly Papa! So intense was his torment, his desperation, that he had hurled himself on to his bed. I even thought I heard him moan. And at that point an odd fear began to steal into my heart. If his passion were as violent as that—and my own blood was no lemon water!—how was I to know that all would stay as it was—Papa and his little girl? My mind refused even a hint of anything so horrible, so against all the laws of Nature. I decided that I must put it all out of my mind.

Steps again. But this time not overhead. I heard them coming down the stairs, approaching, halting before my door.

Papa came in. I felt him sitting down on my bed and watching my face. Then I saw him bending sidewise over me, with his hands on the covers. There were minutes of a tense and unbearable silence. I kept on pretending sleep. But when I heard a deep, quivering, tortured sigh I could not help opening my eyes and smiling weakly at him. "I'm sorry I disturbed you, darling," he said huskily, "but I must speak to you. I must. I am suffering; oh, if you knew how I am suffering!"

"Just tell me, Papa," I said compassionately, sitting up. "Just tell me what you want of me."

His eyes were evading mine, and they looked haunted; but weariness had fallen from him. His hand clasped my shoulder. And then our eyes met and locked. They stayed so for a long moment.

Then, as if by a mutual impulse, they unlocked and turned away. His hand let go my shoulder. The word, the supreme word of human language—Love, the name of the most wonderful thing in creation, but an unnatural and forbidden thing here and now— died on our lips. And then, shamefaced and terrified, I threw myself face down, burrowing into the pillow. While I was sobbing I heard him slump from the bed. Then his head was against my knee and, like me, he in whose eyes I had never seen a tear—wept.

At last he stood up to pace the room. A painful struggle was taking place in his breast. Then he picked up a chair and brought it near.

"I am very unhappy," he said, "to see you so frightened, my poor girl, but I could not help it. What I wanted to tell you must be said at once, and I hope you will help me. I must see Lucrèce. I must see her if but for one time. You must release me from my word of honor."

His words, though they brought immense relief and dispelled a horror, came as a shock. I could say nothing; I could only stare at him.

"You must not be afraid of anything," said Papa. "Just listen to me, and you'll see."

What I heard was the whole story of Lucrèce, with whom Papa had been in love when she was still a girl, but whom her parents had given to Riberolles, a repellent man in both appearance and character. Their decision had turned Papa's and Lucrèce's love into flaming passion. They met clandestinely; and in doing it they had to be very careful to avoid detection by the husband. Not that Riberolles had been jealous: he had small right to be, because for the traffic of the sexes Nature had endowed him but meagerly. Nevertheless he thought it his legal right as the husband to determine with whom Lucrèce should cuckold him; but she refused her favors to men capable of furthering his career, she persisted in refusing herself to Monsieur Bourdeille, governor of Périgord. This Bourdeille had promised Riberolles six thousand livres and a distinguished position in his office as the price of a liaison with Lucrèce. Riberolles became so infuriated against Papa, whom he thought the cause of her stubborn refusal, that he not only pursued him with adultery charges, but presently tried to have him assassinated. Now all his efforts had failed; he was all but penniless; and his one recourse was a renewal of the old arrangement with Monsieur Bourdeille. He was making preparations to go to Pèrigord. If he succeeded and came back to Paris to fetch Lucrèce, she would have to go with him whether she liked it or not, and Bourdeille would have his way.

Lucrèce had struggled desperately, Papa told me. She had yielded neither to Riberolles' brutalities nor to his threat that he would kill her if she didn't obey him this time. At last she had given in for the sole reason that her husband's going to Pèrigord would provide her last opportunity to see Papa, the only man in the world she loved. Her maid Marie—a woman, so Lucrèce wrote, absolutely devoted to her—had handed him a letter near the barracks. In it Lucrèce suggested that, for safety, Papa should not come to her house: that instead she should go to his. Papa, bound by his word of honor, had given a temporizing answer. But now Lucrèce had sent him word that if she could not see him at least once, she would kill herself. Tomorrow Marie would go to the barracks to receive his decision. He was sure that Lucrèce meant what she said. How, then, could he refuse?

Papa's story went to my heart. I could now understand his extreme perturbation. Since Riberolles was to depart, there was scarcely any danger involved. How could I, knowing the pangs of unfulfilled yearning, do less than release Papa from his word of honor and offer whatever help he needed?

7

IN THE FOLLOWING days Papa regained his radiant appearance, and in spite of secret jealousy I was happy to see him fired with expectancy as his reunion with Lucrèce approached.

I knew that with the help of the maid Marie an exchange of letters was going on, and apparently Riberolles had no idea what was going on behind his back. At least, nothing suspicious had happened. But then Madeleine told me of beggars who had appeared in our street in the last few days and knocked at our door. "There have never been so many of them," she said. "But the strangest thing is that this morning one of them sat down at the back door of our garden wall. How much does he expect he can earn there by begging?"

Madeleine's words startled me. She was right. No one but Papa, who used the narrow lane as a short cut on his way to the barracks, would ever cross it. What, really, was the strange man looking for? Président de Verdun's warning came to my mind, together with Riberolles' hateful grimace in the Palais and all the grisly tales of the *cours des miracles* in the Rue Franc Bourgeois, where killers could be hired in that uncanny underground *royaume des Argots*.

I resolved to do something at once. I loaded the pistolet that Papa had bought for me in the Palais and went straight to the alley. The beggar was there. Sitting crouched in the niche, his hair unkempt, his palsied limbs in dirty and wretched rags, and whining alms in God's name, he made a lamentable enough impression. But he did not deceive me. Producing my weapon, I aimed it straight at his breast. "Don't move or I'll pull the trigger," I told him. "And don't think I can't shoot."

The man's eyes and mouth had fallen open. He did not move, but he tried to sustain his masquerade by whining that he was only a sick old man and that for the sake of his poor wife I should leave him unharmed and put the pistol away.

"Take out your knife or whatever it is," I ordered him, "and put it under the stone by your side." He hesitated; but seeing my finger on the trigger and the weapon still aimed at him, he produced a long, sharp knife from under his coat and placed it as I had ordered.

"Now get up and take off your coat," I said.

As he stood upright with his coat undone—he had no shirt beneath it—I saw that this "old" man had a massive, muscular body. But I did not allow myself to be dazzled by the sight of it, and when I had convinced myself that he carried no other weapon—I generously excused him from taking off more when he reached for his belt to let down his trousers—I asked: "How much were you to get for killing Monsieur de Lenclos?"

After a few denials the man said: "Ten livres." When I told him, "You'll get twenty from me for not doing it," he grinned. He said, "That's all right. But you can put your pistol away now. I'm not afraid of it. If I wanted to I could smash you as if you were a flea or a fly with one blow of my fist. But it would be a pity—such a saucy, pretty little damsel!"

"Who hired you?" I asked him sternly. The barrel of my pistolet glittered quite impressively in the sun, and it was still trained on him. He tried to pretend that he didn't know his employer, but when I told him outright that he had been sent by a *cours des miracles* he admitted it. "You'll get five livres extra," I said, "if you'll lead me to your chief."

He measured me with an amazed look. The idea of a young girl's daring to face the Grand Coësre, the all-powerful king of the underworld, seemed beyond his credulity. But when I insisted, disregarding his warning that it was a dangerous undertaking, he finally assented.

I made the man wait in our street, and when I returned from our house with my mantle and his twenty-five livres I let myself be led to the Rue Franc Bourgeois, from which we plunged straight into the ill-famed and dreaded narrow lane.

Darkened by arches and with rotting beams overhead, the lane looked like a subterranean passage. We passed behind old houses swarming with naked children, pigs, dogs, and chickens. I could see faces appear at the holelike windows and forms at

shadowy, cavernous doors—forms that might have
sent a shiver down the spine of the pluckiest of men.
But I could not think of my own safety; I had to save
Papa's life. At last, after we had made our way
through an entanglement of junk piles and garbage
heaps, the passage opened on to a vast, dingy square.
It lay at the bottom of a declivity, buried in dust,
ashes, charred logs, pots and jars, and moldy rags of
rugs. It was like a giant cesspool never cleaned, and
it smelled as it looked. It was enclosed by dreary
ruined houses whose broken walls and fragments of
roofs were jagged against an already discoloring
sky.

We descended the slippery slope. "Wait here,"
said my guide; and leaving me at the edge of the
square, he walked over to a group of ragged men
who surrounded a gnarled tree of broken branches
and a few dusty, shriveled leaves. Then, after the
men had looked around to observe me, I heard my
guide calling: "Come on, come on." And when I
made for the group the ring opened, and I came to a
stand before a man seated on a warped stool—the
Grand Coësre in person.

He was not as I had imagined him, this all-
powerful chieftain of all the outlaws of France. I had
envisaged a burly, grim looking, fierce-moustached
brute. The jawbone and the horselike stained teeth of
this man looked the part, but the rest of the dreaded
being who sat draped in his "mantle of a thousand
pieces," token of his royal dignity, was small, almost dwarfish, hunchbacked, sickly, and fragile.
His ears were long and projecting, his face old, his
lips colorless; but his eyes were diabolically sharp,

shrewd, and glittering and I could well imagine that
they shone in the dark. "Well, young woman," he
said without preliminaries, "what have you to propose?"

"First let me tell you who I am," I said with a
curtsy and a smile. But obviously he was not impressed. "We never ask names," he said. "Just tell
me what you want and how much you offer." But
when I overrode him to say that I was the Ninon who
had saved Yvonne, his whole attitude immediately
changed. He sprang up from his stool and made me a
deep bow, and he did not sit down again until his
men had brought me a warped bench and I had seated
myself. I told him a few details about the affair of
Yvonne and suggested that perhaps some of the men
whom I had met outside the city gates could identify
me; but now he was looking at me appreciatively,
and he said with a chivalrous gesture: "You need no
proof. You don't look like a cheat. Just tell me what
we can do for you."

My request was that he order all the *cours des
miracles* of his kingdom not to accept any commis-
sion that could harm my father; and that he granted at
once. But his sympathy did not stop there. "If you
like, Demoiselle," he said with a most obliging
smile, "it will be a pleasure for us to kill Riberolles." Perceiving my reluctance, he assured me that
his offer had been meant, not as a business transaction, but as just a friendly little gift. "For our
friends," he said, "we do anything. And killing
Riberolles—that's *pas de grande chose*." I thanked
him for his generosity, but told him that neither Papa
nor I was afraid of Riberolles. I assured him that I

wouldn't take his time from more serious business, and that though I appreciated his chivalry, I wouldn't for the time being make use of it.

From somewhere in one of the broken houses an appalling shriek knifed the air. "Oh, don't let that bother you, Demoiselle," the Coësre said with a calm smile. "It is nothing—just a little matter of business routine. We gave that man until sunset to pay his ransom. But apparently his people didn't come in time. So we just finished him. We are very exact in our business."

I had to fight down a cold shudder, and I wanted to go, but my host would not release me. "You had better remain for a while," he said. "The approaches to this place are crowded at this hour; our people are returning from work." I looked about. Groups of ragged shapes were indeed emerging on the edge of the depression, slipping or rushing down the declivity, and scattering over the square; and, miraculously, the lame, the crippled, the blind threw their crutches and sticks away and came running and shouting and swinging bottles of wine and pieces of meat and all kinds of loot. Soon the whole courtyard was packed and buzzing with noise.

Hitherto I had not seen much of life except on its more glittering side, and I must say that the present sight moved me deeply. The Grand Coësre, noticing that it did, became very communicative. "Just look at us," he said, "—at what you rich call the dregs of the people. Look at this courtyard whose bare ground is our home, summer and winter; our bed, our stool, and our table. Do you wonder, you rich, that we too want some of the good things of life that you have usurped? And because you won't share them with us, we take them in our own way. But just wait! The time will come when we shall have defeated you; and then we shall share the good things among ourselves and give to all.'' His eyes gleamed in the dark. ''But that does not apply to you,'' he added. ''You have a heart for us, the outcasts!''

My twenty-five livres were returned to me. I shared wine and roasted meat with my host. I was introduced to the crowd and cheered by them as Sainte Ninon. And after that the Grand Coësre released me, having appointed a bodyguard who escorted me safely back to the Rue Franc Bourgeois.

8

A FEW DAYS LATER we heard that Scarron, whom we had not seen in some time, had arrived in Paris; this time, however, for no spree, but crippled and in excruciating pain. We drove at once to see him in the Faubourg Saint Germain, in whose bathhouse Scarron hoped to find relief and healing. (Its waters had once been known to the Roman garrison of ancient Lutetia Parisiorum.) It was a rainy, overcast day. What we heard from the administrator about Scarron's illness was disheartening, and it was in a rather depressed mood that we entered the dark, rude, poorly furnished chamber. Scarron's pale, haggard face had small resemblance to that of the ruddy bon vivant we had known. But what a surprise! Nothing but cheerfulness radiated from those pain-twisted features; and, lying paralyzed in his narrow bed, he told us his story with inimitable zest, with sly and roguish looks at us, and with endless fits of laughter.

The *malheur*, if one could call it a *malheur*, he said, had happened during the last carnival of Le Mans. The people, masked and gaily costumed, pursued their merrymaking while he, the dignified canonicus, sat at home, lonely and sour. But his epicurean mind revolted against such injustice, and he resolved to join the gay tumult incognito. Having no costume at hand, he undressed, smeared his whole body with honey, and spread it all over with feathers from his *plumeau*, so that he looked like a monstrous exotic bird. It was great fun to mingle with the merrymakers. But the greatest fun was when the girls began to pluck at his feathers. Unfortunately, they plucked so long and so pertinaciously that at last he was completely denuded.

There were, however, grumpy fellows who couldn't take a joke. Some of them, recognizing him as the clergyman of their cathedral, had not only attacked him themselves, but had also stirred up a large mob against him. It pursued him furiously and might have beaten him to death had he not fled, jumped into the river, and hidden himself in the rushes. And there he had stood in the cold water, naked, for hours. He had been sick ever since and a victim of excruciating pain. What kind of sickness it was, the doctors couldn't tell him precisely. Some said it was rheumatism of the joints or sciatica; others maintained that the spine was affected and that recovery would be a matter of years.

Papa and I, carried away by Scarron's humorous way of telling his story, had laughed until we cried, but at the prospect he described we looked at him with compassion. But he was tolerating no commiseration. "Do not think I am unhappy," he protested. "Far from it! You ought to congratulate me and rejoice with me. For that carnival night brought me, besides affliction, the best of fortune. For—isn't it wonderful?—I have been expelled! I am chased out of the church. Canonicus no more! No more pretended dignity! Oh, how I have hated being a hypocrite! But now I am free. I have regained the first of all fundamental human rights: the right to laughter. I undergo pain, yes; but against the dark background of suffering the bright hues of pleasure appear even brighter to me. Let them squeeze and sting and goad me, those damned pains; let them never quit me at all; let them make a permanent cripple of me; I do not care! In spite of them I shall smile and laugh and find the world wonderful."

"Isn't he the most admirable apostle of Epicurus?" Papa said on our way home. "It is easy to be gay and to laugh if everything runs smoothly. But to keep smiling and laughing when pain or sorrow is torturing us—that's the test of an inner true greatness. I hope that such a situation will never come to you, darling, but if it should, then think of Scarron!" Poor Papa, he didn't know in how short a time and for what tragic reasons he would have to remind me of those words.

My appeal to the Grand Coësre and its success had both deeply touched Papa and made him very proud. He wouldn't admit, however, that Riberolles might have planned his murder because of Lucrèce. There was not the faintest possibility, Papa maintained, that Riberolles could know about her intention to meet him. But, though nothing suspicious happened during the next days. I felt uneasy about the whole affair, and I looked forward to Papa's rendezvous with great misgivings.

A few days after we saw Scarron, Papa received a letter in which Lucrèce informed him that Riberolles was to depart at ten o'clock the next morning from the post chaise station on the Place de Grenelles, and that she would come on the very same day after sunset. She asked in her letter that Papa make the proper arrangements for her to enter his house unobserved, and that he work out all the details with Marie. Papa handed to the maid the key to the door in the garden wall and sent word to Lucrèce that, on entering it, she was to cross the garden and climb the outer staircase to the upper floor, where she would find the door on her left unlocked for her.

Everything seemed perfect. But my forebodings would not leave me. Still suspicious, I went the next morning—of course, without Papa's knowledge—to the Place de Grenelles, and there I took a position behind one of the arcades opposite the post station.

Riberolles, whom I recognized at once, was one of the last passengers to arrive and climb into the post chaise. Lucrèce, whom I knew from Papa's description, had come with him. I had to admit that she was beautiful. She was tall, with dark hair and large blue eyes under dark, high-arched brows, and her skin was translucently pale and fine. I could not understand, though, why so great a connoisseur of women as Papa did not see that her eyes were a little too bulging, almost a cow's eyes, and her figure somewhat raw-boned. But perhaps it was only my jealousy that made me notice those little *défauts*.

Leave it to Papa, I thought, to see her as the shining beauty of the age. For my part, I was content to be convinced that her husband had actually gone.

Throughout the day Papa was in an extremely happy mood, full of banter and gaiety and making all the arrangements for his rendezvous with the enthusiasm of a youthful lover. In the afternoon we went shopping, for he wanted to have a cold supper and all kinds of dainty things for Lucrèce to nibble in his room. We bought roasted meats, pastries, and sweetmeats; also armfuls of pink carnations, Lucrèce's favorite flowers. We smuggled everything into Papa's room ourselves, because, save for old Perrot, who slept on Papa's corridor, not a soul was to know our secret.

In Papa's chamber on that night no one would have recognized Maman's former cell. Ever since he had returned it had been a comfortable *chez-soi;* but for this night, with the help of Turkish carpets, brocades and silken hangings and beautiful vases, now overflowing with carnations, he had turned it into a veritable bower of Venus. After I had taken an early supper with Papa I went up to help him with the last finishing touches. The table near the window we covered with linen and laces, displaying on it the delightful blue-patterned plates that Papa had brought from Holland, bottles with old Spanish wine, two golden cups, and all the delicacies we had bought in the city. Nor had I forgotten to bring some silken pillows, which I arranged on the bed.

I did these things to contribute my share to Papa's long-yearned-for love feast, but I could not say that I felt altogether happy. My misgivings had returned, and though I tried to rid myself of a feeling of some great wrong towards Maman, a dread of retribution took hold of me. I imagined that the black cross had returned to the wall and that the Saviour's sad and resentful eyes were watching me through the rose-colored silk hangings. So solemn and so admonitory did His look seem to grow that in a sudden attack of weakness I dropped the vase that I held. It fell to the floor and shattered.

I gave my malaise vent by a little nervous weeping, but Papa begged me not to worry over trifles and told me how wonderfully I had arranged everything. On my way out he gave me the carnations from the broken vase and kissed me good night. "I hope we shan't disturb your sleep too much," he said. "It may become a little noisy upstairs here, for Lucrèce has always been tremendously lively, and I am no corpse myself." I laughed, for I had thought of the tumble-down bed in Loches, but—he shouldn't have said "corpse." On my way out the dismal word made me cast a shy side glance at where Christ hung on His cross. But this time I didn't see Him beneath the pink silken hanging, which was now scarlet and purple in the reflection of the western sky.

In my room downstairs I moved my armchair to the garden window, to watch out for what little could be espied in the deepening shadows. They seemed alive with expectant and secretive whispers. Above, softly touching the tops of the trees, a pink-flushed twilight still hovered, and the tepid breath of love softened the air. Soon Lucrèce would come and fly into Papa's arms. He would hold her to him, and in that moment there would be not the smallest place for me, not even in the remotest corner of his being. Once more I was deserted. A heart-breaking sense of unending loneliness swept over me.

A whisper of music. Upstairs Papa was playing the lute, and the chords sent vibrations of sweetness through the walls. But they were meant, not for me, but for the woman who still delayed her coming, though a tiny edge of the summer moon and a few first stars announced the fall of the night. Then Papa's dear voice mingled with the tremulous lute chords. I knew every tone, every word.

"Spring is Lovers' Paradise . . ."

There was almost nothing in the world—not even a faint accidental resemblance in another man's features, no article, no piece of furniture, no word, no tune—that, if it had even the remotest relevancy to Charles, would not conjure him and our past to my mind. The spring song now played by Papa upstairs struck a powerful chord in my memory, and out of the misty blackness of my lonely room arose that unforgetable afternoon in the Luxembourg. I relived that afternoon with all its colorful brightness: the pink-white chestnut blossoms in an ocean of sunlit green, the glittering stream of flaneurs, the beggar, the crimson robe of the Cardinal, and my dear dark stranger.

Quickly I went and fetched my own lute, sat down again, and, keeping my eyes watchfully on the garden all the while, joined Papa, singing in an almost inaudible pianissimo, first in French and then, as I had done for Richelieu, in Latin:

"Jam nix glaciesque liquescit . . ." Suddenly I could see, with each detail clear in my mind, my

dark young stranger emerge from the crowd, first throw me a kiss, and then bow forward in the pose of the Italian foil fencer, lightning flashing out of his eyes; and I knew now, as I had known then, that that had been the great, divine moment of my life—that moment that had made me his captive forever.

Moved to ecstasy, I looked up. A large bright star twinkled over the treetops, and an unaccountable feeling came over me that at that very moment, in a far-off exotic land among palms or on the shore of a blue sea, my lover was looking up to the same star and pouring out to it what he had once called out to me, over there in the bed, out of his sleep, out of the depth of his soul: "Try as I may . . . I cannot escape you . . . I love you, Ninon. . . Oh, how I do love you!" I could hear the voice as it had sounded, every inflection of it, and a mysterious prompting of my heart told me that, far off as he might be, driven by his yearning and drawn by mine, somehow, somewhere, he would find me again, and we should recapture the whole universe of our love, this love that enveloped everything, soul, body, and mind— this love of once in a thousand years.

A strange and strangely solid assurance, supplanting the misery of my loneliness, brought a deep and beautiful inner quietude to me, and I was jealous no longer when I heard the back door in the garden wall screech open and close again, then hasty steps hurry across the garden towards the outer staircase, which I could not see from my position. In a moment now Papa should be happy. I leaned back again to abandon myself to my reverie.

A loud, dull sound, coming from above, shattered

the stillness of the night. I tried to laugh at the sharp pang of fright that went through me. It had been like the dropping of a body to the floor. I had heard the sound of a body dropping to the floor in that same upper chamber, and it came back to me now, but more as a premonition of catastrophe than as a memory of Maman on the night when she had broken down before the cross—the fall from which she had never been able to rise again.

Madeleine came rushing in, pale, trembling, wide-eyed. ''Someone is in the house!'' she cried.

''Of course there is.'' I was trying to calm both her and myself. ''But we are not supposed to know. You must understand that Papa has a visitor—a lady. So be still and discreet and go to bed quietly.''

But the next moment we heard what sounded like a shoving and overturning of chairs above. Madeleine uttered a wild scream. Other sounds followed, some of them hollow and some a sharp clatter. They seemed to start at one end of the upper room and then shift to the other—a rolling sound mingled with a frantic pounding.

''Come, Madeleine,'' I called out, and with the good woman panting behind me I flew up the stairs. In the upper hall Perrot was peeping out from the door of his cubicle. ''What's going on here?'' I asked him breathlessly.

''The lady is here,'' Perrot said, ''in Monsieur's room.''

''Are you sure? Did you see her?''

''Yes. She had a long, wide mantle, a white veil, and a mask.''

I felt like laughing off my fears, but the silence in

Papa's room after all those wild noises kept me terrified. I knocked, and when there was no answer I pressed the handle cautiously.

The unlocked door opened, and I looked in. The bed was untouched as I had arranged it. When I examined the floor beside it I started back; then I rushed in. Almost on the spot where I had found my mother prone, Papa lay unconscious. No one else was in the room.

Breathless from shock, I knelt by Papa. His face was unrecognizable: it was covered with an adhesive mass of something that I tried quickly to remove. But it took my desperately trembling fingers long minutes to tear off the glutinous stuff from his nose and then from his mouth. When I had done that he uttered a wheezing sound, followed by incoherent whimpers. With the help of Madeleine and Perrot I removed and washed off the last remains of the sticky mask, and by that time he was breathing regularly. His face, blue, with swollen eyelids, and cruelly disfigured by the pain of strangulation, began to relax. His bloodshot eyes had been filled with agony and horror and rolled upwards so that only the whites showed; but now they closed for a moment and then opened a small slit, through which he peered at me in happy recognition. His breath, which he was drawing in through a wide-open mouth, was still panting. But he was alive!

Madeleine, with another terrified scream, pointed to a trickle of blood on Papa's doublet. The small piece of white metal that fastened his lace collar to his breast was surrounded by a red blotch. Madeleine was about to seize what could only be the handle of a small dagger, but I restrained her. "Don't touch it!" I cried, and ordered Perrot to run quickly to Doctor Rochetin, a surgeon in the near-by Rue de la Contrescarpe.

Papa improved astonishingly fast. Presently he lifted his arm, and his hand sought mine. His hand was moist and pitifully tremulous, but it clung to mine; and with my help he sat up and then even got to his feet. I supported him to his armchair, into which he slumped as if after a fearful exertion.

I was kneeling before him, and my terrified eyes were searching his face. "Does it hurt, Papa?" I asked, pointing to the white metal and the blood. He seemed completely surprised, as if he had not even known that he had been stabbed. He nodded his approval of my not having removed the weapon and of my decision to send for Doctor Rochetin.

The surgeon came promptly. He was an elderly man, lean and withered, but very brisk in gesture and speech. Without preliminaries he opened the doublet with a single sharp slash of his knife and with one quick motion jerked out the weapon. Its blade proved to be so thin and so short that it hardly deserved the name of dagger. The wound was insignificant—a mere puncture with blood trickling from it in tiny drops. I watched, not daring to ask him for his verdict. Papa had got hold of the dagger, and, though his hands were still trembling, he surveyed it carefully. The surgeon examined, washed, painstakingly bandaging the wound. "Nothing serious has happened to Monsieur," he decided at last, "for the heart is not touched, neither are the lungs. The wound will heal in a few hours, and you will be absolutely all right."

Papa refused to be put to bed. When the surgeon had gone and we had Madeleine and Perrot off to bed, Papa had so far recovered that he was able to speak, though but slowly and weakly. While I knelt at his feet, my cheek against his knee, he told me what had happened. At the instant of his opening the door and letting in the heavily veiled and masked person, something had been thrown at his face that deprived him of breath and sight. Then he had felt a thrust against his chest and had fallen. Struggling frantically to rid his face of the gluey mask, he had finally managed to open a tiny slit near his mouth. Without that he would have been strangled to death at once. But then he had lost consciousness, not to regain it until we freed him from the mask.

"It was a vile trick," he said. "I am positive that it was not Lucrèce: it was certainly a man, and I would wager that it was Riberolles. But however the thing may turn out, I want the whole affair to be considered over and done with. There must be no court proceedings, no reprisals. That is my express wish, and you must never decide to overrule it."

He was studying the dagger, which he had taken up again and contemplated with an odd, wise smile. He now bade me get up and seat myself facing him. "I think," Papa said, "that you will not be needing me a great deal longer."

"I shall always need you, Papa," I protested, in undefinined dread of what he had in his mind.

"Think of Scarron," he said, "—that pain-racked cripple who smiles and laughs and finds the world wonderful. Do you not remember what I told you?—that you should think of him whenever pain and sorrow come upon you? I did not forsee that your greatness of soul would be put to the test so soon, but —I fear that you must undergo it this very night— right away.''

What was he talking about? Had the surgeon not assured us just now that there was no danger? Was Papa's mind perhaps dazed by the shock? But the knowing way in which he continued to regard the dagger and the reflectiveness with which he studied me showed that his mind was clear, and that the surgeon had not convinced him. ''Promise,'' he said, ''that what I am about to tell you shall be borne with a balanced mind, calmly, serenely, and with the philosophical temper that I expect from you in this hour.''

My heart was all misgivings. But I promised.

''These surgeons,'' he said, ''are good fellows, and they understand their craft very well. Rochetin's diagnosis was correct—but for one little detail that he has overlooked. Look at this knife, Ninon. It is, you see, thin and very sharp, and it looks innocuous enough. But here at the end of the blade—there is no tip. I know this kind of Italian dagger. The tip has broken off: it is still in me. And in the tip there is a poison—one that works slowly enough to give me, I trust, still a little time to enjoy with you.''

''Oh, no!'' I cried, starting out of my chair.

''What did you promise me just now?'' he reminded me. ''Anyway, what does it mean—Death? A natural and quite unimportant incident—a nothing in the course of human events. 'As long as we exist, Death is not here,' the ancients would say, 'and as soon as Death exists, *we* are not here.' Why be troubled, then?''

My heart contracted at his smile of encouragement, for through it I saw his face discoloring to an olive green and his eyes receding into deep purple sockets. Yet there was nothing to do but obey; and, with my lips at least, I answered his smile.

His eyes darted about the room as if to drink in for the last time all the beauty still left to him—the shape and color of the furniture, the hangings, the paintings, the flowers. Then his gaze returned to me, and he contemplated me nodding and smiling, as if he were the artist who has completed his work and found it good. ''I do not leave great riches behind me,'' he said; ''yet there will be enough, if you economize wisely, to let you lead, not a luxurious, but a fairly comfortable life; independently of everyone. You can remain true to your own nature and to the incomparable wisdom of Epicurus, in which I have had the happiness of nurturing you. The eggshell will break, but the wondrous bird will fly out—fly high, high over the swamplands of human stupidity, brutality, baseness.''

For a while he stared into space with a kind of prophetic fixity. Then he said: ''Now let us enjoy this last of our hours together. Hand me my lute.''

He held the instrument lovingly in his arm, stroking its rounded body with a caressing hand, touched the strings with enfeebled fingers, and at last began to play. The chords were weak and distorted, and into his voice came a hoarseness and a weakness. He seemed not to notice: he went on singing until, obviously exhausted, he stopped and held the lute out to me. "Now you take it," he whispered. "Please, play and sing."

I knew that I was blanching with horror and anguish. My hand rather clenched than held the instrument. Yet under the insistence of his wish, I somehow forced my face into a comedien's mask and my lips into a kind of smile. With numb, icy fingers I strummed the instrument and plucked a few chords. But how was I to bring myself to song? My throat was constricted; and I could not fetch forth a single note.

But he was looking at me so expectantly, with so unbearable a wistfulness, that—I had to. Even so, I should not have succeeded had not the Song of Spring, or rather Charles, come to my aid. I fixed my inner gaze on my invisible lost lover; and now I could feel him strangely near, as if my call had made him assume substance and shape.

I played and sang the song to its very end.

Papa nodded happily, but how feebly! His lips vouchsafed me rather a tortured grimace than a smile. Then his face seemed to shrink. He lifted his arm a little and gestured vaguely toward the table. I understood; I filled a cup with Spanish wine and held it to his lips. They took it in, but he could not swallow: it came back, spilling down his chin.

Then his head sagged back. Obviously in delirium and unable any longer to see me, he uttered a few incoherent words. I had to put my ear close to his lips to catch even a few of them: "Lucrèce? . . . I didn't really care. . . . I hoped . . . in her arms . . . But it was only you, Ninon, I loved. . . . Horrible, wasn't it? . . . But now you are safe. . . . The delights and the dreads—all done now. . . . It is better so.''

He had laid his heart's secret open. And at that, as if a last flame were leaping out of its ash, his face suddenly flushed; a kind of wild surge of triumph leaped up in his filming eyes, and he cried out in a rattling voice: ''You will have many of them, many—but not one will ever have you to himself. Not one, ma petite, my only beloved!''

The glow went out; the last vestige of color drained from his face. He collapsed in my arms. Sobbing, kissing him, whispering, ''Papa, dear, dear Papa'' and all the gentlest words I knew, I swore to him solemnly that I would keep my vow.

There was only one promise that I could not make him. I could not tell him that I should never belong to any one human being alone. For, more than ever in the agonizing finality of this moment, I knew that I belonged to Charles, and he to me, and that he was fated to return to me.

Poor Papa! There was still a ghost of the triumphant smile on his lips. But he would never have to worry about Charles any more.

PART FOUR

1

NO ONE, not even the most pedantic attorney or executor of testaments, could ever accuse me of not dutifully fulfilling the legacy that my father, by both his example and his last words, had left me. Day and night I was at my post, enjoying not only all the pleasures of the mind but also, and as unstintedly, those of love, perpetually the same and yet so delightfully various. But never, whether it were with Monsieur Coulon or the Chevalier de Raré or the Chevalier de Méré or the Maréchal d'Estrée or Alexandre d'Elbène—never would I, heedful of Rochefoucauld's advice, call any one of my lovers by his first name. Even the Chevalier de Gersey, with whom, ten years after my father's death, I fell in love, I called only *mon amour*, or, if I wanted to award him a special flattery, *mon petit cochon*.

Gersey bore a startling likeness to my first lover. Like Charles, this tall, narrow-hipped man with the hungry passion in his dark eyes had a strangeness in his composition—a something at once forceful and soft; and, like Charles, he combined with his enchanting manners and striking good looks the most irregular conduct in matters of gallantry. And I, fired by the remembrance of my first passion, was swept away on such a tide of ardor that in my rapture I quite forgot to insist on the use of those dainty precautionary devices that Madame de Senneterre had once recommended to me. In brief, I found myself pregnant.

Though I realized that, in obedience to some dark and devious instinct, I had wanted it to happen, the first realization came to me as a shock. But my heart forbade me to have recourse to abortion or to abortifacient medicines. "Yes, you shall give birth to our child," Gersey exclaimed joyously when I broke the news, "and I will marry you right away."

Marriage, however, was not to my taste. Mindful of Papa's denunciations of the abominable bondage that society had made of wedlock for women, and with no intention of renouncing the gratifications of my own way of life, I declined forthwith.

"You cannot allow our child to be called a bastard and to carry the mark of a liaison *pas respectable* for his whole life!" Gersey objected. But even that argument did not impress me. I wanted the child, but I would not marry Gersey. Had I loved him as I had my Charles, I might have accepted him despite Papa's warning. I could see that he deserved my love better than my first lover, for whereas Charles had been a criminal, Gersey, apart from his philandering, was a perfectly honest man. But what could I do? To me Gersey was not even *la moitié de mon Charles*, and with my passion already beginning to

330

wane, I did not feel like binding myself to him for the rest of my life.

After many an argument he gave in. When my time approached we traveled to Brittany, where he had his estate. There, we agreed, I should be delivered in secrecy; he would entrust the child to a convent; and later on—for both of us hoped that it would be a boy—Gersey would adopt him and bring him up as a cavalier. But, though I reserved the right to see my son, it was strictly understood between us that he was never to learn that his mother was I— an *amoureuse*.

"If he is a boy and looks like his father, then he will look like Charles," I mused as our heavy velvet-lined coach jolted along the roads. They were so bumpy that before we reached Gersey's estate one especially violent jolt precipitated the birth. I was overtaken by labor pains in the coach, and Gersey and his men carried me to a peasant's hut by the roadside. There, in the rough-hewn bed of the farmer's wife, I brought my child into the world.

My heart gave a leap, and I felt as if it must burst with bliss when I held the little screaming bundle of flesh in my arms and knew that it was a boy. Though his tiny dark red face was still shriveled, he seemed to me to look like Charles. Charles's image was, then, to be perpetuated from now on, not merely in my fancy, but in actual living flesh. My happiness was unbounded when Gersey agreed that the boy should be baptized "Charles." But when, a few days later, Gersey took my little Charles from me to carry him to the convent at Jocelin, I burst into wild sobbing in spite of our agreement. On our return trip to Paris it took Gersey a long time to soothe me. For reassurance he promised me that after a few months we would journey to Jocelin together to see my baby.

But that visit was never to be made. A few weeks after my return to Paris Gersey came to announce with a sorrowful mien that his footman, whom he had sent to Jocelin to inquire how little Charles was doing, had returned with the dreadful news that the boy had died.

I was crushed. I did not want to see Gersey any more; I did not want to see anyone. As I had often done in tribulation, I withdrew from the world to my old convent of the Ursulines. And I was persuaded that this time I should never leave it again. A painful burden of guilt was weighing me down. If I had married Gersey, there would have been no need to expose the child in my womb to the hardships of travel and thus to a premature birth. I had been egotistical and reckless and cruel. My little Charles's death had been a punishment from Heaven, and it had given me, I felt, a wound that would fester in me for the rest of my life.

But after a few weeks Life called me back; back to Paris, my house, my lovers and admirers and friends. What was the use of sighs and regrets? "Use then the moments still in view," I told myself. "They fly so swiftly, and so many rosebuds are still to be gathered!"

The first man to whom I abandoned myself after my return was Évremond, and we made up in a happy *liaison* for what we had missed in the past. And when the liaison came to an end we did not part. For Évremond's was a steadfast allegiance to me, and it was to last for the rest of our lives.

After Évremond came the turn of the handsome Pierre de Villard, whom all ladies adored. Villard-Orondate, they called him, after the charming hero in Madeleine de Scudéry's novel *Artamène ou le Grand Cyrus*. He was followed by the proud, swarthy, eagle-faced Louis de Bourbon, the future Prince de Condé. He was the victor of Rocroi, where he had shattered the legend of Spanish invincibility by crushing and exterminating the picked troups of the Cardinal Infanta. Inasmuch as he was devoid of any trait that could remind me of Charles, this masterful prince had a difficult task in conquering me—much more difficult, he said, than his military triumphs. He was succeeded by Henri, Marquis de Sevigné, whom, by reason of his wife's jealousy and his inner conflicts, I dismissed very early and replaced by Monsieur Charleval.

Thus, lover succeeded lover; and in the intervals I abandoned myself to the pleasures of music and of absorbing talk with my friends Évremond, Scarron, Rochefoucauld, and Molière, in whose Illustre Théâtre I would but rarely miss a performance. In my library I went on enriching my mind with all the quintessence of wisdom and poetry. But there were also my *noctes ambrosianae*—those extravagant nights on which hundreds of candles would be burning in my house, and dancing and flirtation would dazzle the young, exuberant hearts of my circle.

Even while Papa was alive and before Richelieu died, and long before my affair with Gersey, my epicurean maxims had swept Paris. I had grown bold and stepped forward as the defender of the right to put them into practice, not only for myself, but for all young women who either could not marry or abhorred marital bondage. In the Palais Rambouillet, in which affectation of speech had degenerated into ridiculous oddities and in which a coterie of aging and anemic habitués was still sticking to antiquated standards, including a conception of love that hypocritically called us women queens and goddesses but in fact treated us as inferior beings, I rose in rebellion against those *platoniciens de l'amour*. ''To the devil with all those senseless epigrams and wearisome rhymed adulations!'' was the challenge that I hurled into their dismayed faces. ''Away with all this nonsensical talk of the sublime! Leave it to the impotent. We young women want warmer and more substantial food. Love is not a skeleton or a ghost. It has cheeks, lips, arms; it has, last but not least, a torso. You men, you know it well enough! but while indulging yourselves in pleasures without restriction, you have hypocritically imposed upon us definitions of virtue that you have no intention of applying to yourselves. I defy this injustice. I demand equal rights for both sexes.''

Those were stormy sessions in the Palais Rambouillet. The day came when I brought about a final break by inviting all who applauded my sentiments to follow me to my house. That day saw the organization of a group of young women in my yellow salon. In contradistinction to the *précieuses* of the Rambouillet, we were known as the *précieuses galantes*. And we did not stop at the mere vocal demand for an equal right to the pleasures of love: we claimed independence of tyrannical fathers, tutors, and husbands and coequal authority in family financial affairs.

There were many who realized that ours was not merely an assertion of licentiousness, but also a first move toward a new freedom for women; that in some perhaps still distant future new social conceptions might evolve from it. And those who applauded us—among them poets, philosophers, and men of the world—were to be found not only in my salon and all over Paris, but even abroad. The young and learned Queen Christine of Sweden, who was said to know more than all the professors of the Sorbonne and all the members of the Académie together, maintained a correspondence with Scarron in which she praised me and my movement in extremely flattering words.

There were those who thought differently. They included women who, lacking charm or intelligence, were excluded from my circle; men jealous of their prerogatives, beneficiaries of the established order who feared a lessening of their authority in the family and in material matters. And we had one pre-eminently dangerous foe: the Compagnie du Très Saint Sacrement. This organization, though its ranks included many priests and bishops, was primarily an association of laymen founded to propagate the true Catholic faith and to engage in praiseworthy charitable work, but it had degenerated into a coterie of political profiteers striving for power. Under the pretext of converting Paris, the "Great Whore of Babylon, into the True Jerusalem, angelic, orthodox, heavenly, and immaculate," they conducted a persistent campaign against the promenades on the Place Royal, against *gorges ouvertes* or the feminine décolleté, against book and picture shops, public amusements, and above all the theater and its actors, to whom they denied even Christian burial. They had conspired so viciously against Molière that to escape persecution he had been forced to leave Paris, and he was now traveling in the provinces in his ox cart with his strolling troupe. And whenever anyone was put to death on the Place de Grève on more or less trumped-up convictions for blasphemy, it was whispered about that the condemned man or woman was the victim of the Compagnie's denunciation. Their most formidable weapon was mystery. They were a secret organization: no one knew the names of their members, the times and places of their meetings, or the details of their policies and activities. They were everywhere—in the churches, convents, cabarets, inns, on the Pont Neuf, in prisons as well as in high places; and nobody was safe from their anonymous eyes and ears. A silent terror of them hung like a gloomy cloud over Paris and over an ever increasing area of the country, and shuddering people would refer to them as the "Invisible Ones" or as the "Cabale of Devotees."

For a long time the Cabale did not dare attack me. They knew my power over many men influential at court, and they knew the devotion that even Gaston d'Orléans, brother of the late Louis XIII, showed me in public; and for some time they restricted themselves to a whispering campaign.

But then they found a willing tool in the person of an old adversary of mine—Madame de Gramont.

2

MADAME DE GRAMONT was that thin dry elderly lady
of the court who had looked at me with a jaundiced
eye on the day of my first tea party in the Louvre, and
who, later on, had had me summoned before Queen
Anne for my intercession on behalf of Yvonne on the
Place des Halles. Those, however, had not been the
sum of her denunciations of me before she joined
forces with the Cabale.

In 1644 this pinch-mouthed venomous scarecrow
had again summoned me before the Queen, to whom
she had made complaint about my adulterous liaison
with Monsieur Coulon, Member of Parlement.
"Deign to consider, Your Majesty," she had said
with an expression of low cunning in her ugly long-
nosed face, "how the innocent wife of this illustrious magistrate must suffer through this dubious
young woman's lack of morals and of common decency."

I had been summoned, not to the Louvre, but to
the lovely little Pavillon Henri IV in Saint Germain.
It was on a beautiful summer day, and I remember

clearly the trees and the hedges that surrounded the terrace and the broad view over the Seine valley—a view that included spacious woods and the massed blue and silver of Paris on the horizon. I was sitting on a low taboret before the Queen, and while Madame de Gramont was speaking I held my eyes dutifully lowered and studied the pattern of green and violet garlands on the Queen's white summer dress. Then, on the Queen's bidding, I defended myself by asserting that Madame Coulon was certainly not the person with whose jealousy Her Majesty should be bothered at all. "Monsieur Coulon complains of her," I said, "that she sleeps with anyone but with him, and that she can bear him no children—not even with the help of his friends." The Queen, herself involved in an amour at the time, was highly amused by my *plaidoyer*. She laughed heartily, and she was broad-minded enough to limit herself to a gentle warning not to jeopardize further the reputation of the young ladies of birth and that in future it would be better to disregard married men.

She was about to dismiss me when a little boy of five or six came running up. He looked droll in a blue silken dress that reached down to his feet and seemed likely to trip him as he ran. When he stopped and caught sight of me he looked at me with a puzzled expression in his enormous black eyes. Then, turning to the Queen, he said: "I don't know her, Mama. Who is she?"

"First tell the young lady who you are," the Queen directed her son. At first a little shy, but then plucking up his courage, the boy said in the tone and manner of a well-learned lesson: "I am Louis,

Dauphin of France, the future King Louis XIV, King of France and King of Ravanna.''

''Navarra,'' the Queen corrected.

''I am Louis, Dauphin of France . . . ,'' the boy recited again, and this time he said ''Navarra'' correctly and was about to start all over again when the Queen lifted her hand and said: ''That will do. And now show the young lady what a great general you are.''

At once the boy took up a little trumpet that hung from his neck and blew with puffed-up cheeks; whereupon boys came running from all sides, swinging small muskets in their little hands, and drew up into a military formation behind young Louis, who marched in front with strides as martial as his long dress permitted. Then he commanded: ''Halt!'' and called over to me: ''And now I shall take the fort!'' He pointed to a heap of sand in the corner. One of the boys pulled in a small wooden cannon on a string, and all the boys shouted ''Boom, bang! boom, bang!'' and then Louis, swinging a little wooden sword, commanded: ''Attack!'' and with all the boys running back with hot cheeks. ''Victory!'' he panted. ''Victory! I have taken the fort and have killed them all!''

His mother looked proud, but he didn't pay much attention to her. Instead he planted himself before me and cocked his head. ''You're a great general, Royal Highness,'' I told him.

''And you are very pretty,'' he said. ''And I should like to kiss you.''

A little confused, I looked at the Queen. But she seemed very pleased—obviously because her offspring seemed not to share the unnatural tastes of his Papa and preferred ladies. "Just go ahead," the Queen said. "I am sure the young lady won't mind." When I bent down to the boy to be kissed he lost all his shyness, jumped spiritedly up on to my lap, and threw his little arms around my neck; and there was not a spot on my face that was not dampened by his lips.

To the great annoyance of Madame de Gramont, I was dismissed graciously. The Queen even assured me that if I could only bring myself to follow the example of many ladies of rank and keep my affairs secret, she would not mind them; she would even be pleased to see me more often.

Some years later, after my tragic liaison with Gersey, in 1651 my so-called "chicken-bone affair" created a great stir in Paris. One night in Lent a priest happened to pass by my house. While he was looking angrily up at my open windows, from which music and laughter and the clinking of cups could be heard, some hard object was thrown through the window. It hit him in the face. When he stopped to pick it up he discovered that it was the bone of a chicken. Here was an outrage: Ninon, for a long time a thorn in the side of the Cabale, feasting—eating meat—in Lent! It was a fresh insult to the Church and her holy commandments. Without delay the priest denounced the heinous business to Père Olier, the leading man of the Compagnie. He, in turn, at once informed Madame de Gramont, who in the meantime had become president of the ladies' association of the *dévots*. At last, an occasion to strike me! Once more I was summoned before the Queen; and this time, really disturbed by the incident, she showed little friendliness.

"I will explain to Your Majesty," I said. "But it is impossible to do so in any other person's presence. If Your Majesty would graciously grant me the favor——"

Madame de Gramont, who had treated me *de haut en bas*, became lobster-red, though her cheeks were ordinarily ashen, and the Queen, too, seemed amazed at my boldness. But she motioned to Madame de Gramont to withdraw.

"On the Lenten night in question," I said, "I was on the point of going to bed, when a company of tipsy roisterers broke into my house, bringing with them a band of musicians and baskets of food and wine. And the leader of this merry company—the one who had the misfortune to throw his chicken bone out of my window—was, I am sorry to say, no other than Monsieur Gaston Duc d'Orléans, Your Majesty's illustrious brother-in-law."

Queen Anne blushed deeply, and after my solemn promise that I would go on keeping the secret she had Madame de Gramont called in. "Mademoiselle de Lenclos," the Queen said, "has become the victim of an evil calumny, and I am not only satisfied but very much pleased with her explanation." The complainant gave me a dutiful and obliging smile, but the corners of her bloodless lips twitched in annoyance, and a vindictive glitter was to be detected in her slate-cold eyes.

For full five years after this setback the Compagnie made no further attempt to cause me trouble.

Then, in the spring of 1656, old Père Luc sent for me to come to see him at once.

I had seen the old priest whenever I went to visit my mother's tomb in the church of Saint Jean-en-Grève, and I had always found him, in spite of his rheumatism, bearing his years rather well. But on this day he was sunk in his armchair, his good gray eyes were filmy, and wrinkles of anxiety had added themselves to the many furrows of his face framed in white locks. I sat facing him in the same small white-washed chamber in which in my childhood he had taught me the catechism. "Great trouble is brewing, my child," he said quaveringly. "A few hours ago two men came to see me. The one was Père Olier; the other, Monsieur Le Cointre, Procureur du Roi au Châtelet de Paris. They were examining me about details of your childhood and early youth—especially about any lapses and sins against our holy Church. They wanted, they said, to complete their files in order to bring forth a mass of accusation against you. A few more facts about your past, they declared, would enable them to prove conclusively that you were always a minion of Hell and ought to be destroyed. They will press charges against you not only for prostitution but also for heresy and blasphemy, because you publicly preached the religion of Epicurus and his heathenish beliefs, making your own sinful life an article of faith. They have sent spies into your house and have collected many of your utterances in sworn statements, as for instance your words: 'I am not godless, for God is present even in my amours.' And you know what such charges mean, don't you?"

Of course I knew. I knew that their accusations could bring about a sentence of one hundred lashes on the Place des Halles, or imprisonment, or even the tearing- or burning-out of my tongue. I might even be burned as a heretic. But I was not at all frightened. "Don't worry, dear Père," I said reassuringly, stroking his withered hand.

"I told them that they should leave you to fight your own struggle with Satan, and that if they were not hard on you, God would give you His bread in due time. And if they should call me as a witness, I said that I would definitely testify against them. They left me, incensed. But what do I care? I am ninety years old, my days on this earth are numbered anyhow, and before God's throne I can answer for my stand. For in spite of everything you are doing, I believe in you, my child, and am sure of your eternal salvation. Come, let me bless you." I felt his fingers quiver as they stroked my bowed head, and tears choked his voice when he blessed me in the name of Father, Son, and Holy Ghost. "You will see, nothing will happen," I encouraged the old man before I went. "Cardinal Mazarin is devoted to me and often comes to my salon. He will never permit such outrageous proceedings to pass."

I did not know then that Mazarin's visits to my salon were to hasten the disaster overhanging me. But the next morning my self-confidence was thoroughly shaken. Mademoiselle d'Escoublon, a maid-in-waiting to Queen Anne, came in headlong haste, saying that she must see me at once. This pretty flaxen-haired girl, with a charming upward tilt to her small nose and the most innocent blue eyes in the world—they never betrayed what an amorous little devil she was—had been a habituée of my circle, but now, under the watchful eyes of the elder court ladies, she didn't dare identify herself with us any longer.

"This very morning," she said, gasping with excitement, "the old witch Gramont introduced a whole deputation to the Queen, and when they came out, Gramont and the rest of them seemed very pleased. They whispered among themselves that you would be finished now for good. And when Mazzi came and was alone with the Queen I did a little eavesdropping. What I heard gave me cold shudders. Mazzi didn't want you to be molested, but you should have heard what a fit of temper she flew into. 'I know you love this easy woman,' she cried at him; 'I know that you are going to see her behind my back, that you did not come to supper the other night because you supped with her. You want to save her for yourself, while I am of no importance to you any longer.' And then she cried and sobbed and sobbed and cried. She knows she's becoming fat and her face flabby and that though she has stopped eating pâté de foie gras and tarts and drinking chocolate she's growing fatter and fatter. She is jealous of every lady at court. 'This insolent courtesan,' she cried, stamping her foot, 'is ruining me. Not only does she take away your love from me, but the people do not even cheer me any more when I drive in the streets of Paris. But when she drives through the city they are fired with excitement. That is an outrage, and I want her to be eliminated forever. I will have it so. And this is my order.

"But Mazzi was firm," Mademoiselle d'Escoublon went on. "He didn't give in. 'The proceedings that Olier suggests,' he said, 'would be a European scandal. The whole world is fond of her. And we cannot antagonize Queen Christine of Sweden, who applauds and admires her and her *précieuses galantes*. The queen is important to our foreign policy, and we must, at any price, woo her from the Spaniards and win her over. I therefore cannot countenance a business that would nullify the efforts I have made to that end.' " Then they had the Gramont called in, and when the witch passed by she squinted at me, suspected that I had been eavesdropping, and sent me to the other end of the Louvre. But when I saw Mazzi afterwards I could see from his sullen face that he had had to give in. That's why I came to warn you. Something terrible, I am sure, is brewing, and you ought to leave Paris at once."

But to that counsel I would not listen. And though I had forebodings of disaster, I was no coward. I resolved to face the issue.

3

THE ISSUE DID not keep me waiting overlong. The next morning—I was sprinkling my flower beds in the garden at the time—Madeleine came to tell me that two old ladies, dry and sharp as thistles, were in the salon and had ordered her to fetch me at once. I was in no doubt that one of those thistles must be the Gramont. In no great haste I finished my sprinkling; then I went up to my bedroom and changed into a lacy and especially provocative white morning gown. Downstairs, in my yellow salon, I found the two women, one of them Madame de Gramont, ironic and haughty, the other Madame Senecé, also a lady-in-waiting, stiff and impersonal. Neither answered my welcome; both remained sitting, silent and solemn as owls. The Gramont measured my silk morning gown with a scornful eye. At last she broke the uncomfortable silence by addressing me in an even more uncomfortable voice of authority: "We are here on an official mission, in the name of Her Majesty the Queen." Without further explanation she handed me a letter adorned with the Queen's

crown and in Queen Anne's awkward handwriting:
"Dear Madame la Maréchale: You are hereby directed to betake yourself together with Madame de Senecé to the house of Ninon de Lenclos and to deliver her without delay to the Maison de la Madeleine pour les jeunes filles repenties, where she is to be sequestered until, through severe discipline and spiritual exercises, she shall appear fit to enter a convent under severe vows and rules; the choice of which convent We graciously leave to the penitent. Anne."

For a moment I felt the blackness of defeat, and the room seemed to heave up and down. But then I pulled myself together. I was not afraid of the Madelonettes, as the Maison de la Madeleine was popularly called. The old scarecrow should not see me cringe and grovel. I kept my face placid, smiled, tilted my head, and said: "As for the convent the choice of which Her Majesty is so graciously leaving to me, I choose the convent of the Cordeliers"—a male order that had recently created quite a stir because of the dissolute conduct of some of its members. "As for the house of the penitent young girls, the Madelonettes, I am somewhat at a loss, for I am not a young girl nor do I repent anything." Madame de Gramont seemed unable to find any answer; her jaw was moving wordlessly. At last she said: "For this impertinence you will be called to account, and I will take care that you shall be beaten for it. Put on a decent dress if you can find one in your wardrobe, and we will go."

Acutely aware that there was nothing I could do to resist Madame de Gramont's orders, without a word

I went up and exchanged my sweeping silk morning gown for an old dark blue house dress. Except for two handkerchiefs, I was allowed to take nothing with me, neither lingerie nor soap nor cosmetics. "You have taken enough care of your meretricious body," Madame de Gramont said venomously. "It is your soul that you now have to cleanse and to perfume."

The carriage rattled down the quiet streets of the faubourg beside green lawns and spacious gardens in which the flower beds were brilliant with color. The morning, bright, brisk, and cool, was ushering in a day that would ordinarily have made me sing and dance with the joy of life. When we passed through the Rue Antoine my gaze took in nostalgically its usual picturesque commotion, which I might not see again for a long time if ever. But Madame de Gramont pulled down the curtain, and there remained nothing for me to look at but the hard faces of the two women.

Having passed the Rue des Fontaines, we alighted at the rear of the Temple. Between it and Saint Martin des Champs the building of the Madelonettes lowered dark gray as a prison. All its windows, except for four at the front, were provided with iron bars. The corridor that we entered was narrow, long, damp, and dark. "Show us to the Mère Supérieure," Madame de Gramont ordered the sister on duty, whose face was hidden under her large hood of gray serge. With my heart pounding in my throat, but smiling as if I considered the whole episode as a mere joke, I climbed the steep, dim stairway behind the others.

When we entered the office the Mother Superior, Mère Anne-Marie Boulain, clad in a worn gray and black habit, carefully mended, stood up behind her writing desk. Her big gray eyes shot a swift glance over our little group, and for an instant we looked at each other. She was, I realized, the Visitandine nun who long years ago had helped me and Évremond rescue Yvonne from the stake; and I wondered whether she had taken it amiss that I had cheated her out of a soul. But she gave no sign of recognition. When the Mère and my two escorts had seated themselves—I remained standing against the wall—Madame de Gramont produced a letter written by the Queen and another by Père Olier and explained the purpose of our visit. "But that is impossible, Madame la Maréchale," the Mère protested. "I cannot possibly receive the demoiselle. We are overcrowded, and we take in only street girls brought to us by the police."

"She is far worse than any street prostitute," Madame de Gramont said icily, "and it is Her Majesty's and Père Olier's wish that she be treated no better than the rest of your inmates. You are to beat the devil of sin out of her body with stick and whip and with iron rods. Make her perceive thus the word of the Lord, and have no false pity for this dangerous harlot. Père Olier will come personally from time to time to hear your report about your penitential measures and about her soul's progress."

The Mère sighed resignedly and bowed; and when the two old women had gone she said to me, as if she guessed what a turmoil was going on within me: "It will not be an easy task for either of us, but we are both under higher orders. Nevertheless, do not be afraid. If you fall into our routine—which in itself will be hard enough for you—we will not persecute you.'' Her austere face was as unmoving as a rock, but its uncommunicativeness seemed to me to be contradicted by her femininely rounded chin and by a spark of compassion that I detected in her eyes; and I took courage.

After she had entered my name on a sheet, she added that I could do work in the kitchen and in the sewing room. (''Knows lace-making and embroidery,'' she wrote on the sheet.) Then she ordered the sister on duty to take me in hand. ''There will be no penitential measures imposed upon her without my express order,'' she informed the sister.

The sister led me downstairs to the wardrobe, where I exchanged my dress for a gown of coarse gray serge. It was joined to a cowl of the same material, which she drew over my head. Then we went to the kitchen. I felt my lungs choked by the vapors and heat and by the stench from a big iron kettle. A few figures clad in the same gray serge dress with cowl stood around the kettle and ''cooked,'' which meant that they were throwing pieces of vegetables into the boiling water. Other gray shapes sat on the floor and did the cutting.

Feeling sick to my stomach, I pressed my handkerchief to my nose. ''Smells like a dog's urine, doesn't it?'' one of the shapes said with a laugh. Another chimed in: ''Why shouldn't it? It certainly *is* a dog's urine, and a foul dog's to boot.'' She spat into the kettle. They gave me a knife, that I might help with the cutting. I sat down on the floor with the others and took a cabbage from the heap before me. It was rotten and full of dirt, and when I drove the knife into it I could see white worms wriggle in the ill-smelling brown mass. With loathing I dropped the pieces to the floor; but the other girls laughed, picked them up, and threw them into the kettle. "Afraid of the worms?" they laughed. "They're all the meat we ever get in this house."

"You're pretty," my neighbor whispered to me. "When we go up to the dormitory, lie down near the door, and I'll come and lie with you. I'd like to make love with you. Remember, my name is Marie." She had a hoarse voice and an old and corroded face, and I shuddered. After a supper consisting of the ill-smelling cabbage pulp thrown upon a piece of black, damp bread and an earthen bowl of stagnant water, we left the refectory and were sent to the dormitory. On our way, while I was racking my brain for some way to escape Marie's love-making, I was summoned to the Mère. "I thought I could place you in a cell where you would be alone and could sleep on a cot," she said. "Unfortunately the cells are all occupied by sick girls, and I shan't have any available for you until tomorrow. But I do not want you to sleep in the dormitory. There is a habit of feminine vice among the girls, and I want to spare you from their importunities and from the danger of infection—for many of them suffer from the Spanish disease. Tonight you may sleep in the kitchen."

I thanked the Mère for her great kindness; and when I went down to the kitchen and let myself fall on the heap of old rugs that the good nuns had prepared for me in the corner, I fell readily asleep. In the middle of the night, however, I was awakened. Through the serge of my gown I felt a hand grasping my bosom. Then another hand was creeping up along my legs, and there was a touch of greasy fingers on my bare skin. "Be quiet, pretty one," a voice whispered hotly. "I know how much better than Marie." We struggled for a while, but the girl was strong, and I was hard put to it to defend myself. Then I heard Marie's voice mewing and spitting: "Get away! Let her alone. She is mine. It was I who made a rendezvous with her for tonight, didn't I, darling?"—"Rendezvous or no rendezvous," my attacker spat back, "it was I that found her here in the kitchen. And if you don't let her alone, I'll kick the last teeth out of your breadshop, you measly whore." And again a hand was on my breast. But fortunately the two women began to struggle like enraged cats. I escaped, darted up the stairs, and spent the rest of the night hidden behind a partition.

The day at the Madelonettes began at four o'clock, when we penitents were marched in line to the chapel in the courtyard. This courtyard smelled evilly from the cesspool in the corner, but from over the wall we got at least a few whiffs of fresh air and a hint of the fragrance of trees. After the services there was breakfast, consisting of a soup made from the leftovers of the previous day's supper and the same damp black bread. The rest of the day until evening we spent in the sewing room, where we made shirts that the nuns sold; they were the main source of the institute's income. The supervising sisters therefore took great care to keep the girls' whole attention on their work. No conversation was permitted, and if a girl grew tired or rebellious and soft words failed, she was brought to terms by threats of stopping her food, or of penitential exercises or whipping, or of handing her back to the police, or—a threat apparently the most formidable of all—of turning her over to the Salpêtrière, the hospital for incurables. The heat in the low and overcrowded sewing room was intolerable, and there was no drinking water from morning to night; for the institute had no well, and water was delivered in a barrel but once a day and had to be saved for the cooking and for supper. But much worse than these hardships, worse than even the dreary monotony, were the fleas. They were omnipresent, and they pricked me with little stings of fire all over my body. There was no escape from them.

I shared all these afflictions with the girls with an even mind, marveling that they did not begrudge me the great privileges with which I was favored. I was exempt from the penitential exercises, such as prayers while kneeling on sharp gravel, and from disciplinary measures, which chiefly consisted of solitary confinement in a darkened cell and of beating. (The beating was performed, not by the nuns, but by a strong woman hired for the purpose.) The only detail the girls resented was my separate cell, which precluded their making me a companion to their nightly orgies. But they stopped teasing me about my aloofness when one of them discovered that I was not Anne Number Twelve (for I was registered under my baptismal name at the Madelonettes), but Ninon; and soon I was their

"Sainte Ninon," come to them to make an end of their sufferings. "I am just as unsaintly as you are, girls," I protested. But it was of little use. "Perhaps according to the catechism of the fine people you are not a saint to them, but to us you are." And it required a great effort to persuade them not to kneel before me and ask for my blessing in the very presence of the nuns. Their doing that might well have involved all of us in prosecution for blasphemy.

In the course of some weeks I acquired another privilege. When I tried to bring a touch of cheerfulness into the monotony of the working day by singing little songs or telling funny stories, the supervising nuns protested; but when they saw that the girls worked better under my method they stopped objecting. One day the nuns gave me thread, and I was glad to discover that I had not forgotten the lace-making that I had learned from Maman. Not only did I produce fine laces myself, but I could teach the girls as well. The shirts with lace sold for higher prices, and the nuns used the extra profit for better food. We now had fresh vegetables and better bread and, on Sundays, even white bread.

Though the girls and the nuns were fond of me, I could not stop the apparent hopelessness of regaining my freedom from depressing my spirit. One day after some three months—it was a gloomy day of low-hanging clouds and a melancholy rain that looked as if it never would end—I was called to the Mère. Her kind eyes were aglow as she told me: "I have wonderful news for you. Père Olier has just come to see me. He tells me that he is much impressed by the favorable reports I have sent him

355

about you. Not only does he praise my efforts on behalf of your soul, but he also permitted me to release you; and if you are reasonable you can go home at once." I could hardly believe my ears. Suddenly the drab room was filled with light, and the raindrops beating on the window-panes were a thousand little hearts beating with joy.

Then the Mère said, handing me a paper: "All you have to do is sign this." I took the paper. What it said was: "I have become convinced that my former views about the rights and duties of women were in contravention of divine ordinances and of the fundamental principles of law, morals, and public order. I, Anne de Lenclos, therefore solemnly pledge myself to renounce the wicked doctrines of the so-called *précieuses galantes* and to lead henceforth a life of modesty, decorum, and Christian virtue. So help me God."

The paper dropped from my hand on to the Mère's desk. "I can never sign this," I said. She gave me an astounded look, and a flash of disappointment rose to her face; but neither her remonstrances nor her entreaties moved me. "Whatever happens to me," I said, "even if they beat me to death, I will never deny myself and my *précieuses galantes*." I defended my position by an emphatic statement about woman's characteristic predicament—the predicament of the single woman who, according to the Scriptures, ought to marry. But what if they cannot marry or do not want to? "Are they to suppress their nature and burn forever?" I demanded. "Are they to become sick or go mad? Or are they to become hypocrites and have lovers in secret?" If she could

356

tell me a solution better than mine and as honest, I
was ready to hear it. "But there is no other way than
ours, I am afraid," I concluded firmly.

We debated for hours. In the end the Mother
Superior, all her arguments having failed, released
me with a plea that I should think the matter over;
and she would pray to God to enlighten me.

Alone in my cell, I was happy not to have suc-
cumbed to Olier's monstrous blackmail—which, on
second thought, seemed a good omen. Certainly my
friends were fighting for my freedom, and Olier
must have been hard pressed to have tried to snatch a
last-minute victory and save his dignity by so miserable a subterfuge.

The next day proved that my growing hope in my
friends was well founded. I was called to the Mère
again, and again she tried to convince me. While we
debated, noises strange to our quiet environs broke
out in the street; and when we looked out we could
see a swarm of cavaliers, among whom I recognized
many of my friends and admirers, all looking up at
our windows. There were outcries of "Where is
Ninon? Let us see her!"

Upon the Mother Superior's request I kept away
from the window. But it was evident that my
cavaliers were resolved on action. Many of them
climbed the roofs of near-by houses. We could see
them measuring the height of our walls. As the
crowd increased, the Mère became so alarmed that
she sent a nun for a patrol of city archers to protect
her institute from the attack that seemed to impend.
The buzzing and shouting in the street kept mounting, and even after I had left the Mère's office I could

hear from the sewing room, though it was situated at the rear, the crashing of stones and the clatter of weapons. The girls grew restless, and all of them agreed that something must be afoot that would bring me freedom. The poor creatures were not thinking of themselves: they only thought it marvelous that I, who had brought them a little solace and a few songs and some white bread, should return to the world.

When night fell I was called to the Mère again, and when I entered her office I could see that it was flooded with a reddish light that arose from the street, together with a tumult of voices. The windowpanes were smashed. Stones lay on the floor. In the corner a group of nuns, huddled together like frightened hens, knelt in prayer. The Mère came forward to meet me. Blood stained her hood. "*Mon Dieu*, what has happened to you?" I exclaimed. "Don't worry about me," the Mère quavered. "But please go to the window and show yourself. I've promised them that they shall see you."

I stepped to the window. The Rue des Fontaines was jammed. In the light of torches and straw fires I could see hundreds of faces known and unknown, lovers and friends; Scarron swinging his crutch towards the window; in front of the rest, Boisrobert the ex-secretary of Richelieu, grown bulky and powerful, now a famous author and just as famous a drinker. With balks of timber he was pounding at the gate, spitting out oaths and vituperations at the nuns. And behind him and my cavaliers there were those anonymous, coarse, rugged, bull-necked figures whom I had encountered before the city gates on that far-off night when I had freed Yvonne from the whipping stake, and who had then vowed that they would never forget me. Here they were, with my lovers and my friends, to help me to freedom.

"We don't want *you*, Sister—we want Ninon!" someone roared up at me, and brandished his fist.

I snatched off my hood. The tumult stopped; and when it broke out anew it was a chorus of "Vive Ninon!" "Vive notre Ninon!" It was dominated by Boisrobert's stentorian shout: "Come down, Ninon! come down. We'll take you home. They will let you go, or we will make this den a heap of ruins."

I signaled that I wanted to speak. Silence fell. "Thank you, my friends," I called down, gesturing and waving to all sides. "Thank you, thank you! I am sorry, but I cannot go with you. It is not the fault of the sisters. They are kind and good to me. What can they do? They cannot release me. I am here by the order of Her Majesty the Queen and of Cardinal Mazarin."

Again the tumult broke loose. "The Spanish whore!" "À bas the Queen!" "And à bas Mazarin! À bas the foreigner!" Fists and clubs were lifted. Eyes flashed wildly, and the clamor rose again to a deafening roar. I could see two men bringing up a heavy iron bar. "Ram the gate!" the crowd cried. "Batter it down."

Suddenly there was the sound of bugles, with the clatter of hooves at a sharp trot. "Cavalry!" someone cried. "Mazarin's men!" And the next moment the fury of the multitude was concentrated on the horsemen debouching from the entrance of the Rue des Fontaines. The officer in charge had his sword drawn; his men were flourishing lances. A stone was flung against the *peloton*, then a hail of stones. One of the troop, hit by a stone, swayed in his saddle. His horse went wild, reared, turned, and ran away, and the other horses followed. Only the officer stood his ground and forged ahead through the dense crowd.

Though stones were still hailing down on the officers, he kept his head. He had the presence of mind to sheathe his sword, stand up in his stirrups, and wave his plumed hat gallantly toward me. I recognized him—Capitaine de Corbille, one of my martyrs—and waved back. At once the attitude of the crowd changed. Those nearest to Corbille began debating with him. When they had got his attention he called out: "Stop this riot, Messieurs, I beg you. I will go at once and report to His Excellency Cardinal Mazarin that you want Mademoiselle Ninon to be set free."

"Mazzi won't listen," someone cried. "He will send reinforcements—a whole regiment."

"Not so," the officer asserted. "If there is no bloodshed or violence, I give you my word of honor he won't."

There was a murmur of doubt. But I called out: "Please, friends, let Capitaine de Corbille go to see His Excellency. I know that Cardinal Mazarin will respect the word of honor given by any of his officers."

My plea seemed to sway them—the more because I had spoken in a firm conviction of Corbille's success. For I knew that Mazarin could not risk a riot against him over a woman. He had an acute ear for phrases like "À bas the foreigner!" They still laughed at his bad French in the taverns, and the outcries of "Spanish whore!" would give him ground enough for defending my release to the Queen. For neither could she risk losing the pitiful remnant of her popularity. "Give the Capitaine a chance to settle things peacefully," I entreated them, "for your own sake—for my sake——"

"Well," shouted a mighty voice from among the dark anonymous crowd, "go ahead, Capitaine; we'll give you an hour. But if within an hour you fail to bring Ninon freedom, we know what to do!"

"One hour—no more," the crowd cried after Corbille as he wheeled his horse about. He waved back reassuringly at me as he rode away. Resolved not to let themselves be hoodwinked, the crowd got ready for a possible attack by the royal troops and for the storming of the building if Corbille's mission should fail. I tried with pleasantries and a show of cheerful calm to ease the tension that was mounting from minute to minute and threatening to explode in violence as the hour drew to a close. But someone cried: "The Captain is coming!" and as the news spread someone else shouted: "He brings good tidings."

Corbille came riding up. The crowd parted to let him advance and stop under my window. He lifted his hat, bowed to me, and then turned to face the crowd. He drew a paper from his doublet. "Messieurs," he announced, "this is my order. If you will disperse at once and go home in peace, His Excellency herewith solemnly promises you in the name of Her Majesty that Demoiselle de Lenclos shall leave the Madelonettes tomorrow morning. He will send his own private coach for her."

A howl of triumph. There were no outcries hostile to the Queen and Mazarin now. Neither was there a single "Vive la reine!" or a "Vive Mazarin!" There were only massed roars of "Vive Ninon!" and between them, like the rumble of an approaching thunderstorm, a choral murmur of "Vive la liberté." Extravagant congratulations were shouted up at my window. I stood overwhelmed by all this love, throwing kisses to all sides and with tears of happiness in my eyes. Free! Tomorrow I should be free!

In the early morning the promised carriage arrived. Not Corbille, but another officer who introduced himself as Capitaine de Coulange, came into the corridor where I was taking leave of nuns and girls, gallantly offered his arm, and helped me to my place in the coach. We drove off. The sun began to break through the mist and played on the tops of the trees, in which the birds were loud and happily busy. Life lay ahead.

"Aren't you taking a long way around?" I asked Coulange when suddenly the bulk of the Porte Saint Antoine emerged from the mist. "We turn to the right, to the Rue Saint Antoine."

But Coulange made no move to correct the coachman. The vehicle drove straight to the city gate and through it. "Where are we going?" I asked, now full of suspicion. He did not answer. The carriage sped on along the open road.

My suspicion turned into anxiety. "Why won't you answer me?" I insisted. "Have you not an order to take me home?"

"I am sorry; I have not. But I may be able to tell you now where we are going," he said, and took a letter out of his pocket. "To be opened one mile outside the city gate," he read; then he unfolded it and glanced at the paper.

"I am truly sorry;' he said," "but I have to take you to Lagny—to the convent of the Benedictine Sisters."

In the Benedictine convent I was put, not in the nunnery proper, but in a small summerhouse that the order had acquired a few years before, together with large gardens and orchards, above the river Marne. My house was surrounded by a high fence; moreover it lay within the high stone wall that enclosed the whole property. A sister especially charged with supervision of my person came several times a day either to bring my meals or to conduct me to the services. I had no personal contact with anybody but the nuns. I was completely cut off from the outside world.

But the master stroke whereby Mazarin, evidently under pressure from the furiously jealous Queen, had outmaneuvered me and the crowd was not to bring him a lasting success. For while I had been in the Madelonettes Christine of Sweden had accepted Queen Anne's and Mazarin's invitation and had made a triumphal entry into Paris. Asked my whereabouts, Mazarin had assured her that I, following an old habit, had retired to the country, leaving no address. Only after Queen Christine had been won over to Mazarin's foreign policy and was on her way back to Rome—which this daughter of the great

Protestant King Gustaf Adolf, after her solemn adoption of the Roman Catholic faith, had chosen as her residence—did she learn the truth from her French escort and *chevalier d'honneur*, the Maréchal d'Albret. His sister was Benedictine nun in Lagny, and he suspected that I was the anonymous guest in the convent of whom his sister had written him. At once Christine turned and rode northward to Lagny.

Had I known all this, my sense of oppression and hopelessness would not have been so heavy upon me as it was when the leaves began to fade and a dreary winter loomed before me in my solitude. I learned of it only on the day when my door suddenly opened and a young woman, high-booted, spurred, and wearing a man's scarlet doublet, a short gray petticoat over her breeches, and a cavalry cap on her blonde disheveled hair plunged in and called out: "I am Christine." Giving me no time to recover from my surprise or to welcome her, she caught me to her and kissed me savagely. "At last, my darling, at last!" she exclaimed. "What would Paris have been to me without my seeing and embracing you?" She sat down on my couch and drew me to her, and, sitting side by side, we began to talk as if we had been lifelong friends who had met after a year's separation. We talked for hours. There were so many things we had in common!—our disgust with marriage, our will to independence, our struggles against the world's conventional prejudices about women, our love of music and poetry, our interest in the philosophers from the ancients down to Descartes. What a brilliant mind she had! No wonder that the greatest spirits of our times admired the versatility and profundity of this woman. She fascinated me not only by the sparkle of her vibrant and forceful personality, but also by the unusual beauty of her large, penetrating gray-green eyes and of her broad face, which, not at all *à la mode,* had the beauty of a wild and proud exotic bird. At last she asked me how it had happened that I was in Lagny. When I had told her my story she jumped up and, slapping her boots with her whip and with her spurs jingling, paced the room, hot with indignation. "That is the most infamous trick I ever heard of," she exclaimed over and over. At last she stopped before me and said: "But we'll pay them back in their own coin. I'll abduct you from here. You shall go with me to Rome, and as my lady-in-waiting you will be protected against them."

I thanked Queen Christine for her generosity and apologized for not accepting her offer. I did not want to flee and give up my independence. She was broad-minded enough to understand; and at once she devised another solution. Asking for paper and quill, she sat down at my desk and wrote three letters. "Now, this will certainly do," she said when she had finished and had sent for sealing wax. "This one goes to Mazarin, and I have dropped him a hint that he will lose my friendship if he doesn't release you at once. And believe me, my dear, he will take great care not to run such a risk. This other letter goes to Queen Anne, to whom I recommend that she take you into her court, which through your presence will evoke the envy of every other court in Europe. And this third and last one goes to young King Louis, who seemed quite dazzled by my conversation with him, and to whom I have written that you, outside of his mother, are the only worth-while woman in Paris. I will make haste to have the letters sealed and sent immediately by courier." And after a final volley of resounding kisses she was out of my room.

Three days later the convent gate swung open for me. And what a surprise was awaiting me! The whole plaza in front of the convent and the small streets of the town were jammed full of my cavaliers and other people who welcomed me back into the world with cheers. Prince Condé had sent his carriage for me, and on my way to Paris I learned from Boisrobert, who sat by my side, that Queen Christine herself, on her way southward through Paris, had broken the news of my whereabouts, which had spread like wildfire. Hosts of Parisians made the pilgrimage to Lagny, and if my release had not been ordered so speedily, they would have stormed the convent as they had meant to storm the Madelonettes. Mazarin, Boisrobert said, had had a hard time persuading the Queen; but young King Louis, flattered that the most famous of all royalties had applied to him, and impressed by her praise of my person, had rebelled against his mother for the first time in his life and had categorically decreed that I be released and hounded no more.

Wherever we passed on our way, people came to meet us in *carrosses*, in litters, on horseback, afoot, and joined us; and what entered Paris was like the endless triumphal procession of a victorious queen. People lined the streets, throwing flowers at me, and there were a thousand outcries of "Vive notre Ninon!" mingled with that other outcry of "Vive la liberté!'' In both there was to be heard a new day approaching.

Olier, I was told later, watched my triumphal entry. ''These incredible Parisians!'' he was said to have murmured, angrily aware that, at least for the time being, he had to postpone further action against me. ''To them the pretty face of a young woman is always in the right.''

PART FIVE

1

MY FIRST WHITE HAIR! I was sitting at my *demoiselle*. It was the same dark polished walnut dressing table that I had used as a young girl. My attachment to the inherited furniture that I had moved into my new house in the Rue des Tournelles was far more sentimental than that to my casual lovers. (People now observed and followed the succession of my lovers with fascination, and knew it better than the students of the Sorbonne know the lineage of the kings and emperors of ancient Rome.)

Save for my dear canopied four-poster, which I now had here on the upper floor, every piece was arranged in its old accustomed way. Only a new modern clavecin and a number of chairs had been added to the yellow ground-floor salon for the ever-increasing crowd of my visitors. Otherwise all was just as my father had left it.

It had long delayed its coming, this my first white hair. How long, I couldn't say exactly. I have never been good at remembering numbers and dates. But it must have been in my fiftieth year. How delicate it looked! faint as a gossamer, but like a fine borderline between youth and age, a whisper of notification.

"I have been combing many more—sometimes even whole white strands—out of my own hair," said Françoise Scarron, fifteen years my junior, who was standing behind me and dressing my coiffure. Good Françoise. Ever since the death of Paul Scarron, her husband, almost ten years before, she had been living with me in my house. As the only one who knew how to cope with my still rebellious curls, she always dressed my hair; and she was especially insistent on it today, on the verge of the great event to which I, as well as all Paris, was looking forward. "I wish my skin looked as smooth and glossy and young as yours," she added sweetly.

I examined my face in what the *précieuses* would call a "councilor of graces" and found that it did actually reflect a young face without sag or hollow. The cheeks on which my lashes cast interesting shadows were rosy without any help of powder or rouge, and my dark eyes still sparkled, "ready to do more mischief to the world than any others," as my present lover, Faucon, had charged. But as I went on contemplating my face I had to cry out over another treacherous innovation. "How awkward of Nature!" I said. "Why doesn't she put wrinkles under the soles instead? Why does it have to be just under the eyes?"

"I can't see anything," said Françoise.

"Just look closer. Here—my first wrinkles."

"Oh, that's nothing. Just a little powder——"

"And tomorrow a little more powder, and a little rouge, and then every day a little more yet, and pretty soon here will be Ninon, the aged coquette."

"Do not make me laugh at you," protested Françoise, fastening a pink ribbon into my elaborate coiffure. "Your face is like a rose petal, and you still look as any charming girl would at sixteen."

"But like one who knows a little about *amour?*"

"Certainly, certainly, but not for very long past," Françoise rallied me; and then both of us laughed. For my observations had touched me but lightly and were soon forgotten, and my mind returned to the more important, the all-important, event of this afternoon. "Isn't it too bad," I said, pointing to the window. Outside the sky was of a hopelessly monotonous gray. Big snowflakes came hovering down slowly, steadily. "Never mind," said Françoise. "Paris is talking of nothing but the *grande résurrection du Tartuffe* and of Molière and of you. Snow or no snow, they'll all come."

I was not so sure. I knew my Parisians and their fear of wet dresses and shoes. It would be too bad if the weather should spoil the chances of an almost consummated victory. Ever since 1658, when Molière had returned from the provinces, he and I had drawn so close that except for Évremond I could call him my dearest friend. We had waged a dogged and desperate struggle against the Cabale of the devotees, hypocritical bigots who under the pretext of defending the church had been able to keep his unique masterpiece *Tartuffe* from the stage.

They had good reason to feel alarmed by this play, those members and friends of the Compagnie who, ever since Mazarin and French policy had lost their need for Christine, Queen of Sweden, had resumed their vicious attacks on me.

The true reason for the Compagnie's present

alarm, which had swept all Paris, was that, with some justice, they took me for the inspiring evil influence behind Molière's modern revolutionary plays—plays that blew like a fresh wind into the foul atmosphere of narrow entrenched prejudices, and especially the prejudices about love and the freedom of women. And now, in *Tartuffe*, they themselves stood exposed, those "traders in piety, those downright imposters." Almost any one of them felt that *Tartuffe* applied to him alone and delivered him over to public ridicule.

What activity, what a storm had they set in motion! After the first version had been played on the King's own stage in Versailles, and fingers had been pointed at many of them—"There goes a Tartuffe!"—they had done everything in their power to prevent a public performance. "Molière is a demon incarnate—the greatest unbeliever and heretic that ever existed, past or present," they had complained to the King; and under their pressure and that of the local clergy, whom they had taken in tow, Louis XIV had yielded and banned *Tartuffe* from all public stages. But Molière had not allowed himself to be beaten. I arranged many readings, and then performances in my house, and soon the fashion spread and *Tartuffe* was presented in the most distinguished palaces.

Then, after a three years' struggle, the King had dared challenge the bigots, whom he disliked not only because they were gossiping about his amours, but also because he hated their falsity. In the last minute before taking the field in Flanders he had granted a *placet* for public performances.

Molière and I had never lost faith in eventual victory. The first public presentation—and for a long time the last—in the Théâtre du Palais Royal had been a great success. But on the day following the first performance, when I had driven to the theater, what a disillusionment, and what a sight! All the posters had been torn down, and the entrances occupied by heavily armed city archers. They barred the entrance to both public and actors. Then came the explanation: No sooner had the King turned his back on Paris than the Président of the Parlement, in charge of the police of Paris, had issued another ban. So all-powerful was the Cabale of the devotees that the King had not dared renew his permission.

But now, two years later, to the utter consternation of the hypocrites, the King had once more granted his *placet*, and today the great event to which all the rest of Paris looked forward was to occur: *Tartuffe* would be played in the Théâtre du Palais Royal. The hour of the great *résurrection du Tartuffe* was at hand!

But I could not feel too confident. It was snowing harder now, and a strong wind whirled the snow masses high and brought on new clouds. And there were, besides, the machinations of the Théâtre de Bourgogne, the stage where the tragedies of Racine and others were presented. By an unwritten law, comedies had been played only after Lent; but now, in order to debar the Cabale from quick counteraction, Molière had made haste and was producing his comedy in the season for tragedies. What a threat to their cash box! The devotees of tragedy had started a campaign of ridicule against *Tartuffe*, and who knew what other tricks they and the Cabale might devise to stop the play at the very last moment?

"If things should go wrong this time," I told Françoise, "I shall go the the King myself. For the first time in my life I would be willing to bribe him with *amour*. I would offer him myself as a pay for holding his own against the bigots."

"Baron Corbille should know that," said Françoise, laughing. She well knew that the elderly courtier and confidant of Louis XIV had many times been the bearer of his master's messages, which, beneath a gracious proffer of greetings, hinted, by the terms in which they were offered, at His Majesty's desire to extend his grace beyond the limits of a mere king-and-subject relationship. But I had always asked the Baron to present only my respects to His Majesty.

While Françoise was still fussing about my coiffure old Madeleine, walking with a stick and with a woolen shawl wrapped around her, came in to bring me the day's mail. Now really old and plagued by rheumatism—only her eau de vie kept her still upright, she would say—she had no obligatory duties, but as a special privilege she insisted on surveying the household and the preparations and arrangements for suppers, on criticizing my lovers, and on bringing breakfast to my bed.

"Just put the letters down on the table, Madeleine," I said, for my mind was on *Tartuffe* and nothing else. But, blinking her eyes rapidly, she handed me one of the letters. She could not read, but by the coat of arms she recognized that it was from

Évremond. I could not resist: hastily I broke the heavy seal.

London, February 1, 1669

My charming, adorable Ninon,

My candles have gone out, and there is only the faint light of the small hours of the night. But I seem to have lost my usual sang-froid, *and I cannot resist the temptation to write to you about something that seems very important and exciting to me.*

Last evening my friend the fat-bellied but subtle literate Sir Crombie arranged a small but exquisite banquet at his house in my honor. He made an effort to give his dinner table a homelike French touch and thus to sweeten a few hours of my bitter exile.

Not only he and Milady Crombie, but also his guests, showed remarkable deference to me, which I at first ascribed to my pathetic role as a refugee rather than to the merits of my pen. But it was neither my satirical poem on Cardinal Mazarin—the cause of the order of my arrest and flight—nor scandalous stories about our Louis and his ministers that they wanted to hear. The only one who interested them, and because of whom I had become the center of eager attention, was you, my darling Ninon.

"Je suis dying for hearing much, very much," *began Lady Blake-Heydyn in the appealing English of the native French, "about your* merveilleuse *friend Ninon, Notre Dame des Amours." With enthusiasm, unanimity, and unusual volume for rigid*

Anglo-Saxons, the others seconded her request. And you would be astonished, my dear, at how much admired you are on this side of the Channel, too. They literally envy us on account of you, without whose delightful personality and sparkling salon Paris would have remained just as hopelessly boring as their London.

I tried as best I could to satisfy their curiosity. I had to report above all about the literary and artistic events in the royaume de Ninon—*about your intimate friendship with our great talents and geniuses, Lulli, Mignard, Racine, Corneille, La Fontaine, and Molière; above all, Molière. Before Charles II returned to the English throne many of the gentlemen present had lived in Paris for years and had often been guests in the Palais Rambouillet. They recalled when you with all your young followers seceded from the degenerating Palais Rambouillet and opposed the asexualized spirituality of the old* précieuses. *They remembered the vibrant vitality of the* précieuses galantes *of your yellow salon, joining forces with Molière and furnishing him not only the idea but many a character and many a line for his* Précieuses Ridicules. *They also know, and a good deal more than I knew myself, of the role that you played in the creation of his* Tartuffe. *Molière himself told Sir Crombie: "Whether Ninon or I conceived the idea of the play, I could no longer tell.*

"When I took the first draft to Ninon and read it to her she was not quite satisfied, and she told me true stories from her own experience—about Jouvenel, the philosophy teacher who tried to make love to her; then about an amorous abbé who tried the same

game under the pretext of saving her soul. And when she had repeated these stories, with all those gentlemen's lives—which split my sides with laughter—I went home and tore my manuscript to bits and wrote it all over again."

So much for Tartuffe. *The ladies were more excited to know about your amours—about the illustrious men who have been your lovers; about de La Rochefoucauld, the Grand Condé, the Duc d'Orléans, and the three Marquis de Sévigné, first the father-in-law, then the husband, and now the twenty-year-old son of our* marquise épistolaire, *who is said to have a good chance with you because your taste has always run to the smooth faces of unripe youth. Three Sévignés—three generations! And what about all those men whom you have discarded because you didn't feel that* frission particulier *which must always announce to you that a man is acceptable to your caprice? What about Richelieu, Mazarin, and—is it true?—also Louis XIV?*

I answered the ladies' questions generously. You should have seen them, my dear, their necks craned, their eyes bulging from under their powdered lids, their mouths open, and their bosoms swelling under their stiff brocade. (Not those of Milady Crombie, because she hasn't any.) And when I paused it was only to provoke a new fusillade of questions that culminated in such as these: "How is this possible? Almost fifty and looking just like a young girl! How in the world does she manage it? And then—this devastating success in love. What does she do, what kind of tricks does she know that we other women don't? Tell us, pray."

"It is as if you were asking me about the mystery of Life itself," I replied. *"But I will try to explain. Think of* aisance—*that relaxed, floating state of a happy mind that the invidious gods bestow on us mortals only at rare intervals. To her they gave* aisance *with a lavish hand. Where we plod, she dances—flies—soars. Where we scowl at ugliness, she smiles at oddity; where we smile, she laughs. Where we solemnly debate, she makes delightful small talk and solves the knottiest problems with a* mot. *Where we moan in the shackles of desperate love, she breaks down passion into passionettes— flighty follies and caprices. That is Ninon—all* légerté, aisance—*always cheerful and sparkling, like the bubbles in this champagne. Vive the genius of* aisance—*vive Ninon!"*

The others echoed my cheers and clinked glasses with me.

There was a silent interval, and in the corner of more than one eye I read a suspicion of envy or self-reproach because of something precious in life missed through lack of the courage to be oneself.

*My host broke the silence. "Your Ninon is a remarkable character—*la fille la plus épouvantable du siècle, *Paul Scarron called her, and he was right; but not merely because she is what she is, or because she has given to French gallantry and conversation that incomparable, scintillating touch that commands, and will continue to command, the envy and admiration of the whole world. She is a great woman."*

At that moment I could see you in my mind's eye as I always do when nostalgia overcomes me. I know nothing better to chase it away than by the memory of the last afternoon, now eight years ago, that I was privileged to spend in your yellow salon, the last refuge in Paris of independent spirits and graceful amours.

And of that afternoon I could not but think for the rest of the night, after I had returned to my lonely apartment. While I have been writing this letter to you I have seen myself standing with friends in a corner, all of us haunted by a foreboding of the catastrophe toward which Mazarin's and the young King's greed for power was driving our France, and wondering which of us would be the next victim of the Cardinal's political purges. And when you came in—fluttered in—in your dainty white flowered frock, and in a flash the whole room was radiant with the lambency of your laughter. It illuminated our faces and flooded our hearts and made us forget all our worries and fears. And that is what my thoughts of you are doing for me now—bringing solace and warmth to me, poor old refugee that I am.

I am, as always, keenly impatient to hear from you at the earliest possible moment. I shall not go to bed at all. The day breaks, and I mean to start right away and walk in the freshness of dawn to the post station and mail my letter. Au revoir, sweet darling of the gods!

In ever devoted friendship, your

Évremond.

P.S. Direct your answer, please, to my address in The Hague, to which I shall return within the next few days. Please write me all the news about Tartuffe.

2

THE WIND HAD turned the snow into rain and the streets into canals of mud, and the Rue Saint Honoré was so crowded that we could hardly advance. People hurrying to the Théâtre du Palais Royal were running and shouting, and it looked as if some serious disturbance might be afoot. Had the Cabale mobilized its ruffians at the last moment to prevent the performance?

Suddenly unable to proceed, the carriage stopped. I asked Faucon, whom I had permitted to see Françoise and me to the theatre, to alight and find out what was the matter. He was a handsome, well-mannered, useful young man, a giant who looked splendid in his cavalry uniform. Faucon was not very bright, but he was bright enough to hold his tongue in the presence of my intellectual friends. He belonged only to the category of my *oiseaux de Tournelles*, and the question of his intellect was not important. After the theater or after supper, when all the other guests were gone, we would have our specific pleasures.

Faucon was gone several minutes. "There is nothing wrong," he reported, "but there is such a mad rush on the theater that people are resorting to fisticuffs to get in. Any number have had their mantles torn or lost their hats. You can't possibly get to the doors. The pressure is so fierce there that women are fainting. But I met a friend who advised me to try a roundabout way through the palace."

We drove to the Place Royale. There were many other *carrosses*, and we, like their owners, were admitted to the Palais Royal. From there, by an interior passageway that Richelieu had originally built for himself, we finally reached the auditorium.

The vast parquet was filled, but people were still pressing in. There were buzzing and shouting, and even in the dimness—for the whole salle was lighted only by six *porte-flambeaux* with thick brown tallow candles—I made out faces flushed with excitement. The interior looked more like the scene of an impending battle than like a great theater.

Normally the parquet would have been occupied by solid burghers, but today there were nobles among them, and also poorly dressed people who didn't look as if they could easily spare the admittance fee. Had they actually made sacrifices to witness the great event, or had someone with ulterior motives, probably malicious, put them there to make trouble?

The two tiers of galleries were occupied to the last seat by nobles of all ranks. The six boxes that Molière had reserved were also filled with nobles, except the one for me, to which I had invited some of my friends. They were already waiting for me, and they stood up to surround and greet me. But they allowed Faucon to take off my fur coat. This was a privilege always granted to my current lover.

"Never since my *Cid* was played in this theater have I seen it so crowded," said my old friend Corneille. He was really old now, bald and furrowed, and the eyes that had sparkled with genius and pride were dimmed and lusterless. There was no envy in his remark, for he loved Molière, who as a comic playwright had never challenged his status as a master of French tragedy. He seemed rather to enjoy seeing the public attention turned away from his young competitor Racine, who with his *Bérénice* and then *Andromaque* had torn the palm of supremacy from his hands.

"Some day you will start writing again," I said, "and have crowded houses once more." Corneille uttered a sigh. "My genius went with my teeth," he said wrily, "and I couldn't keep pace with the new public taste, anyway." He said it in a slightly disparaging tone, for, though he admired Racine for his style and his poetry, he would not concede him dramatic power, and he was sharply critical of his flagrant deviations from historical fact.

Young de La Rochefoucauld was also in my box to kiss my hand and to apologize for his father. "The Duc," he said, "is in too great pain today to accept your gracious invitation, and so—if you don't mind—I am here in his stead." My poor de La Rochefoucauld! What a beautiful charmer he had been! How tremendously vital as warrior, statesman, lover! But since a musket ball had destroyed one of his eyes in the battle of the Faubourg Saint

Antoine he had become nearly blind, and, crippled by gout, he had wearily withdrawn from life and the world. Only rarely would he come to my house, where on request he would read to us some of his new *réflexions* and maxims, acknowledging our enthusiastic applause with the same "misanthropic smile" that emanates from his witty, worldly-wise lines. He had transferred his estate and his titles to his young son, and many times he had dropped veiled hints that he would like his son to succeed him in my favor as well. The son was only a weak copy of his great father, but with my taste running to "smooth faces and unripe fruit"—why not? Perhaps some day——I gave him one of those smiles that promise much and nothing. Faucon, jealous and moody, withdrew to the rear of the box.

There was still half an hour before the play was to start. The crowd, sitting or standing squeezed together, showed signs of impatience and unrest. The heat that rose from them made the air hot and sticky, but nobody moved from his hard-won place. In the box opposite mine, with her son, appeared our *marquise épistolaire*. She was dressed in violet, and under her heavily jeweled coiffure her highly intellectual face looked rather stern, with its long sharp nose and tight lips.

"Look at the Marquise," said Françoise, who was sitting by my side. "She's smiling at you." To my surprise, the sternness had actually gone from the Marquise de Sévigné's face, and she not only smiled but actually nodded in friendly fashion. High-minded indeed, to ignore my liaison with her late husband and to greet me in public! Perhaps there was in her smile a touch of grateful acknowledgment of the refinements of love-making that I had taught him, whereby his escapade with me had turned out to her advantage after all. And perhaps there was also in her smile the admission that she wouldn't mind if I instructed her twenty-year-old son, too.

The boy next to that of the Sévignés was occupied by the people of the Théâtre de Bourgogne, who were whispering among themselves with hardly concealed excitement. "They're exploding," said Corneille.

A tall woman between two men appeared in the Bourgogne box: La Champmeslé with her husband and Racine. Many heads turned in their direction, and not so much for Racine as for the woman who, voluptuous of figure in her wide-sleeved black dress, came forward and, with her nose high in the air, seated herself at the front of the box. Only her husband was a member of the Bourgogne troupe; she herself played in the Théâtre du Marais, where she had tumultuous successes in the role of Venus in a pastorale by Boyer. I myself couldn't see her as a Venus at all. With her dark complexion, her small mordant eyes, and her tall, powerful figure— especially by the side of the feminine-looking Racine, who was said to be her lover and to be paving her way to the Bourgogne stage—she seemed highly unfeminine to me. But the young men seemed to think otherwise:

> *"On se sent le sang tout melé*
> *Voyant la belle Champmeslé"*

—so ran the watchword of their infatuation.

Equally infatuated seemed the dark young stranger standing in the parquet a few paces from me; he gazed at her unmoving, with a breathless undeviating stare, touchingly and helplessly enamored.

The profile of this handsome stranger attracted me at once in an inexplicable way, and to my own surprise I felt myself keeping my eye on him for a long moment. Then came the signal for the rise of the curtain, and, disengaging my eyes resolutely from him, I turned my attention to the stage.

The play begins with the members of the dupe Orgon's family complaining about his having fallen prey to the sanctimonious impostor Tartuffe, who is about to usurp mastership over Orgon's household. While this first scene was being played the buzzing in the audience had still not died down, and only the pert remark of Dorine, the pretty young maid—played by Madeleine Béjart, Molière's charming and extremely coquettish young wife—sent ripples through the crowd. But the mere appearance of Orgon—Molière—who in the following scene returns from his trip, brought instant peals of laughter. What an inimitable grimace! Oh, my dear white-and-green-striped harlequin from the Place Dauphin! And what a comedy of gullible infatuation when he interrupted Dorine's report about his wife's health over and over again: "And Tartuffe?"—"And Tartuffe?"

The audience was roaring. Only the Bourgogne box made sour faces and shot envious glances. "They're exploding," Corneille said again. But I felt a little uneasy about the atmosphere that emanated from the enemy box, and it appeared that the actors felt the same way, as if conscious of a battle about to start at any minute. Only Molière, though I knew him inwardly to be highly nervous, played with his usual sovereign nonchalance. I continued to keep one eye on the enemy box. In the following scene Cléante, the dupe's brother-in-law, warns Orgon that Tartuffe is a dangerous hypocrite who is fooling him with a show of piety, and Orgon replies: "Your discourse, brother, savors of free-thinking." At this point I saw a hand raised behind the Champmeslé; and the next moment cries came from different parts of the theater: "Stop that! Stop the play! Licentiousness! Scandalous! Treason! Subversion! À bas Molière!"

But the two on the stage played on; and when Cléante raised his voice and, more to the audience than to Orgon, exclaimed: "I know what I am saying, and Heaven sees my heart. Would you make no distinction between hypocrisy and true devotion? between the mask and the face? the false coin and the real?" There was a tempest of applause, a veritable uproar. The brawlers were not only cried down, but also roughly handled, and those next the entrance were thrust or kicked out.

After this first crushing defeat of the *cabale*, silence returned, and everyone watched the progress of the play with concentrated attention. There were none of the usual flirtations or covert experimental pawings of feminine neighbors, such as I had observed on other occasions in the dimmed theater. Even the admirers of the Venus of the Marais did not spare a single look from the stage. But—yes, one of them did. My dark young stranger in the parquet stood staring at his Champmeslé. And though I was a little vexed that he paid not the slightest attention to the play, I felt once more mysteriously attracted to this narrow-shouldered youngster, without at all knowing why I experienced an uprush of warm protective pity and a wish that I could somehow help him.

But then the play, the greatest of all the comedies ever written, drew me promptly back under its spell. And how infinitely more it meant to me, who had seen it created, seen it growing and struggling for life, than to most of those who were seeing it! To me it was not only Tartuffe flirting with the maid and trying to make love to Orgon's wife: it was also the actual Abbé Pons pretending concern for my soul's salvation, touching my dress, stroking my collar, and on my protest stammering: "The stuff is so very rich, and the workmanship of this lace so marvelous!" What an experience to hear those lines immortalized in Molière's comedy!

When the curtain fell on the third act the whole place was in a tumult of delight and laughter, and there could no longer be a doubt that the battle was won. In the intermission many came to my box to congratulate me, as though I had written the masterpiece myself. There were La Fontaine and the painter Mignard and Lulli the royal supervisor of music and many others.

Looking down into the auditorium, I caught another glimpse of my young stranger, who, as if unaware of what was going on about him, still stood gazing up at the La Champmeslé. "Do you by any chance know who that young man is?" I asked

Faucon on a sudden impulse, pointing.—'That is the Chevalier de Villiers."—"Would you do me the favor of going down and inviting him to my box? Because I have something important to tell him." Faucon blushed with jealousy and stammered some such excuse as that he didn't know the Chevalier personally. He stayed where he was. "I know him," young Sévigné blurted out—he, with others, had come to my box—and at my request he went forthwith to fetch him. "Don't be silly," I whispered to Faucon. "It is not for my own sake that I had him called." But Faucon remained sulky and stayed in the background.

A few moments later the young chevalier was piloted into my box. He was so touchingly young, so appealing, so confused, and had so hungry a look of passion in his dark eyes! "Should you care to come to my salon for supper after the theater?" I asked him when the Marquis had introduced him. "There will be many guests who might interest you—Monsieur Molière and Monsieur Corneille, and perhaps also Monsieur Racine and—Madame Champmeslé." He blushed violently and his voice trembled when he accepted my invitation. Puzzled again by his mysterious attraction and by a renewed access of protective warmth, I searched his features—the dark complexion, the large, dark, dreamy eyes, the willful chin, the mixture of softness and power. And then it came to me in a flash. He bore a striking likeness to the Marquis de Gersey, a man who had been my lover longer than most. How long ago had it been? Twenty, yes, twenty years ago; twenty at least! Tender memories bound me to that lover who had given me a child. Had that child lived, he might now look as this young man did. What a fanciful stroke on the part of Nature! And suddenly the young man was dear to me. Bent on helping him, I resolved to go over myself and invite La Champmeslé to my house. But I did not have to go, for Racine appeared in the box.

"This is one of the most joyful days of my life," Racine said as he too congratulated me on Molière's success. Also, he embraced his "dear, dear friend and master," Corneille. Of course, he should be glad to celebrate the occasion with us, and to bring Madame Champmeslé; she could recite some parts of his newest play. And if I didn't mind, for the sake of decorum he would extend my invitation to her husband, too.

When the last two acts unmasked the impostor Tartuffe, who for all time to come would remain the archetype of hypocrites, and when he was finally arrested and led off to prison, the tremendous cheers proved that the audience had not only found pleasure in the high comedy, but had fully sensed its profoundly important meaning. Not until after the play was over did Molière lose his sovereign self control. It was with tears in his eyes that he thanked the audience, remembering, too, to pay his tribute to the enlightened King who had made possible this victory over the hypocrites.

On my way home I had Molière in my carriage, but not his wife Madeleine, who had so delightfully played the pert maid Dorine. She had a previous engagement. If adultery were a virtue, she could have been considered the most virtuous woman in

Paris. The actors La Grange and Du Croisy, with the Chevalier de Villiers and the friends whom I had invited, followed in other carriages. "Vive Molière!" clamored the crowd; it was making our drive through the streets a veritable triumphal procession, during which even "Vive Ninon!" was not unheard.

Another triumphal entry came back to my mind—that one of many years ago after indignant Parisians had freed me from the Madelonettes. As the occasion had been, so was this one the triumph of a new age over an old, of freedom over tyranny, of enlightened liberality over prejudice and intolerance. "Vive Molière!" "Vive Ninon!" "À bas the Cabale!" "À bas les Tartuffes!" I was basking in the sweetness of this triumph. I seemed to be at the summit of my life's happiness. For as yet I was without an inkling that a certain event of this afternoon in the theater—one that, measured against the grandeur of *Tartuffe's* resurrection, had seemed but insignificant—was to bring me a still greater happiness, and with it, alas, the most crushing of my defeats and the most cruel of my tragedies.

We were a small but cheerful company at my table. Molière in particular displayed an exuberant gaiety and drew tirelessly on his store of memories. "In the Collège de Clermont—— At the time when I lost all my money on my *Illustre Théâtre* and my father had to bail me out of the debtors' prison—— At the time when the damned Cabale drove me out of town—— Do you still remember, Ninon, the ox cart of Papa Béjart, with whose troupe I had to tour the provinces for more than thirteen years? And what would have become of me on my return to Paris if I had not found you again and made you my ally?'' I protested that he was overrating my help, but he insisted, with his clever brown eyes aglitter under his heavy brows, and what with his eyes and his voice I was outvoted and shouted down by him and all my guests.

Our gaiety was interrupted when at my request Madame Champmeslé recited from *Britannicus,* Racine's newest play. What she delivered was a long speech of Agrippina, the mother of Nero, in which she gloomily foretells the burning of Rome. ''Absurd and incredible and historically nonsensical,'' Corneille whispered in my ear; but Lulli said: ''There is superb music in her voice, and that music will make her our greatest actress.'' Though, with Molière, I preferred the ridiculous aspects of evil to its tragic ones, I too was carried away by the power of her voice, and the somber eloquence of her foreboding sent a shudder down my spine and darkened my mood. And when I looked at the Chevalier de Villiers I saw him shaken, paler than ever, and lost in a stony brooding. By dint of singing to the lute, first some sentimental songs and then some frivolous ones, I finally restored the general hilarity. Only poor Villiers still sat rigid, as if unable to recover from his dejection.

I was incensed at La Champmeslé. I had seated my young protégé by her; but she, concerned with nothing and nobody but her ''adorable Racine,'' paid no attention to him, and as often as poor Villiers would take heart and address her she would even snub him by affecting not to hear. It was outrageous. "Do not worry," I told Villiers, taking him aside when he and my other guests were going. "A woman's resistance is no historical fact. Come to see me tomorrow, and together we will devise some way to break it down."

When he and the others had gone I patted Faucon's cheek and told him: "It is a shame, my good lad, that I neglected you the whole time. But here is the hour for you and your special intelligence." And upstairs we went, to the promised land of my bedroom, where I recompensed him generously by allowing him to pluck a rich and colorful assortment of blossoms from the vast flower bed of my amorous experience, until, from overmuch stooping and plucking, his knees grew wobbly and he fell asleep.

In the morning, blinking through sleepy eyelids, I saw him fully dressed, sitting by my bedside and watching me.

"Adieu, *mon chéri*," I said, stretching a hand out to him. I knew at that moment that I did not want him any more. It was always like that. The *frisson* had come over me—how many days ago was it?—and now it was gone.

"It's adieu forever, isn't it?" he said.

"How do you know?" I wondered at his unusual acuity.

"Because you're in love. In love with the Chevalier de Villiers. I knew it at once—yesterday in the theater."

"Nonsense!" I protested, starting up.

"And this time it is not just play, as with me. This time it is serious. I watched you the whole evening."

He was at least partly right. But I couldn't tell him that my warm feeling for the young Villiers, my desire to help and protect him, was more maternal than anything else.

3

WHEN FAUCON had gone I hurried to take my ice-cold morning bath; then I went back to bed, and Madeleine brought me breakfast. I meant at first to get up and to take a long morning walk in the open, but Madeleine said: "Pray remain in bed a while, ma petite. In no circumstances would I let you go out in this weather." She drew the curtains open. The sky was as black as yesterday's, and a nasty wind was sweeping rain and snow across the blurred landscape. There was nothing for it but to obey and to bury in the pillows the weary inner darkness and emptiness that always came over me—though even my most intimate friends did not know it—when I had satiated my caprice and had done with a lover. It was a malaise that would not stop plaguing me until I was embarked on another affair.

Not until late forenoon did Madeleine come to wake me and announce that Molière was waiting for me downstairs in my salon. It was not my habit to receive in my bedchamber men whose friendship I cherished too much to prejudice it by such intimacy as I reserved to my *oiseaux*. But today my fit of melancholy had me in so firm a clutch that I could not feel like getting up, and I invited Molière to come up to see me.

He came storming in, still exuberant with his victory. "This morning brought me twenty invitations," he said breathlessly, "from all the great princes to play *Tartuffe* in their *hôtels*, and there is such excitement all over Paris that everybody wants to see it. You wouldn't believe it. The Rue Saint Honoré is already jammed with people standing in the rain to make sure of getting in this afternoon. And the King sent for me and had me breakfast with him. He overwhelmed me with congratulations and ordered me to share them with you. And he talked about you much more than usual—so much more that his message struck me as meaning more than just a gracious gesture."

"Won't you make your last line a little more clear to your audience?"

"He told me that you and he have met once before, and he wanted me to find out whether you still remember that meeting."

"Of course I remember it. And you can tell him that I remember with great pleasure the day when as a small boy he sat on my lap and embraced and kissed me."

The bafflement on Molière's face was no comic acting.

"I'll tell you the whole story if you like," I said, highly amused and feeling that the recital of that droll occurrence might cheer me a little. I recounted all its details as vividly as I could manage.

Molière was highly amused, but he declined to believe that that was the occasion to which the King had referred that morning. I granted that he was right and told him about an encounter of a much later time, though still many years ago. "One day I was driving in my carriage to the forest of Versailles; but when I had passed the village of Versailles I found the road impassable. This was when they were building the new royal castle, and the present channels and lakes were still ditches and holes. The road was crowded with carts carrying stones and sand and hundreds of trees that had been uprooted from here and there to embellish the new royal park. So, in order to reach the forest I had to take a roundabout way—a narrow and very uneven lane. And there, at a turn, I met a young man on horseback." I remembered him vividly as he looked then, with his slightly pockmarked but still handsome face—a broad face, with a thin moustache over full red lips. He was smiling at me and raising his large black hat—a hat with one simple red feather in it. He bowed, and that called my attention to the long, dark curls that hung down to his shoulders. I answered his smile; and I had a feeling that he had stopped his horse when my carriage had passed and was looking after me. I wondered about his shyness. Why had he not turned his horse and come after my carriage?

"Oh, I see," said Molière. "This was he—the King."

"Yes. But I didn't know it then, he was so simply dressed. I thought he was one of the architects; there were any number of them around."

"That meeting seems to haunt his memory very

agreeably, and there is no doubt that he wants another one. But from the way that he takes occasion over and over again to refer to 'our charming Ninon,' always very enthusiastically, I am obliged to conclude that there is much more to it than the mere wish for a fleeting encounter.''

''Don't frighten me, Molière.''

''You certainly know that the star of Madame de Montespan is waning. It is whispered all over Versailles that her days and her nights are numbered, and that the King is already on the lookout for another *maîtress en titre*. Intrigues are being spun and wild guesses made, for every lady's dream is to draw this good fortune. But I think that he is on no lookout at all. I think that he has decided already, and that his choice has fallen on you.''

''I cannot believe it, but I am glad to know. In any event I thank you kindly for the warning.''

''And what answer am I to take him about your remembering your encounter?''

''Just tell him about the day at Saint Germain and how he jumped on my lap and kissed me. That ought to amuse him.''

''And nothing else?''

''No, nothing else—only lay my humble respects at His Majesty's feet, inasmuch as I always send exactly that message by the Baron de Corbille. Imagine me becoming a slave to the whims of a man— and what other relation could there be between and a self-centered king? I had rather give up love-making altogether! If he does ask you about me, please tell him quite clearly how I feel.''

But Molière made so unhappy a face over being

charged with so embarrassing a misson that I spared him and told him to leave it to me. There was no doubt that the King would send the Baron de Corbille for a preliminary inquiry, and it would be to him that I should say a quite clear and definite No.

Not that I would take the situation too lightly, either. Throughout Molière's struggle Louis had been and still was a very consistent and reliable ally, even if a cautious one; and we meant him to remain so. It had been in his own interest, to be sure: by reason of his amorous propensity the King was naturally opposed to the Cabale and to its censure of his affairs. Nevertheless, I was myself deeply in debt to him. It had been on Louis' insistence that I had been released from my imprisonment in the Convent of Lagny and had been let alone from that time on. It would, then, be painful to say No to a man to whom I owed my freedom. But the mere thought of the smallest curtailment of my freedom of choice upset me so that I resolved to defend myself energetically and at whatever cost.

After Molière left me the weather became even gloomier and the sky as black as night. My depression returned. Moodily I pulled the bell rope for Madeleine. While helping me to dress she told me that Françoise had gone to the Carmelites on some important errand, and that the Chevalier de Villiers had come and was waiting for me. "I cannot help it," she said, "but he reminds me of someone." When I asked her if it were not of the Marquis de Gersey, at first she nodded; but then she mumbled, shaking her head: "I don't know—I don't know.

Perhaps it is of him—and perhaps it is of someone else. I can't place it. Sometimes I think I'm getting stupid and old.''

My yellow salon, with its gilded picture frames and chairs reflecting the fire in the hearth, was particularly cozy in contrast to the gloom outside. But for all that there was gloom enough present when I went down. The young chevalier, when I bade him welcome and seated him facing me near the chimney, sat brooding and preoccupied, with his head resting on his long-fingered hand. ''I thank you for what you are doing for me,'' he said; and there was a desperate undertone in the fresh young voice. ''Without the hope that your help gave me I should have despaired yesterday, and by now I might be—dead.'' His words shocked me, and my yearning over him grew. ''Very theatrical and impressive,'' I said. ''But that is no way to get what you want. What you are looking for, I can see, is simply an interesting adventure with an interesting lady. If you will proceed by my advice, I can almost guarantee you success. But do away with your tragic mien and with the ridiculous posture of a lover who insists on dying for love. It doesn't suit you.''

''I am a very melancholic person,'' he said, ''and very unhappy. And that is why I fell so madly in love with Madame Champmeslé. It is the tragedy in her voice that speaks to my soul and holds it captive. I experienced it when I saw her as Venus in the Marais. But how much more am I swayed by it since last night, when she recited Racine! The very essence of her soul is tragedy—which is likewise the very essence of my own existence.''

"But these are terrible things that I hear!" I said, assuming a light, bantering tone. "We can make no headway with our conspiracy if you won't let me get to the bottom of all this. What is this dire tragedy that weights you down so, my poor Chevalier?"

"This——I had rather not say."

"Confide in me," I coaxed him, putting as much tenderness into my voice as I could.

His resistance wavered. He uttered a moan. "My mother——" he said at last in a very low voice.

"What about her?" I insisted.

"She is dead."

"My poor, poor Chevalier," I said, putting a hand gently on his shoulder, "I understand your grief. But that is still no tragedy."

"It is," he said; and then, in an uncontrolled outburst:"——because it was I who killed her."

I gave a little shudder.

"She died when I was born." The gravity of his voice seemed to carry a heavy burden of guilt. "She gave me life in pain, and in return I gave her—death. And that is what is haunting me. Perhaps if I still had my faith, I could find peace of mind. I had it; I was devout and God-fearing. But I fell a prey to modern ideas. My faith is gone. It is as if I were hanging in the air, with no ground to stand on. And there is more. I became prey to a strange passion. I love my mother, but not with the spiritual affection with which I ought to hold her in my memory as something sacred—almost like the Holy Mother herself. Rather, I am on fire with a *physical* desire for her that I can never satisfy in this world. I don't know why, but deep inside me I have the feeling that to you, you

alone in this world, I can speak openly and confide
my innermost thoughts. I want her—my mother—
not only in her soul, but—think of it!—in her flesh as
well! I have a mad craving to touch her flesh, to kiss
her breasts, to bury my face in them—to bury my
face in the lap that bore me; to creep back into it and
lie there—in her womb—and nevermore to come
into this world.''

His words struck me as mad; as the expression of a
strangely warped spirit, which, if someone did not
intervene in time, must, I feared, sooner or later lead
him to suicide. And, moved as I was by his likeness
to Gersey and by the memory of my own dead child,
I decided that it must be I who should help him to free
his mind.

His father, I learned, a Chevalier de Villiers, was
a country gentleman who owned a moderate estate
near Cognac. His mother had been a very beautiful
girl with large light-blue eyes and dark hair, which
she wore—as I could see in the miniature that, with
his hand trembling, he showed me—in thick braided
tresses like a queen's crown. Before coming to Paris
he had not seen the world at all, for his father had
kept him within the lonely walls of their isolated
provincial manor. Great pains had been taken with
his instruction. His father's brother, abbot of the
near-by Jesuit convent, had sent the best teachers he
had to serve as his tutors. He himself had been
promised to a daughter of one of their neighbors, but
he didn't care much for her. A year ago, his father
had sent him to Paris to finish his studies at the
Sorbonne; for though the old man, bowed with grief
since his wife's death, was lonely without him, the

last and only scion of their family and sole heir to the manor, he would do anything in the world to make an accomplished and perfectly happy man of him. But how could he ever think of being happy? The only relief for him, he said, and the only way that he could overcome the morbid passion for his dead mother, would be for Madame Champmeslé to respond to his love. "She must be as unhappy as I am," he said, "and she must have a great and beautiful soul."

I didn't think so. Anyone with her *instinct du théâtre* had to be somewhat calculating and cold. But I didn't tell him that, lest it hurt him or make him lose his confidence in me. But I encouraged him: "With all the great qualities that Madame La Champmeslé undoubtedly has, you must not forget that she is no goddess, but a woman—a human being with human weaknesses and faults. If you want to conquer her, you must look for rifts in her armor. And I can tell you exactly what they are. She is an ardently ambitious artist, and, like every great artist, she wants recognition and praise. Write to her. But not about any of the sentiments of your heart, or your passion for her, but only about how you are carried away by the grandeur of her art. Write that you admire the power of her voice and all its nuances, and that you consider her the greatest *tragédienne* of the century, and that all your friends, among whom you are spreading her fame, think likewise, and that soon all Paris will be at her feet. It will be an exception to all my experience if she doesn't answer you with a few lines at the very least. But it won't stop at that, I predict.

"If you wish, come at any time and tell me about the progress of your siege. And when I next invite you and her together I shall see to it that there is an opportunity for you to talk with her alone and unwatched by others."

He took to coming every day. First he came with a draft of a letter to La Champmeslé (I had to throw it away and dictate him another). Then, exuberant with joy, he came with her answer—three short lines containing polite thanks for his appreciation, but he held it pressed to his heart in a glow of confidence. Then we would make plans about his next moves. He sent other letters and flowers and gifts, and new answers came to keep the flame of his adoration alive. I had the great satisfaction of seeing his melancholy ebbing away. There came color to his cheeks, vivacity to his gestures, and a sparkle of hope to his eyes. I was delighted by the progress of his education; it was to me almost as if I were bringing my own son up and steering him around dangers. I lost my own depression—and this time without even taking a new lover; wherefore all Paris took to wondering what had come over me.

The young Chevalier, who now became my daily guest—and from within the somber cocoon what a charming creature had developed under my guidance!—was not only my own pet, but also Madeleine's. "Do you know whom he looks like?" she told me one day. "I've got it after all: Monsieur Charles de Beaumont. Every time he comes I think it is that Monsieur Charles who has returned to my petite after so many years."

At first I would not believe her. But, observing him intently, I began little by little to respect her penetration. The Chevalier looked like the sweet scroundrel who thirty years before had conquered my maidenly heart in the Luxembourg Gardens, to conquer a few weeks later all the rest of me.

As to the likeness, I could only marvel at the strangeness of so much coincidence. The Chevalier looked like Gersey. And he also looked like Charles, my first lover. But there could be no connection between the two facts. There was, as I had found out by inquiring of Villiers, neither a Gersey nor a Beaumont among his ancestors. Charles Beaumont had disappeared in the Orient and had never returned, and the Marquis de Gersey was not known to Villiers even by name.

I never stopped puzzling, but I accepted with pleasure the astonishing set of facts, for I had begun to draw considerable delights from this likeness. Now, with the agonies of my first love far behind me, I could freely play with fond memories and, helped by the new Charles's unwitting presence, summon back those happy unhappy days of long ago.

What a pleasant play it was! It even set me to rummaging in my old boxes for keepsakes of that far-off time; and my search was richly rewarded. For not only did I find the round rosewood box that my first lover had given me, and a few of his letters, turned yellow and gray, but also Richelieu's parchment with the lovely old Song of Spring that I had forgotten in the course of the years. Trying it once more with my lute, I discovered what a precious jewel of medieval song it was; and I promised Lulli, whom I told about my discovery, to sing it at the *matinée musicale* that I was going to arrange in my house.

4

IT WAS NOT UNTIL that occasion that I could redeem my promise to Charles de Villiers to bring Madame Champmeslé to my house. It was notorious in Paris that she shunned any salon whose mistress commanded over-much masculine admiration. But with the help of Racine and the prospect of her reciting from his works before an illustrious and highly literate company, I succeeded; and when the day arrived it only remained to solve the problem of the promised undisturbed tête-à-tête.

My house and my garden were more crowded than ever on that unusually warm, almost summerlike March day. Not only my closest friends and my *oiseaux* had come, but also everybody who counted himself in my circle. Lulli, who had promised to play his newest compositions, was one of the first to arrive. Taking me aside, he said with his red-rimmed eyes blinking: "Today I shall play something that I have composed just for you—a message from heart to heart." He was the only one still unable to reconcile himself to the sharp distinction that I made between friends and lovers. He was too inordinately conceited to admit that his coarse face, bulbous nose, short squat body, and unappetizingly sweating hands disqualified him for the second category. But I was saved from the affliction of his attempted advances when Molière and Corneille joined us. Molière had to go early, for *Tartuffe* was still running in the Palais Royal and drawing a full house every day. "What a satisfaction to your genius," Corneille said, "and to your conscience and morals!"—"And to my cash box," Molière said, and laughed throatily. "So far I have made over two thousand livres."—"Two thousand livres!" exclaimed Corneille. "What a beautiful rhythm those words possess! I must tell Racine; he will be delighted." He chuckled, rubbing his hands.

In the meantime the invasion had started. Boileau came, and Fontenelle, Bussy-Rabutin, Charleval, La Bruyère, and many of the younger ladies and gentlemen of the Court; the young Sévigné, both Rochefoucaulds, and the warrior prince the Grand Condé, eagle-faced victor of Rocroi. Last year he had taken the Franche-Comté, but he was still saying that of all the conquests of his life he valued the most that of young Ninon twenty years before. Even in the time of my deepest humiliation he had never passed my carriage without stopping to alight from his own and gallantly kiss my hand in public.

There was also the blonde, blue-eyed *savante* Madame Sablière, with her original short haircut, wearing a sober dark red frock. A striking contrast to her was the always gay Duchesse de Bouillon with a whole train of her cavaliers and protégés, among them La Fontaine the eternal day-dreamer, whose genius for fable and tale was said to have been inspired by her. The Grand Condé congratulated her on her delightful pink lace dress, focusing his eyes on its most conspicous feature, an extremely short skirt. Her bright eyes were sparkling mischief when, with her impudent little nose tilted up at the giant, she said: "I was tired of having you men always trying to lift my skirts, so you see I have spared you the trouble." She was renowned for her pretty little feet and the graceful shapeliness of her legs.

The last to arrive were Racine and La Champmeslè. With her big breasts, columnar neck, and sharp cheekbones she seemed to me less attractive than ever, but that impression did not alter my determination to bring her and Charles de Villiers together.

"As our great composer Lulli has said," I addressed my guests when they were seated, "Madame Champmeslé's voice adds to the spoken word the same impression and the same moods that are ordinarily conveyed only by music. Her voice is itself music, and I have asked her to open this *matinée musicale* with her recitations from Maître Racine." I could not have hit on anything better calculated to persuade her of my good will than this flattering introduction; and I completed the effect by leading the prolonged applause that followed her recital, which Lulli exuberantly summed up as "a great chant."

Then Lulli took his place at my clavecin and played pieces he had composed to Molière's comedies, an *Air Tendre*, an *Amour Malade*, a few minuets, and a sarabande. "But the piece that I composed for you, my dear, will come later." His wet, fleshy lips sprayed the words into my ear during an intermission in which sorbets, sweetmeats, and fruit were served to my guests. "Later—later on—when the shadows are sweeping across the lawn and the trees whisper dreamily."

When the program came to an end Lulli reminded me of my promise to sing to the lute my rediscovered Song of Spring. But there was no time now to comply. Many of my guests were on the point of departure; others were on the way down to the garden, where supper would be served for my most intimate circle. It was high time now to approach La Champmeslé—take her aside and make my plea for Villiers. "He's so ardent an admirer of your art and your person," I coaxed her, "and bruits your fame so zealously to the whole youth of Paris! You would be doing yourself a service by granting him a short tête-à-tête." Convinced as she was of my good intentions and not averse to a little private adoration, she assented. After a few maneuvers—one of which was to engage Racine with Corneille in a heated discussion about the dramatic unities—I piloted her into the bower at the far end of my garden. "Now go in," I said to Charles, who had followed us at some distance and stood outside, expectant but still very shy. I felt a little pang of nostalgia when I saw him disappear into the bower, for I had no doubt that from now on the Champmeslé would keep him in the train of her intimate devotees, and that my maternal protection and my re-creation of the past in fantasy had come to an end.

Walking back to my guests, I encountered my old Rochefoucauld. He stood alone by a clump of evergreen shrubbery, warming his bony, gouty, blue-veined hand on the shoulder of a sunlit white marble nymph. Our eyes met, and we both smiled in reminiscent understanding. The park of Loches. The marble faun. My hand stroking its back. And then——

"I would give all my possessions and all my literary and other fame for a single moment of that time," he said with a sentimental look at the bushes, "if I could only, once more——"

I felt sorry for him and for myself that he couldn't. I kissed him lightly on his withered cheek and hurried on to join the others. He had aged so much more than I!

"The jewel of a song that you promised——" Lulli reminded me once more; and there was no putting him off any longer, for he himself brought my lute down and handed it to me, and all the others echoed his importunity.

I strummed the chords.

The Song of Spring! There were no chestnut blossoms over my head, but with the sun filtering through a fine greenery and with a crowd of listeners surrounding me it was like that day when I had sung and played this song before the Cardinal in the Luxembourg. I could see myself, a young girl of almost seventeen, in a simple fluffy light-blue frock, and everything seemed the same to me, as if no years had intervened.

And while I played and sang, lost in gracious memories, a strange thing happened. Once more the lank, narrow-shouldered figure appeared before me; and it was not a phantom of imagination, but a reality. I knew that it was Charles Villiers, but for the moment it was exactly as if it were Charles himself—Charles my first lover. And, as then, his eyes flashed at me. They did not reach down into my heart so poignantly as of old, but they did send a sweet little thrill through me; and, as then, I stopped and missed a bar, with my fingers improvising modulations and my whole self filled with a heady delight.

"Getting old," I sighed to myself while acknowledging my guests' applause. "Living on memories! Like poor old Rochefoucauld."

Charles de Villiers came forward, looking at me with too expressive eyes. "I must speak to you," he whispered hotly. Suspecting that something had gone wrong with La Champmeslé, I took him aside. "Were you too demanding?" I asked him. "Did you pour out your feelings too passionately? Did you try to kiss her?" He shook his head mutely. "What was it, then? Tell me. Was she cruel? Scornful?"—"No, she wasn't," he murmured, gnawing his underlip. "But something else happened. When I entered the bower, when I sat down by her side, quite alone with her, everything that I had ever felt for this woman, or rather what I had thought I was feeling—suddenly died. She was very pleasant; she tried to encourage me. But I could not bring out a single word—felt cold and remote, and all I could think of was running away." He stopped for a moment; then he burst out: "Running away from her—to you. Because—I realized that it is only you whom I love. Only you."

True, I was not the least displeased that he didn't care for La Champmeslé any more. I was also vain enough to feel agreeably tickled by the thought that I had outdone the young woman, and without even trying. But the passion in the boy's words and looks shocked me. "What a funny young man you are!" I said forbiddingly and sternly, "—a boy who does not know what he wants. Don't say such foolish things to me again."

But he was not going to let himself be suppressed. "I cannot help it," he said. "Ever since I have known you I have become another, a better, a happy man. It is you who have lifted from me all the gloom and heaviness that oppressed me. You gave me back to life. Only in your presence can I breathe and live. I love you; believe me, I love you."

I decided to make an end of this nonsense once for all, and when he continued to stammer and even spoke of love eternal, I cut him short. "I have done for you, my dear Chevalier," I said nervously, "everything that I promised. If you don't love Madame Champmeslé and must love at any price, then please go and find another object of your romantic fancies. But spare me, I beg of you. And fare you well." I was astonished at my own brusqueness; it was not my habit to let myself flare up that way. But I turned away and, leaving him there, went to my guests.

On the lawn and under the trees tables had been set for supper, decked with my best Valenciennes tablecloths. Madeleine, propped on her stick and wearing her thick woolen shawl, directed the valets and maids like a general ordering his troops, sending them here and there with dishes, plates, and silver candelabra until everything was ready and my guests could sit down. A little orchestra had arrived—a surprise from Lulli—and the maestro stationed it behind shrubbery, whence the tones of violin, viola, and flute, mingled with the whisper of leaves and the chatter and laughter of my guests. But, try as I would, I could not get rid of my nervousness, the aftereffect of my embarrassing scene with Charles de Villiers. Where was he now? Had he gone? What was he doing? He was so vulnerable and so strange! If anything happened to him I should never forgive myself.

The shadows lengthened. The paling sky, the multicolored lanterns among the trees, and the flickering candles painted the garden with an exotic light. In the middle of the supper Lulli stood up and, looking significantly at me, went over to his orchestra. Now, I knew, he would try to tell me through his music how much he loved me. And heart-moving indeed were those liquid sounds that floated to me on the evening breeze. Yet, while all the rest stopped eating and listened enraptured, I got up and slipped away from the table.

Wandering about the garden, I searched for Charles. At last I found him in the bower. He was sitting on the bench, dejected, head in hands. Upon my entering he looked up, and a sudden light passed over his face.

"Don't be silly," I said. "Come and have supper with us."

"Then you won't send me away?" he asked, at once fearful and hopeful.

"Listen to me," I said gently, sitting down by his

side. "I don't want to send you away. I like you. I even love you. But in the way a mother would love her child. You are young enough to be my son, and if you will let yourself be treated as that, then stay, and we can remain good friends. Will you?"

Impulsively he took my hand and kissed it. "Whatever you say," he said devotedly—"if only you won't send me away."

He kept his word. From that evening he remained gallant, devoted, respectful; and, seeing that I wanted and chose only the best for him, he let himself be guided in everything by my counsel.

But in addition to the maternal solicitude that I could lavish on his education, there was still the different, the strangely compelling pleasure that I continued to draw from his presence—from my play with him as I played with my own past. From his eyes those of my first lover still seemed to gaze at me. And when I counseled him on making love to other women I delighted in so choosing my words that, in my own mind, they were addressed rather to my first lover than to him. A charming enough comedy this was—and a hazardous one.

5

BEING HAPPY in this new and singular way, I had still, after two months, chosen no new lover from my waiting list. There were guessers who connected this extraordinary fact with another: to wit, the reluctance of the King to look for a successor to Madame de Montespan, though his separation from her was said to be imminent. The frequent visits of the Baron de Corbille to my house—and he was known to be the confidant of the king in his amorous affairs— were eagerly commented on, and not without reason, for the King's messages to me were more and more pressing. So, too, were my answers more and more decisive, for I meant to keep my independence whether or no. And though I knew that the struggle was not over and that the worst was to come, I laughed at all surmises.

Françoise made me very unhappy one day by saying: "I have trespassed on your generosity long enough. For years I have been living in your house, contributing nothing to your expenses. You give me beautiful dresses and all the delights of good company. I love staying with you. But it cannot go on this way. I have arranged with the Carmelites for a small room for myself, and they will ask no rent until I have found some way to earn it, by handiwork or copying or whatever."

I could understand Françoise very well. Though lively and witty in conversation, she was basically serious. Life had been never too gracious to her. As a penniless young girl she had married Scarron and had devoted herself wholly to the task of nursing him. Poor Scarron! Ever since Papa and I had seen him in the bathhouse in Saint Germain he had remained a cripple, though one who "smiles and laughs and finds the world wonderful." All that he had left to Françoise on his death ten years ago had been his debts; and had I not paid them and taken Françoise into my house, she would have lived in utter penury. Always a faithful wife to Scarron, she had remained faithful to his ashes. I had often enough urged her to fall in with the atmosphere of my house and to take a lover. It would not have been difficult for her to find one. She was of a superb exotic dark beauty—people called her *la belle indienne*—and in spite of her outward show of coldness, any discerning observer could tell by the veiled fire in her almond eyes and by her delicate, mobile nostrils that inwardly she was smoldering. "I could only associate with a man," she had told me once, "if I were joined with him by the holy sacrament." Deeply religious, she had no use for the *libertinage élégante* of my other friends, though she was tolerant enough to respect their point of view.

"I won't keep you back, dear," I said. "I can understand your wanting, after all this time, to have a life of your own. But do let me see to it that you find a better occupation than handiwork or copying—something worthy of your intelligence and your beauty." At the same time I got her to agree to the compromise of staying with me until summer, when I would move to my country house in Cordeliers.

On a fine May morning I was dressing for a drive to the woods. As usual I chose a comfortable, simple dress such as I liked for country wear. "Do you know," I asked Madeleine, who was helping to dress me, "where I am driving today? To the forest of Vincennes, as I was on the day Maman went on a pilgrimage."

"Then I must give the coachman a woolen rug for you, lest you catch a cold from sitting in the grass." She gave me a sheepish look. "It's with him, Monsieur Charles, that you are going, isn't it?" I nodded. "I thought so," she said. "And I keep wondering why you have never been with him at night."

"Don't talk nonsense, Madeleine," I said. "He is still a child, and I wouldn't think of it, and neither would he."

Madeleine smiled. "Wouldn't he? Every night when he goes he comes back to our street and hides behind a tree and looks up to your window. Why don't you be good to him, ma petite?"

Her coaxing was interrupted when Françoise came rushing in, her face all flushed. "You must go down," she told Madeleine, "and tell all the servants to keep away from the yellow salon and the entrance hall.'' To me she said: ''Baron de Corbille has come, with the Vicomte de Vigny, who wants to pay you his respects.'' When Madeleine had gone she said: ''It's no Vicomte de Vigny. It's the King himself. What a handsome man!''

''I think you have caught fire,'' I teased her. ''Wouldn't it be better if you told him I have gone out and entertained him yourself?'' A great deal was at stake, and I didn't really feel at all like jesting. The decisive moment had come.

''You must select an elegant dress,'' Françoise suggested excitedly. ''Perhaps the reseda-green one with the Malines lace?'' But I said no, I had been notified of the presence of a simple Vicomte de Vigny, and why should I change from the dress I had on for my outing? It was a white dress printed with pink roses—a little _légère_, for it was designed to give sun and air access to my skin.

I had never thought of preparing myself for a surprise attack such as I had now to face, and on my way downstairs I was wondering—as La Fontaine had written—how to manage that ''the lion should have his fill and the gazelle remain whole.'' Not knowing my enemy's tactical plan, I decided to rely on good sense and intuition. Two unknown gentlemen stood guard at the entrance to my salon. They opened the door for me, allowed me to enter, and closed it softly.

My first glance at Louis, I must confess, took me by surprise. This was not the great Roi Soleil whom I had seen once in Versailles, preceded by glittering heralds, clicking his heels, staff in hand, strait-laced, haughty, attended across the polished parquet by nobles overawed by his magnificence. The man standing in the middle of my room was the same dark-complexioned, full-lipped young man whom I had met once in the wood of Versailles, and he was in the same dark, simple dress and with the same black broad-brimmed felt hat with the one red ostrich feather. He was a little plumper, and his chin was more pronounced and domineering, but he had the same charm and grace that had once brought a smile to my lips.

Had he stuck to his role as the young man of the woods, I do not know how his visit would have turned out, for in spite of myself I was thrilled. But fortunately enough for me, after this first appeal to romantic nicety he changed his tactics. Instead of coming forward to meet me, he stood rigid and self-conscious; and the smile that was about to take possession of my lips was frozen before it reached them.

"What splendor for my humble house," I said ceremoniously. With a condescending nod he permitted me to approach and curtsy to the floor. Inwardly I was enraged. I, a woman, obliged to assume an almost kneeling position before this man! Only wait, I said to myself: in a little while I'll make you kneel before me, and you will get for it nothing that you want! At last, with a gracious gesture of his hand, His Conceited Majesty allowed me to rise. We stood face to face. But I couldn't bring myself to smile at him. My first kind feeling for him was gone.

"I suppose," he said, and his voice was pompous, "that Baron de Corbille and Monsieur Molière have not failed to convey to you the great interest that

I take in your charming person. The answers that they brought me, however, were not very encouraging, my dear lady. But it is always so: whatever I do not do myself is never done properly. And so I have put aside a very important affair of state this morning and come to see you in person."

I offered the King my largest armchair, near the fireplace; and not only did he accept it, but he did not even protest when I seated myself humbly on a low taboret facing him. From his superior elevation his royal eyes deigned to examine my face, and then to descend past my throat to the narrow line of my pinned décolleté.

"My visit to you has been prompted by very serious considerations," he went on. Meanwhile his eyes, leaving my bosom, graciously and sympathetically traced the curves of my arms and my legs. "And I am convinced that you, whom I regard as the most intelligent lady of my realm and one accessible to arguments of reason, will fall in with the plan on which I have decided in the interest of my country."

"At your command, Your Majesty," I said weakly, "there would be no sacrifice too great for me to offer willingly on the altar of France." My answer and the earnest mien that I maintained—to do it I had to bite back an ironical smile—appeared to convince him that his plan of attack was right. He vouchsafed himself a brief cessation of hostilities, and used it to let his eyes go on another reconnaissance.

"If Your Majesty is interested in counting the roses on my dress," I remarked, "then I can spare you the trouble. They have been counted by others;

422

and I have been told, not once but again and again, that they number sixty-nine precisely.''

For a moment he looked a trifle disconcerted: then he said gallantly: ''They are growing on the loveliest hills and valleys in France, and happy are those who are allowed to pluck them,'' and he touched some of them with romancing fingertips. Then, ready for serious battle, he resumed the attack:

''First of all, before I let you know my decision, I wish you to have some understanding of my person and my kingly office, which, in the interest of my country, are and must be one and the same. I am no private person; not ever; not for a single moment. Everything about me, even to my sleep and my dreams, belongs to France and to mankind. First, a word about France. It can certainly be no secret to you that out of a country which throughout the centuries has been in a lamentable position, torn by disunity, afflicted by invasions, under a constant necessity of defending her borders, I have forged a united whole. The Flemish towns are mine, Burgundy is mine, and the Dutch and the Habsburgs tremble at my powerful army. For they know what I have in mind.''

I gave a start. ''Wars?'' I exclaimed. ''Will there be wars again?''

He favored me with an indulgent, slightly mocking smile. ''Of course, wars, my little lady; what else? In peace a country perishes. Only by wars can it become great. It is the heroic spirit of the soldier that creates the world and lays the foundation of all culture.''

''And the people?'' I said, distressed. ''The poor

people, burdened with conscriptions and taxes—the widows—the invalids——''

''The people? Pooh! They will mind neither sacrifices nor wounds nor death if only I make their France great and glorious. You can watch them when I return after new conquests, when I shall have elevated France to the place where she belongs—to the top of the world. How they will hail me!'' And with an expansive gesture of his arm he raised his hand.

''I hope Your Majesty does not plan to introduce that gesture as our people's salute.''

''Why not?''

''Because in ancient Rome it was the salute of the slaves.''

''The hard discipline of the Roman slaves and the Romans' fear of the fasces of their rulers were the very foundation of the grandeur, the world domination, of ancient Rome, and only by hard discipline of the French can I lay the foundation of the world empire that I have always dreamed of, which I am resolved to build on the ruins of the Second Roman Empire of the Habsburgs.'' At that moment he seemed oblivious of the real purpose of his visit, for now his eyes were staring, not at my sixty-nine roses, but prophetically into space. ''And all the peoples of Europe shall be united in this new Roman Empire of mine,'' he exclaimed, ''with me as successor to the emperors of ancient Rome—the Sun, center not only of France, but of the whole world.

''There is no vainglory in these dreams,'' he went on, his eyes returning to me, ''—dreams that I have never confided and will never confide to any other woman. For I know that you combine with your woman's charm all the honesty and discretion of a true gentleman. What I have in mind is, in its ultimate scope, the salavation of mankind. Instead of a mixture of states great and small, there will be only one highly concentrated and all-powerful state. Instead of fighting each other, the peoples shall devote themselves only to the works of culture and peace. And there is—for history wills it so—no other person in this world called to bring this about—but me."

"A tremendous task Your Majesty has taken upon your shoulders," I said; but he seemed not to notice the touch of skepticism in my voice.

"Is it not?" he exclaimed. "And now you understand perfectly, as I do, that there is no move, no word, no minute, no second that I have not to calculate in advance, to make it serve my great purpose—a purpose that not alone I, but *everyone* in France will be called upon to serve." His eyes bored into mine.

It was not difficult to deduce from this circuitous approach the role that I was supposed to play in world history. "I understand, Your Majesty," I said with a smile of comprehension. "Even the hours of your most intimate privacy belong to the state and to mankind, and in the interest of the general welfare they must be used to relax the terrible strain of your overworked mind through the delights of the body."

"How admirably expressed!" he exclaimed, and proceeded to convert theory into practice by drawing his armchair nearer and placing his hand on my shoulder. "Thanks to your fine understanding," he

said, "I can come nearer now to the decisive point. It
is not necessary for me to tell you what a tantalizing
woman you are. Looking at you, sitting here near
you, enveloped by your intoxicating atmosphere, I
must confess that you transcend all my expectations.
And were it not that I still have much to tell you, and
were it not for a certain resistance that I still sense in
you—which makes me fear lest I break something
very precious—believe me, I should become even
more impatient than I already am. But it is not only
that for which I look to you. I need a woman—a
sparkling feminine spirit—to whom I can speak my
mind. With the poor Queen, as all world knows, it is
unendurable to try to converse; she is, *entre nous*,
stupid. Madame de Montespan? I am weary of her
tittle-tattle, her intrigues, her scenes, her passionate
ados. Molière and Corbille must have told you how
highly I think of you, how often I quote you, and
how often I ask them: 'What would Ninon say to
that?' In short, I need you; I want you about me. And
so I have decided to appoint you to the highest post in
Versailles that I can give to a woman—to make you
the uncrowned, but actual, queen of France."

He had decided! He had not bothered even to ask
me. Simply decided. As if everything and everybody
belonged to him.

"I am deeply touched by the honor," I said sub-
missively. "To be *maîtresse en titre*–that is certainly
the dream of every woman in France. But since Your
Majesty attaches so much value to my advice, permit
me to direct your attention to certain points. There is,
I fear, a serious difference between our views, so far
as Your Majesty's ingenious and far-reaching plans

are concerned. I do not understand anything about politics; I have never cared to and never shall care to. But—perhaps because I am only a woman—I cannot see how conquest and war can lay the foundation of a happy future. You will see glory in it, but I shall always see only the tears of the desperate women whose husbands or sons or lovers are going off to war, or returning from war as cripples, or not returning at all. Mine is, as I say, just a woman's outlook, and therefore it may be a narrow one. But I cannot help that. It is the way I feel. And, sorry though I am to say it, I shall never be able to hail the conquering hero. How, then, can Your Majesty hope to draw inspiration from me? For my part, I can foresee only disillusionment and, sooner or later, quarreling.''

Louis frowned a little. The idea of outright opposition seemed not even to have occurred to him. But presently a smile flitted over his face. ''Well,'' he said, ''if you say that you don't understand politics and don't even care to, I agree that politics shall never be mentioned between us. But there are still many other considerations to make me stand by my decision. There is, for instance, Versailles, which I have tried to build into a stage at which all Europe shall look with envy. The best plays are performed there, and there are ballets and masquerades, *carrousels*, fêtes, and water and garden parties in endless succession. But, to tell you the truth in strict confidence, I have not succeeded. It is all elaborately contrived; it is superficially glittering; but at the core it is monotony and boredom, and it is an ugly spider's web of intrigues. It is devoid of finesse, of charm. But in your salon there is everything—good taste, elegant conversation, the delicacy of all the *beaux esprits* who flee to you to recover from the boredom of Versailles. And it shall be your task to transfer this spirit of the Rue des Tournelles to my Versailles. Can you not see how much I need you?''

I felt cornered, but I was prompt with another objection: "Has Your Majesty considered that my presence in Versailles would be a slap in the face of all the people who have criticized me and denounced me as a courtesan?''

The King jumped up. The blood rushed to his face. "In this country it is I," he almost bellowed, "who must decide who is a courtesan and who is a virtuous woman. Have I not done enough to smash the Cabale? Did I not free you from your confinement? Have I not dissolved the Compagnie that defamed and persecuted you? No, my dear demoiselle. Your *préciosité galante* is no disadvantage: it is a jewel. *Amour* can be a deadly commonplace, a groveling business; but your genius has transformed it into an art—the art of all arts." Standing face to face with me, he blinked confidentially. "Can you realize," he said, "how important it is to me for this amorous spirit of your house to pervade my Versailles? When that comes to pass, my nobles, their heads completely bedazed with amorous intrigues, will have time neither for conspiracies nor politics. They will be glad not to put their noses into the affairs of my government, and to leave those affairs completely to me. And who could better create this peculiar atmosphere than you, past mistress of love as you are? Have no fear: what pleases me is the law. I would severely punish anyone who ever dared whisper a word against you.''

It was an embarrassing moment. Louis stood there triumphant, persuaded that I had exhausted every possible argument against the decision he had already taken. He had, moreover, reminded me of my debt of gratitude towards him. How could I possibly continue to evade him? But I could not allow myself to be beaten. And so, in this impasse, I turned from argument to entreaty. ''But—please,'' I said with girlish helplessness, ''I beg Your Majesty to think it over. Consider, please, that *amour*, as I see it, can spring up and live only in freedom. It is the unconstraint, the naturalness of the whim that produces all its graces. It comes, you don't know when or why; it is simply there. And then it fades as a flower fades. It knows no law, no reason, no purpose beyond itself. You have said that to let yourself be carried away by impatience would be to feel as if you were breaking something precious. What a subtle understanding you have! You have perceived that it is not there— the whim, the *frisson*, the little thrill, the unmistakable sign of my caprice coming to flower. And without that, without the freedom of my caprice, my *amour* wouldn't be that of Ninon at all. It would be quite worthless. Please, do not do this to me. I have struggled for the independence of my caprice my whole life long. Do not imprison the fickle bird in your golden cage!''

Irritation had visited his face. He stood frozen stiff, saying not a word. I lowered my eyes, realizing that I had nettled him. Worse, I had wounded his pride; and not so much the pride of the King as that of the man. There was no other woman in France who, when Louis wanted her, would not at least pretend love and passion; and I, the *amoureuse,* dared say that I felt no *frisson.* But a flash of inspiration came to my help. With a sigh and a look that could have melted a rock I pleaded: "What a pity that you are the King and not the nice young man whom I met in the wood!"

At that the irritation left his face, and in another moment it was positively beaming. "So—you recognized me!" he exclaimed. "I had Molière sound you out, but all I learned was about Saint Germain when I was a little boy and could not yet really appreciate what it meant to sit on your lap and smother you with kisses. But you *do* remember me in the woods! Why didn't you tell me at once?"

"Because when I came in I could see only the dark suit and the red feather in the hat of the young man. The young man himself was gone. In his place stood His Majesty."

Louis seemed suddenly aware of the blunders he had made. "And if in the King's stead," he ventured with a romantic vibration in his voice, "only the unknown young man had come to you?"

"Then——" I said, leaving my sentence unfinished, but giving him a smile of the half promising, half prohibiting kind. It was enough to draw him still a little nearer to me—near enough to put his hand on my knee. "The young man in the woods," I said innocently, "was so disarmingly shy——"

The hand was instantly withdrawn. "You did like him, didn't you?" he asked; and the tone of the arrogant King had been replaced by that of the anxious and hopeful admirer.

"I liked him tremendously," I said. "I should be belying myself and you if I didn't admit frankly that he gave me my *frisson*—actually a rather extraordinary one. I had several sleepless nights. And—I went to the woods several times, dearly hoping that I should see him again."

"What a pity that you didn't!" exclaimed Louis, flushed with triumph and sure now of victory.

Having thus cajoled him enough, and judging by the restlessness of his hands that it was high time to dash his spirits a little once more, I said: "But I did see him again. It was near the woods, but from some distance away; and instead of giving the coachman an order to proceed, I had him turn at once and drive me home. For by that time my *frisson* had gone."

"Gone? Why?"

"You see, on my way to Versailles I could observe hundreds and hundreds of laborers working on your castle and your park, and many of them came up to my carriage begging for a few sous. It seemed strange to me that those who were working so hard for you needed to beg. But they said that they were being ground to death; that for their work from dawn to dusk they had nothing but a few crumbs of evil-smelling, putrid food; that every day numbers of them died, some from hunger, some from exhaustion, some from poisonous food or water. And when you appeared at a distance they pointed fingers at you and said: 'There he comes—our murderer.' "

Louis was beside himself. I should have told him, he said. Nothing of the kind had ever reached his ears. When he had personally inquired about the workers, everyone had told him that the food was good and everything to their satisfaction. He asked me urgently to forget about it.

"I will try," I said. "But I cannot change the fact that you are the King and the young man in one person."

"Forget the King," he exclaimed. "Let me from this moment be nothing but the young man." He seemed delighted and excited by his idea. "Perhaps then the *frisson* will return to you?"

Having thus maneuvered him into this position, I felt that it was now I who dominated the field; for, though he was no stripling in *amour*, I, with my much vaster experience, was certainly his superior. And by a reflective silence, eked out with a purposeful byplay of eyes, hands, and feet, I succeeded in getting him where I wanted him; for the next moment he had stood up and then let himself down on one knee, from which position he was gazing wistfully up at me.

"Why not?" I said, passing my fingers over his hair and with the other hand taking him under the chin. "Why should my *frisson* not return, my very handsome young man? You look just as you looked then. But, like all my other lovers, you must be patient and wait until my caprice comes and promise to leave me without remonstrances when it goes. Just a pretty fugitive adventure—why not?"

He capitulated completely, unconditionally. Before he left me, though, I made him sit down again in his chair and had another word with him as the King. I told him how sorry I was that I had had to disappoint him in connection with his plans, but that if he cared for my advice, I had a splendid idea for solving his problem.

Seeing him eager for it, I told him about Françoise, who truly seemed to me the ideal woman for him. She was beautiful, cultured, entertaining, witty, and spirited; she had a sterling sense of humor, a great strength of will, and a capacity for absolute devotion to the man whom she chose to belong to. She was not easy to win, I told him, and nobody had won her since her husband died; but *he* would certainly know how to conquer her. "How excited she was," I told him, "by your looks, and how she did blush when I teased her about whether she had not fallen in love with you at first sight!"

"I should have preferred to have the problem solved in my way," he said. Of course, he would consider my counsel. The lady whom he had seen, the one who had rushed up the stairs to fetch me, was beautiful indeed. He was looking, he said, for a governess for his two children by Madame de Montespan, and he would see to it that Françoise should be nominated to him for this post, that he might have her near and study her. And then he would see. But since I myself had addressed him again in his capacity as King, he did not want to go without discovering whether he could not do me some favor.

"There is really nothing I could ask for," I said, "because, thanks to you, I enjoy what is the one thing most important to me—a complete and unrestrained freedom." Nevertheless, on his continued insistence that he wanted to do something for me, I asked him to permit my friend Évremond to return from exile. Assuring me that the reasons for this exile were long since obsolete and that he had no objections, he promised to see to it that a pardon should be issued at once.

About to go, he took my hand and gallantly kissed it. "This kiss of the hand is from the King of France to the Queen of Charm," he said. "But what about the young man? Does he get nothing for a farewell and for the token of a possible revoir?"

I held my lips up to him. He kissed them warmly; nor did he by any means confine himself to them, but, like the little boy of Saint Germain, he smothered my whole face. And the next thing I knew, it was not only my face, for by some sleight of hand he had made my pin disappear. His arms around me were holding me close. And how strong he was; *mon Dieu,* how really royal! But at the critical moment I gently freed myself.

"And when can the young man hope?" he murmured.

"I don't know," I whispered into his ear. "But I think soon—very soon."

6

WITH THIS EPISODE satisfactorily concluded, I told
Françoise about her eventual post as governess of the
King's children. I also told her that the King had
found her beautiful. She blushed again, and in my
mind's eye I could already see her in the position of
the King's *maîtresse en titre*. I did not dream then
that her will and her principles would prove so un-
yielding that in the end the King would marry her, or
that as Madame de Maintenon and his morganatic
wife she would actually become the uncrowned
queen of France.

When the King had gone and the guards posted in
front of my house had been withdrawn, I expected
Charles de Villiers to arrive to have luncheon and
drive with me to Vincennes. But when he did not
come I became first nervous and then seriously worried. I was increasingly haunted by a foreboding. An
unusually strong desire took possession of me to
have him with me and to be affectionate to him. It
was not until toward evening that he came.

Madeleine had found him behind the trees across the street, with his face pale and distorted and a pistol in his hand. The foolish boy! He had thought I had had him driven away from the entrance in order to get rid of him for the sake of undisturbed amorous hours with one of my lovers. He had thought that he could not survive the humiliation. I explained to him as tenderly as discretion admitted—petted him, fondled him, whispered endearments to him. But he would not let himself be calmed.

"I am no child," he protested passionately, "but a man, and a man in love with you. And if you can't respond to my love, what else is left me?" At that point my resistance broke down; and it was not only fear for his life, but also my own heart, that made me realize how far from indifferent I was to his passion. The past had advanced upon me faster and closer than I thought. Reality had replaced my dreams. I was in love with Charles de Villiers!

In love! In love again! Not just another *affaire d'amour*, but in love! All the thirty years between my first Charles and my new one seemed wiped out, as if no clock had struck between then and now. My Charles had returned to me! Of what avail was it that I struggled against such unreason and blindness, or that Françoise kept warning me: "Are you mad, Ninon? What will you do when this boy has had his fill and left you, as sooner or later he must? Will you cling to him then, run after him, beg for this youngster's pity, and go through all the agonies of a frustrated passion?"

No, there was no reason in it all. I was in love; I was the ardent, radiant Ninon of other days, in whose life moods of melancholy had no more place. I was light as a bird and strong in the glorious certainty that this was the happiness that had once been taken from me. In this exuberant mood it appeared to me neither absurd nor foolish when, one day, Charles announced that he had written to his father. For he was determined to marry me and to withdraw with me to his ancestral mansion, where we could live only for our love, undisturbed by the world.

In those lovely May days, invested with glamour and glory, I enjoyed a happiness comparable only to that of my first courtship. Wanting to perpetuate this happy stage as long as possible, I granted Charles—save for words of love, furtive pressures, and a few rare kisses—no familiarity that might destroy the tender spell. There were other explanations, to be sure, of my reluctance—some belated joy in the pleasures of purity in love, the prospect that I was to become his wife, and certainly a residue of the maternal affection that I had felt from the very first moment of seeing him in the half-dark of the Théâtre du Palais Royal.

But then my old troublemaker, my passionate disposition, claimed me for its own. I began to want him. I longed to have him against my breast, to kiss the life out of him. And when, one night, he left me after supper and as usual planted himself beneath my bedroom window to gaze up at me with eyes full of restrained but passionate longing, I could control myself no longer, and I motioned to him to come up to me.

Reclining on my couch in a negligee, I had not the slightest doubt what would happen when he came storming in and flung himself impetuously on to his knees by the couch. I kissed him, whispering sweet nothings into his ear, and at the same time permitting my negligee to open. He stared enraptured at my body, its outline veiled by nothing but an almost transparent gauze. Even that slipped away when he grasped my shoulder.

But then there happened something unexpected and very strange. Instead of taking the whole of me, he stared wordlessly at my denuded bosom with a rapt adoration that I had seen in no one else. Only after he had contemplated my breasts for a long while did he approach one of them with his lips, tracing the bare flesh softly and lovingly. He hung on my breast like a child. A sweet thrill went through me, but with an icy and peculiar shiver. When at last he let my breast go, I hastily gathered my negligee about me, wrapping myself tight. "That is enough for tonight," I said. "Now good night, dear."

But he would not go. "I am languishing, dying with love," he exclaimed. "Why did you call me? To send me away now that it has just begun?"

I could understand him. His blood was kindled. Youth is youth; it was claiming its own; and what right had I to refuse him what I had given to scores with whom I had not even been in love? But by no means could I bring myself to continue with him that night. I must first free myself from those inane thoughts of him as a boy who might have been my son—a formidable stumbling block to my passion. "Do not press me, my love," I begged him. "Let it be tomorrow—tomorrow night—our first great love feast, with all the bliss, all the wonders."

He yielded at last. And, as we had planned, we drove to the Luxembourg Gardens the next morning and promenaded arm in arm under the pink-white trimmed chestnut trees and kissed each other in the grove, whose trees, having grown gigantic in the course of the years, offered us shelter from both observation and heat. We had luncheon in a little tavern on the *quai* of the Seine, and then I drove home. There would be no guests admitted tonight, I promised him at parting. We would have our supper in my boudoir, just the two of us. And then we would withdraw to our happiness.

Having dismissed last night's hesitations, I could hardly wait for the night to come. I went down into the garden. All the flowers of this glorious May day should be ours in the night to come. I cut lilac, laburnum, white narcissi, irises, even a few roses that had just opened their buds, and placed them carefully on the long, cool grass while I went to cut a few blossoming apple branches.

At that moment a shadow fell across the lawn, and then across me, and here came Madeleine, hobbling toward me. To my surprise, her face looked worried. "A monsieur has come," she said hesitantly.

"But I won't see anybody today. Didn't I tell you?" I said.

"It is a Monsieur de Villiers. But not our Monsieur Charles. An old one. It might be Monsieur his papa, I'm afraid."

"Oh, there is nothing to worry about," I said lightly—though there was everything to worry about, for I should have to invite Monsieur to supper, and our evening would be spoiled. But, after all, he was the father of my beloved one, and it would be a pleasure to meet him. "Just go and tell the Chevalier de Villiers to come out. I will see him here in the garden," I ordered her.

When the elderly Villiers came out of the house I went forward to meet him. He was a substantial broad-shouldered man with deep furrows on his sun-tanned forehead and cheeks—a sturdy, typical country gentleman hardened by weather and work. He had sharp light-gray twinkling eyes, and it occurred to me that he bore as little resemblance to his son as Charles did to his mother, whose miniature he had shown me.

When Villiers came nearer I was surprised to find that his look was firm, like that of someone who has to acquit himself of an embarrassing task. But at my smile of welcome his mien lightened somewhat.

We exchanged greetings, and I invited him to the bower, where we sat down in shade. He seemed extremely embarrassed, and though I encouraged him by welcoming speeches he was long silent. Finally, when he had several times cleared his throat, he began to speak. But, apparently unaccustomed to making speeches, he brought his words forth as if plowing heavy clods; and the words that came out were as awkward and gnarled as his hands. He apologized for having come alone and in secret. His son did not yet know that he had arrived in Paris. He had just come from the post chaise station, but he had not dared visit me until he had learned that his son was not with me and would not be until evening. This, then, would be a good chance to have a few words with me without his son's knowledge. And I must excuse him for being still in his traveling dress. With his fingers he wiped dust from his leather collar.

"There is no need to apologize," I said. "My Charles's father is welcome to me in any apparel." My politeness seemed to embarrass him even more. Nevertheless, with an obviously heroic effort he mustered all his forces and blurted out: "My son wrote me that he wants to marry you, Mademoiselle. I cannot imagine that you yourself would ever dream of such a foolishness. He is young—very young. Besides, he is engaged to Claire Brinbal, a niece of the late poor Marie, and he must marry her when the time comes. She is young and healthy and will bring him an heir to our estate. She is the woman my son, a country gentleman who cares for his heritage, will need. You wouldn't be that sort of wife to him, would you? You wouldn't want to leave this fine house—leave Paris and all your grand friends and bury yourself in a simple mansion away off out of the world. You must help me to bring my Charles to reason."

"If that is what you have come for, Monsieur," I said, laughing, "then you won't find the right conspirator in me. Oh, I can spare you the trouble of setting forth everything that speaks against my marrying your dear son. There are my age—his age—my past—my way of life—many things. But against all this stands the one all-important fact: Charles and I are deeply in love. Our love has rights of its own, and a beauty of its own, and it has nothing to do with age or morality or the interests of your manor."

Villiers shook his head; his hard and bitter mouth seemed to tell me that his outlook did not reach beyond the universally accepted standards and the interests of his estate. But I had guessed wrong. For a human and very gentle inflection had stolen into his harsh voice when he said: "Don't think, demoiselle, that I do not know what love is. I, too, have loved, and I had the unspeakable happiness to marry my beloved one—Mademoiselle Marie de Brinbal, my neighbor's daughter. But poor Marie died in childbirth." A tear glittered on his thick eyelashes.

"Yes, I know," I said sympathetically.

"And now," Villiers went on, "Charles is the only one left to me. He is the last scion of a family that has defended and cherished our mansion and our fields and woods from generation to generation. I always hoped and still hope that fate will be kinder to him than it has been to me. But he has always given me so much sorrow, the poor lad! Yes, from his childhood on. What a thin, pale child he always was! and melancholy. No wonder—a boy deprived of the warmth of maternal love. And how different he was! Instead of caring for the farm and hunting, he was reading all the time. I loved him, and so I didn't mind his burying himself in books. From my brother, who is the abbot of the Jesuit convent of Cognac, I got the best teachers for him. He was also very devoted to God and His church. But as nothing seemed to cure his melancholy, I sent him to Paris last year to live with a sister of mine and carry on studies at the Sorbonne. But what happened? He got into circles of freethinkers. First he fell in love with an actress and then with you. Now he wants to marry you. But I can tell you I won't permit it—not in any circumstances." His voice had risen almost to a shout, but it seemed to me that he was shouting at himself more than at me.

"You who have known what love is," I said, "you can't rob me of him."

The big, heavy man seemed to shrink. "I don't know what to say," he murmured helplessly, "but it cannot be. It cannot."

For a while our struggle went back and forth over the same ground. But at last, when all his arguments and pleas had failed, he said: "I wanted so much to spare you the truth! But I see that I must tell you. Will you promise me that what I am going to tell you now you will keep secret?"

"If I possibly can," I said cautiously, "then you have my promise."

My words seemed to satisfy him. "Do you still remember Monsieur de Gersey?" he said.

A little shock ran through me, leaving a sick feeling behind when it was gone. What did he know about Gersey? What had he to do with him? "Of course," I said, "I remember him." I looked at Villiers, wondering what more he might know.

"You had a boy by him."

My unease was growing. "Yes, the poor child died a few days after his birth," I said.

"When you were pregnant you were traveling with the Marquis de Gersey to his estate in Brittany. But you did not reach the estate, and it was in a small hut by the country road that you brought the boy into the world. You wouldn't marry the Marquis, and you agreed to entrust the child to a nunnery. And

443

perhaps you may have been not too sorry to hear afterwards that the poor boy had died.''

My head sank.

''But he did not die.''

The truth was dawning on me, or at least over-hanging me like a thundercloud. ''Go on,'' I urged him. ''Let me have the full truth.''

''You brought the boy into the world on the very day after my poor Marie had died in childbirth. And not only had she died, but the child too. I don't think I need do much more explaining. I was in despair over the loss of Marie and the boy. Knowing that I would never marry any other woman, I saw that this was the end of my estate. It was doomed.

''But then I learned about you and your child, and it was like a miracle and a gift of God. I made an arrangement with the nunnery and a gentleman's agreement with the Marquis de Gersey; and, ever since, your boy has been my son. And now, you know, too.''

I refused to believe Villiers. ''My boy was born in Brittany,'' I protested, ''and yours was born near Cognac.''

''My boy was born in Brittany, make no mistake. But I could not stay on in a mansion in which I had been so happy with my Marie. I sold my estate in Brittany and moved to my other estate in Cognac.''

A tumult of emotions raced through me, and I did not know which of them prevailed—whether the happiness of fulfilled maternity, pain at the loss of my lover, or the shame that left me horrified at myself. I was principally aware of a great need to cry. By a stern effort I managed to deny that need.

Taking Villiers' gnarled hand, I said in a low, re-signed voice: "Then, of course—everything is over. Finally, irretrievably, over and done with."

For a long time he did not break the silence. Then he said: "Poor demoiselle, it is hard for me to ask a favor of you at such a time, but it must be done. Since no one, and least of all Charles, must know the truth, I still need your help. He is desperately in love with you, and it will be of little use for me simply to refuse my consent. You are the one that must let him know that everything is finished between you. You must not tell him face to face. Just write down a few lines and give them to me. Write him that you have come to realize that it was all a mistake—that you don't love him, or that you have decided on another man, or whatever one writes on such an occasion. You would know better than I."

"The poor boy has a strange leaning toward death," I warned him. "I am truly afraid that such a letter might kill him."

"I know my boy," said Villiers. "I know that there will be a difficult time with him. But I understand how to handle him. He loves me and he respects me. And if I tell him that his mother's last deathbed wish was that he should marry a Brinbal, he will do it. Just write the letter and give it to me and you can leave everything else to my own judgment and my own responsibility."

My legs trembled when I walked, or rather swayed, with Villiers towards the house. The lilac, laburnum, narcissi, and roses that I had cut for that night lay withering in a pitiless sun.

7

Cordeliers, May 25, 1669
My dear, my ever faithful friend Évremond,
I have good news for you. The King has granted you a pardon that will enable you to return to France and to me and to the whole circle of our common friends. But to me our revoir will be of particular importance, for I shall have more time than ever to dedicate myself to you and your friendship. I must warn you, though, that on your return you will find an altogether transformed Ninon. Yes, my dear friend, after a crisis of agony and despair I have arrived at a point from which there is no turning back.

Crisis, despair, agony—strange words from the pen of your "ever cheerful and easygoing Ninon," are they not? And I hasten to explain them to you, though some things in my confession may cause you an unpleasant surprise.

The first thing apt to surprise you is that the cause of the turmoil that has brought my life on to another plane is—a man; and, although it will be hard for

*you to believe it, he was one of those smooth, un-
formed young men—unripe fruit, to which, as your
London friends know, I had a lifelong leaning. And
here is another almost unbelievable surprise: this
was no liaison, but love—a love so absorbing that I
decided to marry the young man and to withdraw
with him to his country mansion.*

*I should have known from the very beginning that
it would be impossible—I, the almost-fifty-year-old
amoureuse, married to a boy of twenty. Though such
marriages have taken place before, the whole world
would have laughed as they did when the old Comtesse Évard married her stableboy. I should not have
cared about that. But there were other and even still
more important reasons that made the young man's
father stand in the way of so supreme a folly; reasons
that, for considerations of discretion, I am forbidden
to reveal even to you, my most intimate friend.*

*I should have endured the parting that I speak of
with a more balanced mind, doubtless flinging myself into the arms of a new lover, had I merely loved
my young man. But I more than loved him. It was a
passion, the most consuming of which my sex is
capable.*

*Apropos my sex, I must confide to you a truth that
I fear must once more greatly disillusion you. I feel
like pouring my heart out to you in all candor;
because you are not the cold bitter cynic that you
pretend and have been a warm-hearted and understanding friend from my early girlhood. The truth is,
then, that my sex is not the soft, playful kitten of my
capricious galanterie légère, but—a Monster.*

And what a dangerous, vicious monster it is! I do

not want to be ungrateful and to condemn i
wholesale. Though I often wonder whether what
have had was worth what it cost, I would not hav
missed it. I had learned to tame the monster. M
father taught me to lead it on silken strings, and i
could be charming and pretty and capable of givin
much pleasure to me and to others. But there wer
times when it was a primordial beast of prey again
giving me neither peace nor truce and bringin
tragedy to those whom I loved.

No one can conceive the cruelty of my inne
struggle last night. You know that, in spite of m
libertinage, there has always been a religious strea
in me. It asserted itself in my youth, vanished, an
reappeared like one of those strange rivers that los
themselves in sand, flow underground, and then fo
other stretches resume their course n the surface
There have been times when, for my own sake an
aside from my involuntary confinement, I withdre
to a convent. Last night I appealed to the poo
remnant of religious strength in me.

But no God, no angel, would come to my aid; an
in the end it was only myself, my own reason, traine
in the philosophy of the stoics—the philosophy th
you and Papa once taught me—that mastered m
passion.

C'est fini! As I cannot have the one whom I love,
have irrevocably decided to have done with the plea
sures of sex. I have said adieu to passionettes, t
flirtations, to adventures. I am no longer Ninon th
amoureuse, the fickle, easygoing maîtresse de
plaisirs. Rather, from now until the end, and to th

whole world, I am Mademoiselle de Lenclos who lives only for her friends, for her books, for music and art, for all the pleasures of a tranquil mind. Is not that wonderful Évremond? Overnight I have become an old lady—thank Heaven, with only a very few wrinkles so far, and with no more white hairs than I can count on my fingers—but an old lady who is ready to take pleasure in her old age.

I write this letter sitting in the garden pavillon *of my summer house. Its glass doors are wide open, and I look out into the foliage of the trimmed lime tree alley. And though I am still tired from the awful struggle just ended, I take great pride in myself. For I have won my battle with the weapons of philosophy and have called on no Saint Augustine or any other supernatural powers to help me. I feel only commiseration for those who need religion to guide them through their troubles. One feels so free, so light, so strong if one knows that, not the phantom of an invisible God, but the steady clarity of one's own mind is shaping one's fate and is the measure of life.*

Come soon, my dear friend, to enjoy in my company all the rich pleasures that this beautiful world has still in store for us!

Yours at last really happy and always affectionate
Ninon.

I put the quill down, read the letter over carefully, folded and sealed it. Through an opening in the cupola overhead a shaft of dazzling sunlight slanted down on to my table. Standing up, I withdrew to the back of the *pavillon* to lie down on the divan in the shade. Looking up through the opening in the cupola, I could see a patch of blue sky. From it my gaze wandered along the gracefully carved columns and the pink walls, gaily painted with those old tormentors of mine, a troop of pretty little chubby-faced amoretti. But they were to do me mischief no more to the end of my days.

I stretched languidly. Though sheltered in the half darkness, I felt the heat of the afternoon penetrate the walls and vibrate in the air. I was sure of my privacy. No one knew that I had gone to my summer house in Cordeliers; and moreover I had strictly enjoined Madeleine not to admit any visitor. Nothing was to be heard but the sweet and peaceful drumming of bees. Peace—peace at last—peace. I closed my eyes, and after a time I fell happily asleep.

Suddenly I came out of this peaceful sleep with a start. It was as if two lascivious hands had been laid upon me, pawing, groping. My eyes flew open.

"Charles!"

Young Charles was here. His dress was disorderly, half undone. His hair was disheveled, his face aflame, distorted, his eyes wild.

"Leave me alone!" I cried out. "I beg of you, go away, go away. How did you come here? How dare you——?"

He heeded neither my resistance nor my question. "I must have you."

"I do not want it," I cried into his face. "I do not want you."

"That is not true. You love me. You want me. I know it from the very way you look at me." Taut with manliness, he was about to seize and to take me.

It was to me as if I had fallen into the fiery mouth of a grotesque and obscene hell, but when I tried to wriggle from his arms I felt my strength fail me, and my lips, despite myself, were smiling at him.

Only at the last second before his final approach did I clench my hand into a fist and thrust him back. "You don't know what you're doing," I cried out to him. "Go, go!" And when, in his rage, he would not listen, the words of my supreme anguish sprang from my lips: "Don't do it, Charles! I am your mother. Do you hear me? Your mother."

I stood leaning back against the wall for support, panting, facing him. His eyes were devouring me greedily.

"If you have not understood me, let me say it to you again. I am your mother. You are my son. My flesh and blood. I swear it."

He was staring at me now with all the fire gone out of his face. It was deathly white. "It is not true," he cried out.

"I did not know it myself. I have known it only since your father told me."

"He lied to you. He made it up. He made it up to separate us."

Still leaning against the wall, trembling all over, in frantic words I told him the full truth. While I spoke he stared at me listlessly. When I had ended and he knew that what he had heard was truth, he looked like a trapped beast. Then he moaned and hid his face in his hands.

I should have liked to go closer to him, compassionately take his hand, and fondle him; but I did not dare. "You should be glad," I said, "to know that you did not kill your mother—that you have a mother who lives, and who loves you. For your own sake it must be always a secret between you and me and your father. But I will do everything for you that a loving mother can do——''

His hands left his face. His eyes were fastened upon me in an uncanny way that sent a shudder down my spine. ''Mama!'' He gave a peal of bitter laughter. It was laughter that said I had robbed him of the divine ideal that he had made for himself. His mother stood before him now divested of glamour, an elderly *amoureuse* whom he had all but possessed. I could see that he could not help it, but in his eyes the pain of disillusion was still struggling with his lust.

''You had better go now,'' I said. ''Go back to your father. He must be in great anxiety for you. Be a good son to him; marry the girl who is worthy of you; and in some future time we shall meet as good friends.''

He seemed defenseless against the gentle smile that I gave him. He stood up, came near, took my hand, and, bowing down, kissed it. I felt his lips quivering as they touched it. Then, not looking at me, he said ''Adieu, Mama,'' turned, and walked away down the path.

I stood on the threshold, very straight, my eyes following him. ''Adieu,'' I whispered. ''Adieu, my lover—the only love of my life; my strange, my wonderful love. And adieu—my son.'' I repeated ''son,'' and there was intolerable pain in my heart, and yet it was overflowing with sweetness.

I wished that he would turn around, once at least, so that I could see from his face whether he had forgiven me. Had I wished it intensely enough to force my wish into reality? For he did suddenly stop; he did turn around; he lifted his hand. I lifted my own arm to wave him a last good-bye.

In his uplifted hand the barrel of a pistol flashed in the sun. I tried to cry out, but no sound came. I tried to run toward him, to tear the weapon from his hand; but I stood rooted to the earth.

The shot exploded. I saw Charles drop to the gravel of the path. Only then was I able to run toward him, and the next moment I was by his side. Blood trickled from his temple and from his lips. His body lay at my feet, lifeless.

On my knees and with my hands upraised I cried to the Heaven: "Lord, O Lord, help me; let it not happen; let him not die!"

But my prayer had come too late. A great gush of blood came from the wound and from his mouth, and the beloved eyes, quenched of the last spark, grew strangely fixed and dim.

"He is dying—our poor Monsieur Charles is dying!" I heard Madeleine's voice call out. In my turmoil I had not seen her rush from the house and hobble to my side.

"For Heaven's sake," I implored her, "run. Run as fast as you can. Fetch a priest."

For I was seized by an inexpressible anguish for the eternal life of my dying beloved.

Epilogue

THE SHADOWS ARE falling. My eighty-first birthday.

I was an *amoureuse* no more. From the day of the tragedy in my summerhouse in Cordeliers I had withdrawn from my follies, and it was now only to my mind that I conceded enjoyments. In the intervening years my salon had reached such a degree of distinction that it drew even those who still lived in terror of the Cabale, which, though officially dissolved, still wielded an uncanny power. One after another of them had joined my circle, and to it belonged increasingly not only the social but above all the spiritual elect of Paris. How gay, how graceful, how well-balanced was my life now that, tormented no more by the tyranny of passion, I could give myself to friendship, conversation, music, books, and my daily walks alone in the beautiful parks!

It is true that, *distinguée* or no, I condescended to small escapades now and again, but rarely and *très discrètement*. The one with the young Abbé Gédouin on my eightieth birthday, I decided, had been the last.

On the night preceding my eighty-first birthday I wondered what would happen if Gédouin should return the next day, and if he were foolish enough to present his bill and tempt me. I was surprised that some insignificant part of me even wished that he would. But as this was not the better part, I decided—for his sake as well as for mine—that I would stand firmly by my decision, and that there should be no birthday surprise this year. But why this guessing, this unrest, this anxious insistence on my decision? There was nothing to be afraid of. The whole year had brought no word from him. Most probably he had received some canonicate; or else he had forgotten me and his church—as I had always assumed he would—in the arms of some blonde Gretchen or fiery Spaniard.

On my birthday morning, after breakfast and bath, I prepared for my walk. In front of my window the walnut tree flamed in autumnal splendor. Sparrows twittered merrily in its branches. And though I had not even the slightest premonition of the great adventure that lay before me—the most wonderful I had ever met in my life—I felt in the air the promise of an unusually beautiful day.

There were a great many letters in my mail, but, *Dieu merci,* none from Gédouin. Knowing that he was well-mannered enough not to come without informing me in advance, I could leave my house with a quiet mind. But at the last moment a messenger arrived with a basketful of the most splendid roses and—a letter from Gédouin.

Not caring to read it right away—I could guess its silly contents—I put it into my bodice. "In case that Monsieur Gédouin should come in my absence," I ordered my maid, "say that I beg him to excuse me, but that I am not receiving today—either him or anyone else."

At the entrance to the Tuileries gardens I left the coach and wandered among the clipped hedges and flower beds until I reached the music pavilion, and there I seated myself on one of the benches and gave myself up to the spell of the autumn day. But I had not reckoned with the danger that lurks in those incomparably sweet autumn days in Paris—days dappled with blue and gold and warm as summer, but with the cool smell of discoloring leaves in their breath, with the nostalgic warning: "Don't be a fool! As long as there is still a trace of summer in you, take it—enjoy it." And at that point, Gédouin's unopened letter began to tickle me under my bodice. It tickled me so that I had to take it out. And once it was in my hands, I opened it and read it.

You fool, you silly young fool, I whispered while my eyes scanned lines overflowing with devotion, with passion. ". . . I count the hours, the minutes, the seconds, that I must wait to fly into your arms . . . The time of our separation has altered nothing of my love, nothing of my decision that, to have you, I will not only give up my *collet*, but, just as readily, my soul's salvation. . . ."

Poor Gédouin! Not only did he love me, but I could see from his lines that passion had precipitated him into a fierce inner struggle whose agonies I could well understand. But no, I assured him in my thoughts, he had nothing to fear for his eternal soul; at least, not from me. On meeting him, I decided, I would tell him outright: "No, no, indeed, my dear abbé. Go and serve your Church, and let me, an old woman, alone."

But when I returned to the garden entrance I didn't climb into my carriage. A sudden anxiety made me hesitate. Should I really have the courage to tell him No when I faced him? "Drive home by yourself," I told the coachman. "I will walk." Before he drove off I hastened to add that the cook was not to expect me for luncheon. What a coward I was!

"Coward! Coward!" I repeated to myself as I wandered along the Seine, and then to the Place de la Bastille, and to the Place Royale, and on and on until I reached an unknown area of obscure narrow lanes of old, rickety houses. Where was I going? Going? No—I was fleeing. Fleeing from Gédouin, but just as much and perhaps even more from myself.

At first what I felt had been a mere slight titillating unrest. But the longer I wandered, the more aware I became that in spite of myself I was longing to go home—longing to have the fellow in my arms. At the same time I was seized by anger, bewilderment, self-contempt, and at last by headlong panic. My blood ran chill and hot. I, eighty-one years old and with thirty years of a completely balanced mind behind me, thrown once more into such a whirlpool of passion at the edge of my grave! Where would this lead, this grotesque, obscene, macabre emotion that was playing havoc with me? Was I to make love to my last hour? Was I going to make my tombstone dance above me to the rhythm of my antics in the earth?

But no self-mockery would help, and—what was even worse—neither would the most frantic efforts of will and reason. Where now was all my philosophy? where the Stoics, Montaigne, Papa? No one, no one at all, was there to help me.

"Some white asters for the altar, Madame?" I heard a voice say; and, coming to myself, I saw an old woman in a ragged shawl, huddled in the shadow of a doorway, a basket of flowers before her. Just to be kind to the poor woman, I bought a bunch of her white asters. "What fine weather for All Saints' Day!" she said gratefully, and when I said Yes and turned to go, she said: "God bless you, Madame."

God bless you! The words struck me with so affecting a sweetness that I could not go on. As if to bask in them for a moment, I stepped into the doorway. Looking out from it on to the small irregular square, I caught sight of a little ancient church. Mass was apparently over, for a crowd was issuing from the open doors. It was all so peaceful, so solemnly gay, with the people in their best dresses and the sun pouring out her gold upon them and upon the old stones!

Should I go in?

No, I told myself. What help could I expect from a God in whose Church I refused to believe?

Not that I had not tried to believe. In my youth, in Ursulines' convent, and on the several occasions when, tired of pleasures, I had retired to a nunnery, I had followed the mystical voice that my dear mother had set vibrating in me. And ever since that fateful day, when, in my summerhouse in Cordeliers, I had launched into prayer—a belated one, alas—I had tried, not occasionally, but systematically and with honest effort, to get inside the Church. Many as notorious libertines as I was had tried and succeeded—even Évremond, the most profound freethinker I had ever known. Living still in exile because he didn't trust Louis XIV and his ministers, and financially dependent on the allowance that Charles II of England had granted him, he had given up his liberal ideas and embraced the Church.

But I had not succeeded at all, though many clerics, apprised of my desire for honest conversion, had made a great effort to help me. "I can believe in the divinity of Christ's words," I had said to Père d'Orléans, a disciple of Ignatius de Loyola, "but I can believe neither in the divinity of His birth, nor in the Immaculate Conception, nor in other miracles. All these appear to my intellect absurd, nonsensical."—"Then at least go and offer your incredulity to God," Père d'Orléans had advised me. Another abbé asserted that "Heaven would think twice before refusing to let so charming a lady in." Many others had employed their whole armory of theological weapons, but my reason simply refused to believe the unbelievable. What, then, had I to do with this ancient little church across the square?

My desire to enter it was growing on me. I was unknown in this neighborhood, I supposed, and I could steal in unobserved and do as I had done in my youth when touched by the spell of faith: I could pray. Still I hesitated. But there, out of the shadows of the doorway and out of the past, figures emerged, and familiar welcoming faces. It was as if I could see my mother's old lovely smile, as if I could hear her whisper: "Ma petite, God's beloved darling——" And then, between shadows and light, I thought I recognized a strong round head with a flattened nose and bushy overshadowing brows—a face entirely plain, but radiating a light that had penetrated the gloom of the day on which he had come to see my dying mother. Vincent de Paul! Monsieur Vincent! "Let not your heart be troubled," he had said. "There is a human kindness in you that can come only from God, Whom, indeed, I can see in your face. Yes, God loves you, my child. For you the kingdom of the Lord will be opened." And so vividly did I remember the words and the sure way in which they had been spoken that it was as if they had been spoken just now, and not more than sixty years before. Deeply touched and encouraged, I took heart, crossed the square, and entered the church.

A gentle mellowness reigned inside it. Wisps of blue smoke floated quietly through the air. Silver candelabra glistened in the sunlight that streamed through the frontal rose window, and with the scent of incense mingled the chaste perfume of white asters. And I remembered—remembered——Yes, that was how it had been in the Ursulines' chapel, on the day when Beatrice had taken holy orders. Then, too, the church had been decorated with chaste white flowers—all white.

It was strange, all those images of a far-off past returning to me with a clarity that laughed at time. And sitting there on one of the last benches, I felt as if I had just witnessed the ceremony of the Vows, with Beatrice's voice re-echoing still from the archways: ". . . to the One Whom the angels serve and at Whose beauty the sun and the moon stand in wonder . . ." And then, as my eyes wandered about the church, I discovered His image. Like the one in the convent church, it was a painted wooden figure on a big black cross; and, as then, my lips whispered: "When—when? . . ." and again, exactly as before, I felt myself drawn toward Him by a gentle but irresistible urge.

But when I arrived before him I did not, as the young postulant had done, pull myself up on to the railing and fling my arms around Him and kiss Him on His lips. Tired and shamefaced, I dropped to my knees and with my lowered eyes added my bunch of white asters to the others at his feet.

There was complete silence in the church.

"Don't stand on ceremony, my dear," I heard a voice say suddenly. Was I dreaming? The voice went on: "Stand up, my darling, and look at me with those bright eyes of yours."

I could not trust my ears. But how could I withstand such charming gallantry? I rose to my feet and looked at the Saviour. On His bowed face there was a welcoming, winning smile.

"Are you not angry with me, then?" I asked timidly.

"Angry? Why?"

"For my behavior yesterday," I said weakly. "I mean, a few years ago, when I was a postulant and behaved so indecently toward you. You remember?

You must have been very much displeased with me then.''

"Displeased? I was delighted. I enjoyed it. How else could you express your love for Me at that time, but by holding Me in your arms? You could not love what you couldn't embrace. And you were so charming!''

"They told me I had committed sacrilege.''

"Poor Père Guillaume. His intentions were of the best. But he was too much prejudiced by the theories of the Sorbonne to understand you. I was afraid that you would become dull under his influence, and I arranged for you to leave the convent.''

"You are so generous to me! But I know that I don't deserve it. In Your eyes I must be a great sinner, much worse than Mary Magdalen before she met you.''

"Yes, my dear, you are one of the greatest sinners of history. But I didn't make you out of stone; and, looking at you, I don't wonder——It only shows the Devil's good taste, that he chose to wrestle for you and so desperately tries to keep you for himself.''

I still didn't know whether I was dreaming or seeing visions and hearing inner voices. "I thank You for Your pleasant compliments,'' I said, "and I am sorry indeed that I shall have to miss your company.''

"What makes you think you will?''

"Because you are in Heaven, and I shall have to go to Hell, of course.''

"Oh, there I must protest. By no means could We bear to miss a presence so enlivening as yours. We count upon you to give Us the pleasure of coming to live with Us."

"I—in Paradise? Would not that be, say, a little *déplacé?*"

"If you had only your pretty little head and your sparkling eyes and—but for a pair of wings, of course—nothing else, that would be enough to make you one of our most attractive angels."

"And my sins?"

"Well, you have sinned gravely and many times, but it will give Me no little pleasure to forgive you your sins. For you are kind in your heart, and have a great sense of humor, and those two qualities are the very essence of man's faith in Me."

"Humor?" I said wonderingly. For this was exactly the opposite of what I had been taught by learned doctors.

"Of course. For what do you think I died on the Cross? Only that all who come after Me shall be happy and smile and laugh. He is not a good man who does not love humor. He gravely misunderstands my supreme sacrifice. But you are full of humor, ma petite, and so you will understand that I should begrudge the Devil possession of you."

The prospect that I should gain access to Heaven and that I could be gay there and humorous filled me with joy; and my joy mounted into bliss when it occurred to me that I should meet there so many dear ones with whom I had thought I had parted forever. Maman would be there, and Charles my son (to whom in the last moment a priest had administered the Holy Sacrament), and there would also be my dearly remembered old Madeleine. But then I asked anxiously: "But what about Papa? Poor Papa is in Hell, isn't he?"

"I ought not to tell you, for if other people knew this secret, too many would light-mindedly rely upon it. But I know you are discreet. My Holy Mother, Tower of Mercy, is sometimes so deeply moved by the cries of the eternally damned that she steals behind the back of My Heavenly Father and opens the gate of Hell a bit so that a few poor souls can slip out. Then she begs My Father so insistently to leave them in Heaven that He relents. And such a thing, fortunately enough, happened to your Papa."

My bliss increased. But then I was bold enough to ask about Charles. "What about him?" I said. "Charles Beaumont, my first lover."

"You'll find him in Heaven, too. He died in a convent."

"In a nunnery, I suppose?"

"No," He replied. "After many adventures he found his way back to me and became a monk in a far-off order."

Suddenly He was a painted wooden figure again. For just at that moment the soutaned figure of a priest emerged from the sacristy door and brushed by me. Still not sure whether I had dreamed or not, I followed the priest and asked him to hear my confession.

In the booth I said my Confiteor and then launched into my confession. It must have lasted for hours, and I felt sorry for the good father, that I kept him so long from his luncheon, but he persisted in wanting to hear more and more and more of my interesting temptations. At last I had confessed all my sins remembered and asked him to forgive me them.

"Do you feel sorry for your sins, my daughter?" he asked dutifully.

"I am sorry," I said truthfully, "that I am not sorry at all; on the contrary, I am glad that I missed none of them."

There was an embarrassed silence behind the grating. But then, in a tone of enlightenment and triumph: "But you *are* sorry that you don't feel sorry?"

"Will that do?"

"If you are firmly resolved to sin no more——"

That I affirmed from my very heart.

"That will answer," the priest said gently.

"But, Father," I said, "I must tell you the full truth. Does my confession not come too late? I am very much past middle-age—eighty, eighty-one."

Another obviously astonished silence; then he said solemnly: "Your age does not matter. The workers who come to the vineyards at the eleventh hour are paid the same wages as those who have borne the heat and burden of the day."

He made me say my Confiteor, gave me absolution, and imposed a penance, the first part of which I had to perform right away.

As I knelt at the altar, absorbed in my prayers, there shone suddenly upon me a moment infinitesimally brief, yet at the same time eternal, and I knew with a lucid certainty that the Lord's Grace had just touched me. It was not like what I had been told by many. This was no experience of mountains falling from my shoulders. No flood of blazing light descended; no shudders racked me; I did no soaring as on clouds. It was all so simple! It needed no evidence, for it was simply truth—an understanding of the faith that is beyond human reason. I was as a deaf person who has read much about music, but can never really grasp its wonders until the day when the gift of hearing is granted. Filled with a sense of harmony and perfection, I finished my prayer and arose.

To my surprise, the church was not altogether empty any longer. There must have been at least a few who spread the news of my conversion, for I saw familiar faces. *"Benedico te,"* I heard a sonorous voice exclaim, and there was Père d'Orléans standing before me and kissing my forehead. "You don't know, dear demoiselle, what a great service you have done us today. The whole world knows of the honesty of your convictions. It knows that you wouldn't go to the confessional and do penance if you were not converted and did not fully believe in Him and His Church."

There were whispers and murmurs about me. In front of the church and in all the streets that I passed through, people gathered and discussed the news of my change of heart. A little courtesan with painted lips and cheeks tripped towards me. She looked like Yvonne, with her red hair and her fluffy green dress, and she reminded me of the girl whom I had once freed from the whipping stake. "Our Saint!" she said adoringly, kneeling before me and asking for my blessing.

I was not so pretentious as to aspire to the rank of a saint. I was glad enough that I should be admitted to Heaven at all. There I should dwell on a white cloud—men had always found me dazzling in a white, cloudlike nightgown—but I didn't want to disappoint the poor girl, for she was right in feeling that her profession, too, being officially tolerated by the police ministry, deserved its patron saint. I gave her the blessing she asked.

The sky was deep blue now. Bells were ringing out, and a soft wind like a messenger from Heaven was stroking my cheeks. And, most wonderful of all, the thick red fog that a few hours ago had beclouded my heart was gone. The fever of my blood had died down. As if bathed in floods of light, I was chaste. Chaste, at last! And I could understand at this moment what Mère Clothilde had told me in the Ursulines' convent: that chastity is not just absence of lasciviousness, but a special grace, a positive gift of God that cannot be earned by merit, but is given freely to whom it pleases Him to give it, and that receiving it is a joy so much beyond all other joys that the pleasures of lust appear poor and worthless beside it. I was pure; I was happy; and I walked as if I were already riding on clouds.

On the Place Royale I saw Gédouin rushing toward me, breathless, with flashing eyes and eager gesticulations. "At last!" he called out. "Where have you been, my adored one?"

I did not mind his kissing my hand. I even took his arm, which he gallantly offered, and I permitted him to see me to my house, patiently listening the while to his passionate protestations of unquenchable love. But at the entrance of my house I dismissed him.

"I may not go in with you?" he said.

"No, no, indeed, my dear abbé," I said jauntily. "For since this morning I have acquired another

468

Lover, and my time is so taken up with Him that I shan't be able to find any for you.''

"And we shall never meet again?'' he stammered.

"We had better not. But, yes—perhaps, later on. Sometime in Heaven.''

He made so puzzled a face that I could not suppress a chuckle. And when a raindrop fell on the tip of his nose, and I looked first at his nose and then wonderingly up at the blue sky, I thought I could see God the Father in Heaven laughing with me. And I knew in that moment that by His grace the best, the gayest part of my life was still to come.

There are a lot more
where this one came from!